The Spectrum Handbook 2018

- **Spectrum valuation framework**

- **Sources and timing of new mobile spectrum**

- **Break-out of mobile wireless spectrum allocations, demand and fundamental business dynamics**

- **International comparative analysis of spectrum regulation and allocation**

- **Explanation of spectrum and wireless technology issues**

- **Overview of fundamental regulatory and licensing issues**

- **Explanation of spectrum usage in all major frequency bands**

Acknowledgements

We would like to thank the following people who generously donated their valuable time and expertise providing input on various drafts of this publication and the 2013 edition:

Peter Curnow-Ford (Viatec Associates), Juan Deaton (Idaho National Laboratory), Howard Del Monte (formerly with Ofcom), Brian Goemmer (Allnet Insight), John Hane (Spectrum Co.), Timothy Horan (Oppenheimer & Co.), Jan Kruys (Spectrum Consult), Neal Mellen (Wireless Spectrum Management, LLC), Drew Svor (Sheppard Mullin, LLP), J. Pierre De Vries (Silicon Flatirons), Brian Weimer (Sheppard Mullin, LLP), Chip Yorkgitis (Kelley Drye & Warren LLP).

Any remaining errors or omissions remain those of the authors.

Praise for *The Spectrum Handbook 2018*

"Spectrum is the information pathway of the 21st century. Understanding the basics of spectrum - from the physics to the applications - is therefore an essential skill. The Spectrum Handbook lays everything out in a way that makes it indispensable."

> Thomas E. Wheeler
> *Former Chairman of the FCC, and Senior Research Fellow at*
> *Harvard Kennedy School*

"Everything you ever wanted to know (and more) about spectrum, a key resource in the Information Age, is here in this amazingly inclusive primer and reference guide. Kudos to the authors for producing such a highly valuable handbook."

> Richard E. Wiley
> *Former Chairman, Federal Communications Commission*
> *Founding Partner, Wiley Rein LLP*

"An exhaustive compendium for the spectrum guru or the spectrum novice, *The Spectrum Handbook 2018* is also extremely well-indexed and accessible. The valuation section and detailed descriptions of the full range of spectrum-based technologies are particularly valuable. A timely resource as we move into new spectrum frontiers."

> Michele C. Farquhar
> *Communications Practice Leader, Hogan Lovells LLP*
> *Former Chief of the FCC Wireless Telecommunications Bureau*

"Comprehensive guide to spectrum management and policy. A go-to reference!"

> Paul Kolodzy, PhD, Kolodzy Consulting
> *Chair, IEEE Dynamic Spectrum Access Network Conf. Steering*
> *Committee and Former Senior Spectrum Policy Advisor, FCC*

"*The Spectrum Handbook 2018* offers comprehensive and accessible answers to just about every question one could have about spectrum management and the wireless business. Authors Armand Musey and Barlow Keener have made a truly worthwhile contribution to the literature by compiling this indispensable resource. You will use this primer frequently."

> Rob Frieden
> *Pioneers Chair and Professor of Telecommunications and Law*
> *Penn State University*

Praise for The Spectrum Handbook 2018 (Con't)

"As pervasive as wireless services are today, the wireless revolution is just getting started. Whether you invest in startups or public companies in technology, media or communications understanding how radio spectrum is allocated, licensed, used, shared, bought and sold - and which bands support different services - will give you an edge. With the 2018 update the Summit Ridge handbook is an even more comprehensive desk reference for investors - just the right amount of information on a huge range of topics in a manageable size with extensive references for further research. I don't know of anything like it."

John Hane
President, Spectrum LLC
Former partner, Pillsbury Winthrop Shaw Pittman LLP

"*The Spectrum Handbook 2018* is an invaluable resource for anyone looking to get up to speed and stay current on spectrum policy. Whether you have spent years dealing with these complex issues or are just getting started, this compendium of knowledge is the go-to guide. From the basic physics of radiofrequencies to the complex regulatory regimes around the world that govern it, the authors have covered it all in this well-organized and comprehensive guide."

John Heitman
Chair of Communications Practice
Kelley Drye & Warren LLP

"Spectrum and wireless data are the fundamental building blocks of cloud computing and hence our economy, and this fabulous book describes these assets and technologies better than anything else we have ever read."

Timothy K. Horan
Managing Director
Head of Communication and Cloud Services Research
Oppenheimer & Co., Inc

"*The Spectrum Handbook 2018* is an invaluable resource for operators and investors in the fixed and mobile broadband ecosystems. Summit Ridge Group has distilled the technical, regulatory and practical elements of understanding spectrum into an easily digestible and referenceable format. There really is no other publication out there like it."

Jeff Kohler
Co-Founder
Rise Broadband

"There is a wind of change in spectrum use; learn where the wind is blowing. The breadth of the handbook overwhelms by covering technology, economics, law, and regulations affecting the use of spectrum bands in the U.S. and globally. I compliment the authors for collecting and presenting deep spectrum knowledge with juristic accuracy but without losing readability."

Dr. Heikki Kokkinen
CEO and Co-Founder
Fairspectrum Oy, Finland

Praise for The Spectrum Handbook 2018 (Con't)

"Summit Ridge's handbook is a boon for academics and practitioners seeking to engage the difficult issues of valuing, transacting, and planning wireless investments. It provides a comprehensive and holistic overview of the technical, legal, and economic challenges of spectrum management in a single and easily accessible volume that still manages to go deep in addressing the challenges confronting the experts today. In light of the fast pace of innovation, we are lucky to have a recently updated and expanded Spectrum Handbook 2018!"

> William Lehr, PhD
> *Research Scientist*
> *Massachusetts Institute of Technology*

"An extraordinary comprehensive and well-organized overview of the multi-faceted complexities of spectrum issues, including technical, economic and regulatory considerations. *The Spectrum Handbook 2018* is an invaluable primer for both those new to the field and a handy reference for experienced practitioners."

> Andrew D. Lipman
> *Partner and Legal Practice Group Leader*
> *Morgan Lewis*

"*The Spectrum Handbook 2018* is a rare – and extremely valuable – guide to the business and regulatory issues affecting the use of spectrum in the 21st Century. The Handbook goes beyond the typical review of US regulatory issues by supplying the technical overview that is so often lacking from other handbooks. Additionally, the Handbook provides an excellent review of global markets, plus an insider's discussion of the valuation process. The Handbook is a great reference guide for both experienced telecoms professionals and those new to the industry."

> Lee G. Petro
> *Special Counsel, Pillsbury Winthrop Shaw Pittman LLP*
> *President, Federal Communications Bar Association (2018-2019)*

"A very comprehensive book covering, every aspect and issues related to spectrum, a necessary resource for all wireless services. Excellent read and reference source for anyone involved in spectrum from new to the field to experienced practitioners, they are guaranteed to learn something."

> Veena Rawat, O.C., Ph.D
> *Senior Spectrum Advisor and CEO, Expert Strategies International*
> *Former President of Industry Canada's Communications Research Center*

"*The Spectrum Handbook 2018* is a comprehensive survey of spectrum regulation, key technologies, and the state of the wireless business. It focuses on the United States, but includes surveys of key countries world-wide. It would serve well as either a primer for someone entering the field or as a handy reference for those well-versed in the field."

> Pierre de Vries
> *Co-director, Spectrum Policy Initiative at Silicon Flatirons Center*
> *University of Colorado*

About Summit Ridge Group, LLC

Summit Ridge Group is the premier provider of valuation and financial advisory services specializing in the satellite, media and telecom sectors. We provide business appraisal, intangible asset valuation, strategic consulting, custom research and litigation support service. The client needs we service include transactional support, financial reporting, financial analysis, market analysis, strategic analysis, regulatory support and litigation support/expert witness testimony. Visit us at:

www.SummitRidgeGroup.com
Blog: www.SummitRidgeGroup.com/blog
Twitter: @SummitRidgeGrp

J. Armand Musey, CFA, JD/MBA

Mr. Musey is the president and founder of Summit Ridge Group, LLC. He has worked for over 20 years in telecom finance for a wide variety of clients including corporations, investors, and governmental agencies. He regularly speaks at major telecom industry conferences and has been frequently quoted in leading trade publications and by national publications as an expert in satellite communications finance and in corporate governance. He authored "*The Spectrum Handbook 2013,*" and his recent industry research has been published in leading law journals.

Mr. Musey is a member of the Federal Communications Bar Association, the American Society of Appraisers, the New York Society of Securities Analysts, and the CFA Institute. He holds a J.D. degree from Northwestern University's Pritzker School of Law, an MBA from Northwestern University's Kellogg Graduate School of Management, an M.A. from Columbia University, and an A.B. from the University of Chicago.

E. Barlow Keener, JD, MA, CIPP

Barlow Keener is a Managing Director at Summit Ridge Group and serves as its Chief Information Security Officer. He has over 20 years of telecommunications, spectrum, Internet, and privacy law experience. He also earned a CIPP/US (Certified Information Privacy Professional) from the IAPP (International Association of Privacy Professionals). Barlow has provided counsel and in-depth regulatory and financial analysis for clients involved in innovative FCC related spectrum issues, satellite spectrum matters, terrestrial radio technologies, small cell technologies, long-haul fiber networks, and data centers.

Mr. Keener is a member of the Federal Communications Bar Association, is a principal at Keener Law Group, and was previously co-founder of a New England facilities-based CLEC. In addition, he served as General Counsel at a Boston-based marketing firm and was in-house counsel at BellSouth Telecommunications (now AT&T). Barlow regularly speaks at major industry spectrum and telecom conferences. He holds a J.D. degree from Emory University School of Law, an M.A. from North Carolina Central University, and a B.A. from the University of the South.

The Spectrum Handbook 2018

J. Armand Musey, CFA
Founder/President

E. Barlow Keener
Managing Director

Samantha Lynch
Research Associate

John A. Tardio
Vice President

Fan Jia
Associate

Daniel-John Perez
Analyst

For additional copies or inquiries please contact:

Summit Ridge Group, LLC
535 Fifth Avenue, 4th Floor
New York, NY 10017
Phone: +1.646.843.9850
Email: Admin@SummitRidgeGroup.com

Published in the United States of America in 2018
By Summit Ridge Group, LLC
All Rights Reserved. Printed in the United States of America
978-0-9892962-4-3   Hardback ($149.95)
978-0-9892962-6-7   Paperback ($119.95)
978-0-9892962-5-0   Ebook ($79.95)
978-0-9892962-7-4   .PDF ($79.95)
Library of Congress Control Number: 2018910924

IMPORTANT DISCLOSURES

- **This document is not a recommendation to buy or sell securities of any type.** It is designed to facilitate an understanding of communications industry topics. Please consult an appropriate professional advisor before making significant business or investment decisions.

  o This document expresses summary views and therefore does not include all views of Summit Ridge Group, LLC or its professionals.

  o General views expressed in this report may or may not be applicable to a given situation. Adjustments and/or changes may be needed to address the particular circumstances of that situation.

- Forward looking statements expressed in this report are not guaranteed in any manner and may ultimately prove to be incorrect.

- Data in this report, including but not limited to financial information, company and industry information was derived from a number of sources that we believe to be accurate. However, we have not independently verified the data and therefore cannot assume responsibility for its accuracy. Please verify any data before using it as the basis for an important decision.

- Comments about regulatory issues should not be taken as legal conclusions or advice. Consult an appropriately qualified attorney before making important decisions requiring regulatory analysis.

- Views expressed in this report are subject to change. Summit Ridge Group, LLC does not assume responsibility for updating its contents. Please contact us for our most current views.

Executive Summary

This updated Handbook has three objectives: 1) to serve as a primer for explaining the complex issues around the use of electromagnetic spectrum; 2) to analyze, from both an economic and a legal perspective, the regulatory processes being considered or underway to reallocate or change the use of spectrum bands; and 3) to be a reference source for industry professionals. Part I of the Handbook provides an overview of the spectrum and the regulatory process. Part II provides an in-depth overview of various spectrum bands, discussing their range, location, and physical properties and how these impact their ability to be used. Part III explains the various Regulatory Dynamics. Part IV provides a comparative international overview. Part V is an overview of valuation methods and trends. An analysis of the current allocation of these spectrum bands in the United States follows. Throughout the Handbook, we provide links in the footnotes to sources for additional information.

From a macro-perspective, regulators worldwide are in the middle of a spectrum reallocation, primarily for 5G, that is unprecedented in its size and speed. This is occurring at a range of spectrum bands. The most noticeable change since our 2013 Handbook is the clear trend towards increase demand for higher frequencies, most notably, millimeter wave spectrum in the U.S. In addition, the unlicensed spectrum and spectrum sharing movements have graduated from a niche into the mainstream. Various forms of spectrum sharing are now supported by major companies such as Google and Microsoft. In a sense, they may be a portend a long-term upheaval of the sector by Silicon Valley players; however, mobile operators are ahead in deployed infrastructure.

In addition, regulatory bodies, including the FCC, repurposed and reallocated spectrum from 2012 to 2018 for both licensed and unlicensed use. This has dramatically increased the availability of spectrum, AWS-3, AWS-4, H-Block, 600 MHz incentive auction and others. And the process is continuing. The 3.5 GHz Citizens Broadband Radio Service, or CBRS, spectrum sharing proceeding, which will begin operating by the end of 2018 will add 150 MHz of new mid-band service for mobile and fixed use. The 2018 FCC proceeding to study proposals for satellite vendors to repurpose spectrum from 3.7-4.2 MHz will in the near future add up to another 500 MHz to the 150 MHz at 3.5 GHz. The 24 GHz and 28 GHz auctions are expected at yearend 2018.

Software defined networking technology has also increased the flexibility of communication networks in all areas from satellite to terrestrial wireless to submarine cables. Moreover, new technologies to increase spectrum efficiency, such as MIMO, spectrum sharing, small cell densification, beamforming antennas and spectrum aggregation (licensed and unlicensed) have evolved at unexpectedly rapid rates. As a result, not only has spectrum availability increased, but the historical near linear relationship between bandwidth demand and needed capacity has been broken. This makes evaluating carriers' need for spectrum an increasingly difficult exercise.

THE SPECTRUM HANDBOOK 2018

Table of Figures

Critical Dates in Spectrum History

The history of wireless communications mirrors that of many fields of science. After many centuries of little progress, significant new technological developments occurred during the Enlightenment. Progress has generally accelerated ever since, responding to the increased communications needs of modern society.

- 5th Century B.C.
  - Greek Pre-Socratic philosopher Empedocles opines (correctly) that light travels at a finite speed
- 1600s
  - Isaac Newton opines that light is made-up of particles (1672)
  - Christiaan Huygens postulates the wave theory of light (1678), a dualistic understanding (waves and particles) that continues today
- 1700s
  - Leonard Euler (1740s) and Benjamin Franklin (late 1700s) support Huygens' controversial theory which supports Newton's view
- Early 1800s
  - Thomas Young confirms Huygen's wave theory of light (1803)
- Mid 1800s
  - James C. Maxwell formulates the mathematical equations for classical electromagnetic fields using Michael Faraday's discovery of electromagnetic fields (1861)
  - International Telegraph Union (later to become the International Telecommunication Union) founded in Paris (1865)
- Late 1800s
  - Heinrich Rudolph Hertz proves electromagnetic waves exist (1886)
  - Guglielmo Marconi transmits and receives the first wireless signal
- Early 1900s
  - Reginald Fesseden makes first voice radio transmission (1900)
  - Guglielmo Marconi transmits first transatlantic wireless signal (1901)
- 1910s
  - Titanic tragedy emphasizes importance of radio communication (1912)
  - During WW I, the U.S. Navy takes control of all radio technology
  - After WW I, the Radio Corporation of America (RCA) established to take over patent control from the government
  - First AM licensed radio station, 740 kHz KCBS AM, San Jose, CA (1909)

- 1920s
  - First radio program transmitted on a daily basis (1920)
  - Marconi discovers short wave radio can reflect from ionosphere (1920)
  - Working television is demonstrated in London by John Logie Baird at Selfridge's Department Store (1925)
  - First color television transmission is delivered in Scotland (1928)
- 1930s
  - Frequency-modulated (FM) radio invented by Edwin Armstrong (1933)
  - The Federal Communications Commission (FCC) established (1934)
  - First FM station, WAAF 107.3 MHz Westborough, MA (1937)
- 1940s
  - Wartime military needs encourage deployment of radio services
  - Radiotelephony commercialized
- 1950s
  - First Soviet satellite, Sputnik 1, launched, followed by the first U.S. satellite, Explorer 1
  - First color television introduced in the U.S. (1953)
- 1960s
  - Telstar I satellite relays transatlantic television signal (1962)
- 1970s
  - LORAN becomes leading navigation system
  - The FCC allocates 40 MHz for cellular service
- 1980s
  - Cellular spectrum given to local Bell operating companies and ATT (1983)
  - The first commercial handheld mobile phone was approved by the FCC (1983)
  - Bell Breakup (1984)
  - First cell phone services begin (1984)
  - FCC allocated ISM bands for unlicensed use (1985)
  - First generation of GPS satellites completed (1985)
  - First Internet services provided through dial-up connections
- 1990s
  - Second generation (2G) cellular technology (digital) launched
  - First text messages sent from cell phone to cell phone
  - FCC conducts its first spectrum auction (1994)
  - Internet commercialized and opened up to the public in 1995
  - FCC finally publishes unlicensed Wi-Fi standards allocated in 1985 (1997)
  - Digital television broadcasting begins (late 1990s)
  - Wi-Fi is trademarked by the Wi-Fi Alliance (1999)
  - Apple adds Lucent Wireless LAN into the new iBook and Airport (1999)

- 2001
  - Third generation (3G) cellular technology launched
- 2006
  - Fourth generation (4G) cellular technology released in South Korea
    - 4G not launched in the U.S. until 2008 by Sprint Nextel
- 2008
  - First reallocations of U.S. spectrum bands in the 700 MHz range
  - Analog services phase-out to digital service begins
  - Licensing TV white spaces accelerates share spectrum movement
- 2015
  - 4G LTE penetration reaches 100% of the U.S. population
- 2018
  - 3GPP or Third Generation Partnership Project, defines 5G standards

PART ONE: BACKGROUND ON SPECTRUM AND ITS REGULATION

I. Electromagnetic Spectrum and Radio Waves

A. Electromagnetic Spectrum

Understanding electromagnetic waves is the foundation for understanding the regulation and use of wireless spectrum

We would not have radio, TV, or mobile phone service if Michael Faraday and James C. Maxwell, working together in the 1800's in London, had not discovered electromagnetic fields and then determined the mathematical formulas for the fields. Understanding electromagnetic waves is the foundation for understanding the regulation and use of wireless spectrum. Electromagnetic spectrum is the range of all frequencies of electromagnetic radiation. Electromagnetic radiation is a form of energy that moves in a wave-like form as it travels through space. These waves have different transmission characteristics depending on their wavelength.

Spectrum is often described in terms of its frequency, which is the number of waves that pass a given point per second. The number of waves made in a second is typically referred to in units called Hertz[1] (Hz), where one wave, or cycle, per second, is one Hz. Frequency may also be referred to by the absolute length (in metric units) of its waves. As electromagnetic waves move at a constant rate, the speed of light, the wavelength, and the frequency are inversely related. The longer the wavelength, the lower the frequency and vice versa. Mathematically:

$$frequency\ (in\ Hz) = \frac{299{,}792{,}458\ m/s\ (speed\ of\ light)}{wavelength\ (in\ meters)}$$

and graphically illustrated in Figure 1-1 below. Spectrum is commonly referred to in units of kilohertz (kHz) – 1000 waves [hertz] per second, megahertz (MHz) – 1,000,000 waves [hertz] per second and gigahertz (GHz) – 1,000,000,000 waves [hertz] per second.

---

[1] Named after the German physicist Heinrich Hertz (1857-1894) who provided conclusive proof of existence of electromagnetic waves.

Figure 1-1: Relationship Between Wavelength and Frequency

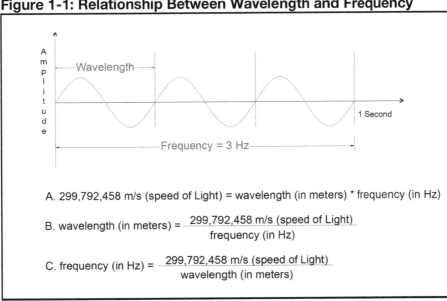

A. 299,792,458 m/s (speed of Light) = wavelength (in meters) * frequency (in Hz)

B. wavelength (in meters) = $\dfrac{\text{299,792,458 m/s (speed of Light)}}{\text{frequency (in Hz)}}$

C. frequency (in Hz) = $\dfrac{\text{299,792,458 m/s (speed of Light)}}{\text{wavelength (in meters)}}$

Source: Summit Ridge Group, LLC analysis

Radio waves occupy only a relatively small part of the electromagnetic spectrum. Other parts of the electromagnetic spectrum include X-rays, visible light, and gamma rays. A brief summary of the radio spectrum is given in the Figure 1-2 below. A more detailed analysis is contained in Appendix II at the end of this Handbook.

B. Radio Waves

Radio waves occupy the portion of the electromagnetic spectrum, namely that between 3 kilohertz (kHz) and 300 Gigahertz (GHz).[2] In the U.S., radio waves with frequencies between 9 kHz and 275 GHz only have been allocated for any use, government or commercial, so far.[3] Common allocations are listed in Figure 1-2 below. In general, radio services that require the transmission of signals over long distances, such as LORAN long-range navigational services,[4] use waves with low frequencies of 2 MHz and thus long 160-meter high wavelengths, while services that are more restricted in terms of the geographical

---

[2] The U.S. regulatory bodies (the FCC and the NTIA) as well as the International Telecommunications Union (ITU) define radio spectrum as including all frequencies below 3,000 GHz.

[3] FCC Encyclopedia, *Radio Spectrum Allocation* (June 12, 2018) http://www.fcc.gov/encyclopedia/radio-spectrum-allocation

[4] Long-range navigation a hyperbolic radio navigation system developed in the United States during World War II. Until 2014 it widely available as a backup for GPS navigation systems. Recent funding plans call for building a new enhanced or "eLORAN" system.

PART ONE: BACKGROUND

area in which they are provided, such as Wi-Fi devices, use waves with high frequencies 2.4 GHz with 4 inch wave and 5 GHz with a smaller 2 inch wave and therefore short wavelengths.

Figure 1-2: Uses of the Radio Spectrum

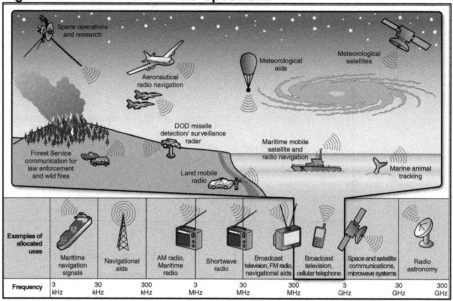

Source: GAO. (2011). Spectrum Management: NTIA Planning and Processes Need Strengthening to Promote the Efficient Use of Spectrum by Federal Agencies.

C. Polarization

Polarization is an expression of the orientation of the electric waves on an electromagnetic field

Polarization is the expression of the orientation of the electromagnetic waves in an electromagnetic field. It is the plane in which the electromagnetic wave vibrates. Polarization is used in satellites, in mobile base stations, and in fixed broadband radios to make more efficient use of the approved spectrum. The simplest form of polarization is linear polarization, where waves can either be vertically or horizontally polarized, and the orientation of the wireless antenna corresponds the polarization of the radio waves received or transmitted by that antenna. Vertically polarized electric fields are perpendicular to the Earth's surface, and horizontally polarized fields are parallel to the Earth's surface. To optimize the signal of an antenna, the polarization of the signal and the antenna should match and they should be located in exactly the same field. Both directions can be used simultaneously on the same frequency with different receivers. Linear polarization is most widely used for radio communications applications.[5]

---

[5] Intelsat, *Circular Polarization vs. Linear Polarization* (2013)
http://www.intelsat.com/wp-content/uploads/2013/02/Polarization.pdf

Figure 1-3: Polarized Wave

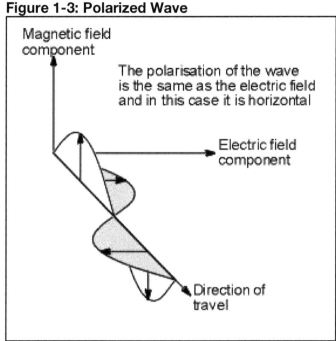

Source: Link Communication Systems[6]

The data capacity of spectrum is generally proportional to the amount of bandwidth used

D. Bandwidth and Capacity

The data capacity of spectrum is generally proportional to the amount of bandwidth used. Generally, digital satellite transmission (with its weaker signals caused by distance between the satellite and the receiver) can achieve approximately 1.5 bps for one Hertz of spectrum while newer high-end Long-Term Evolution, or LTE, systems can achieve closer to 11.2 bps per Hz, and future 5G technology is projected to be anywhere from 10 to 100 times faster than LTE or 1120 bps per Hz. The theoretical limit of bits/sec per hertz is represented by the Shannon-Hartley theorem[7] (often referred to as Shannon's Law). Mathematically, the formula is:

To date, communication technology has not been able to approach the full theoretical limit of capacity using spectrum bandwidth

Capacity (bits/sec) = Spectrum Hz x Log_2 (1+ S/N)[8]

To date, communication technology has not been able to approach

---

[6] Link Communicaitons Systems, *Circular and Linear Polarization* (Aug. 10, 2017) https://www.linksystems-uk.com/circular-linear-polarization/

[7] Named after American mathematician, engineer, cryptographer, and MIT professor Claude Shannon (1916 – 2001) who largely invented the idea of digital communication and is considered the founding father of the electronic communications age and American electronics researcher Ralph Hartley (1888 – 1970) who contributed to the foundations of information theory.

[8] S/N is the signal to noise ratio. S is the signal power in watts and N is the noise power, also in watts.

the full theoretical limit of capacity use of spectrum bandwidth. However, some advanced systems have achieved utilization approaching the Shannon Limit, as illustrated in the Figure 1-4 below.

Figure 1-4: Bandwidth Enhancement Technologies Plotted with Shannon's Limit

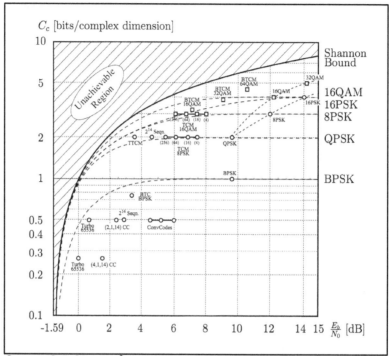

Source: C.E. Shannon[9]

This suggests that while there is potential for additional improvement in spectrum technologies, it may be limited. The demands for data vary by application. Data demands of typical applications are listed in Figure 1-5 below:

---

[9] C.E. Shannon, R.G. Gallagher, E.R. Berlekamp, *Lower bounds to error probabilities for coding on discrete memoryless channels, Inform. Contr.* Vol. 10, pt. I, pp. 65-103, (1967).

Figure 1-5: Data Rate Requirements of Common Applications

Application	Data rate
Voice call (low quality)	3 Kbps
Voice call (medium quality)	30 Kbps
Voice call (high quality)	90 Kbps
MP3 music (standard quality)	128 Kbps
MP3 music (high quality)	256 Kbps
Television (low quality)	1 Mbps
Television (standard definition)	2 Mbps
Television (1080i high definition)	5 Mbps
Television (4k UHD)	20 Mbps
Television (8k UHD)	50 Mbps
Telemedicine (detailed x-rays, MRIs)	10 Mbps

Source: Summit Ridge Group, LLC analysis

Service providers can limit signals to a smaller area... then install another antenna in an adjacent area to allow reuse of spectrum... This process is known as "Cellularization."

Spectrum capacity can often be increased reusing it. Depending on the power levels, topography, antenna design, modulation, and spectrum selection, service providers can limit signals to a small area. They can then install another antenna in an adjacent area to allow reuse of spectrum without interference. This process is known as "cellularizing" or "densification" and is, of course, where the name cell phone service derives. Cellular reuse is illustrated in Figure 1-6 below.

Figure 1-6: Cellular Reuse

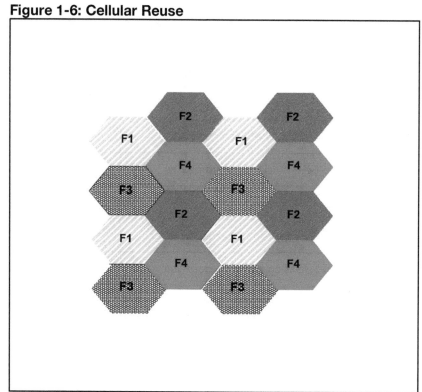

Source: Summit Ridge Group, LLC analysis

Figure 1-6 above shows an example of frequency reuse with four frequencies. The image shows an idealized situation with perfectly hexagonal cells; however, in a real network, the cells are determined by geography and building size. The cell on the top left uses frequency F1. The cells next to it use frequencies F2 and F3. By a carrier using different frequencies that are adjacent to one another for its mobile services, cellular reuse allows each cell base stations to transmit into adjacent cells without causing interference in the adjacent cells as seen with the first cell is using F1 frequency while the surrounding cells are using F2, F3, and F4.

Mobile handsets served by the carrier are able to move from one frequency to the other as the mobile handset moves between cells. Thus, the carrier can provide uninterrupted coverage over a large area with many base stations without transmissions from one base station interfering with cell of the base station next to it. Prior to using this pattern of cellular reuse of spectrum, a single antenna covering a large area was the only method of delivering service to a large area. This frequency reuse pattern is typical for a digital wireless system.

II. Bandwidth Enhancement Technologies

Improved compression technology and modulations schemes generate greater bandwidth efficiency

Wireless satellite, mobile networks, wireline networks, and cable technologies have experienced continuous advancement in network bandwidth capacity since their beginnings through the improved capabilities of several core technologies. For example, approximately every ten years, the efficiency of has roughly doubled to provide better quality and faster speeds for transmitting video data. Improved compression technology and modulation schemes generate greater bandwidth.[10] The following technologies in Figure 2-1 deliver more data over the same amount of bandwidth, thus increasing the efficiencies of spectrum data transport.

Figure 2-1: Bandwidth Enhancement Technologies

Method	What it Does	How it Helps
QAM	Changes amplitude of carrier waves	Increases capacity of spectrum
Video Compression	Receives duplicate bits from video transmission	Allows video to require less bandwidth
MIMO	Multiple send/receive antennas	Allows reuse of frequency in cell site by sending more than one signal simultaneously
Beamforming	Sends data to specific direction	Can reduce cell sites needed and increase capacity of cell sites

Source: Summit Ridge Group, LLC analysis

A. Quadrature Amplitude Modulation

Quadrature amplitude modulation (QAM) is used to in many mobile and fixed radio systems. QAM conveys data, through both wires and radio transmissions, by changing some aspect of a carrier signal, or wave, in response to a data signal. Modulation differs from compression because rather than removing redundancy from the data

---

[10] NAB, Steven J. Crowley, *Capacity Trends in Direct Broadcast Satellite and Cable Television Services* (Oct. 8, 2013) http://www.nab.org/documents/newsRoom/pdfs/Capacity_Trends_in_DBS_and_Cable_TV_Services.pdf

(which is how compression works), QAM is a system of modulation in which data is transferred by modulating the amplitude of separate carrier waves out of phase by 90 degrees, and the resultant output consists of both amplitude and phase variations. QAM is a combination of analog modulation, where only one wave, either amplitude modulation (AM) or frequency modulation (FM), is transmitted, and digital modulation, where multiple waves that are adjacent to each other are transmitted at same height and speed. Thus, using this technique, the same wave of spectrum can carry twice the amount of data. In QAM, the waves are separated so that the peak of one wave occurs at the same instant the second wave is in a valley, such that the waves are out of phase with each other by 90 degrees. The 90-degree difference in phase is where the term "quadrature," or a quarter of 360 degrees, comes from. QAM descriptions start with a modulation quantity such as 2 QAM, which is a binary, 16 QAM, or 64 QAM. These quantities are the number of states. For example, in 16 QAM creates a symbol of 4 bits through 16 distinct signal points, or variations in amplitude and phase. A symbol includes multiple data bits. For 256 QAM there are 8 bits per symbol and the rate per second of symbols is 5.361 million. For DOCSIS, the video channel bandwidth is 6 MHz. The raw data rate for 256 QAM is 8 bits x 5.361 million symbols per second, which equals 43 million bits per second (Mbps).[11] The overhead for transmitting the data is approximately 5 Mbps, leaving a downstream speed of 38 Mbps.[12]

QAM is widely used for data communications because it enables more data to be transmitted on the same carrier signal, which increases the efficiency of transmission and reduces the amount of bandwidth required, promoting spectral efficiency. 16 QAM, 64 QAM, and 256 QAM are used for LTE and 1024 QAM is being considered for LTE-Pro and 5G technologies.[13] Additionally, 2048 QAM is used primarily by wireless Internet service providers. It follows that the higher the modulation, the higher the capacity. However, the higher modulation schemes do come with tradeoffs. Higher QAM levels

[QAM] enables more data to be transmitted on the same carrier signal, which increases the efficiency of transmission and reduces the amount of bandwidth required

---

[11] 1 Megabit per second (Mbps) = 0.125 MB/s (megabytes per second). A byte contains 8 bits. Cable, DSL, and wireless speeds are measured in Mbps or bits. Speeds are measured it "bits"; files sizes are measured in "bytes. For example, a 100 MB audio file being transferred over a 100Mbps Internet will take 8 seconds.

[12] *See* Communications Technology, Ron Hranac, *Spectral Efficiency* (Oct.2012) http://www.scte.org/TechnicalColumns/12-10-01%20spectral%20effieciency.pdf for an excellent description of QAM.

[13] FierceWireless, Monica Alleven, *With 256-QAM, what's good for the small cell is good for the macro: Report* (October 17, 2016). https://www.fiercewireless.com/tech/256-qam-what-s-good-for-small-cell-good-for-macro-report

require more processing power and are more susceptible to noise and interference due to the increased amounts of data being processed. T-Mobile was the first mobile provider to utilize 256 QAM for downloads and 16 QAM for uploads in September 2016. The following year, Verizon and AT&T both announced in February that 256 QAM was being leveraged on their mobile networks. The capacity gain in higher-level modulation schemes is shown in Figure 2-2 below.

Figure 2-2: Capacity Gain Using Different QAM Levels

Bits Per Symbol	Modulation	Capacity (In Mbps on a 56 MHz Channel)	Incremental % Increase
8	256 QAM	370	
9	512 QAM	421	13.8%
10	1048 QAM	472	12.1%
11	2048 QAM	523	10.8%
12	4096 QAM	575	9.9%

Source: Oppenheimer & Co report[14] and Summit Ridge Group, LLC analysis

B. Video Compression

Video compression is the use digital technology to reduce the number of bits needed to send a video wirelessly. The more efficient the video compression technology, the fewer bits needed for each video feed program stream, and the more video that can be sent over a satellite provider's fixed bandwidth. Conversely, more advanced video compression allows the same bit rate to be used to send higher-resolution and higher quality videos. Although simplified, the basic concept of video compression is that redundancy within a video frame and between frames is removed while retaining the output quality seen by the viewer.

The basic concept of video compression is that the redundancy within a video frame and between frames is removed while retaining the output quality

1. MPEG-2

MPEG-2 is most widely used as the format of digital television signals that are broadcast by terrestrial cable and direct broadcast satellite television systems. MPEG-2 was created to be able to deliver video for VHS over a telephone network copper wire DSL or a T-1, which

---

[14] Oppenheimer & Co, Timothy Horan, *Wireless Set to Transform Communications/Cloud* (June 21, 2018) (*Oppenheimer & Co. Report*).

delivered 1.5 Mbps. Released in 1994, MPEG-2 was the second of several standards developed by the Moving Pictures Expert Group. MPEG-2 is a "lossy" video compression method. Lossy means that data is lost, or thrown away, during compression, so the quality after decoding is less than the original picture. The objective is to maximize the amount of data thrown away while maintaining a minimal effect on the viewing experience for the end user. In a video this means only transmitting the bits that change from one video frame to the next.

2. MPEG-4 Advanced Video Coding (AVC)

The development of MPEG-4 began the same year MPEG-2 was released when it became apparent that further improvements could have been made to MPEG-2. It was initially introduced in 1998. MPEG-4 offers benefits in applications and services composed of many different streams with low bandwidth and data-rate requirements and where efficient transmission is requested in terms of overhead, delays, and synchronization, and as of 2014, it is one of the most commonly used formats for the recording, compression, and distribution of video content. MPEG-4, in addition to enhanced experience, provides an advanced video coding (AVC) compression process that cuts the bit rate by as much as 50% for the same image quality as MPEG-2.[15]

MPEG-4 AVC is not only used by video streaming sources such as YouTube but also by web software such as Adobe Flash Player, in addition to HDTV broadcasts over terrestrial, cable, mobile and satellite. One disadvantage of MPEG-4 is that it required different, more expensive hardware than MPEG-2, causing the transition to MPEG-4 to be slow, especially in developing countries.

3. High-Efficiency Video Coding (HEVC)

The latest video compression standard is High-Efficiency Video Coding (HEVC). It was developed by MPEG and ITU-T and approved in early 2013. In comparison to MPEG-4 AVC, it offers about double the data compression ratio at the same level of video, or significantly improved video quality at the same bit rate. However, like MPEG-4 AVC, it works by comparing different parts of a frame of video to find the areas that are redundant, both within a single frame as well as in subsequent frames, which are then replaced with a short description instead of the original pixels. Consumer hardware for HEVC is not yet widely available because of high licensing costs, but it has the

---

[15] EE Times, Richard Quinnell, *Introduction to MPEG-4 Video Compression* (Sept. 15, 2004) https://www.eetimes.com/document.asp?doc_id=1275756.

potential to make ultra-high definition over satellite more cost effective in the long run.

Figure 2-3: Relative Bit Rate for a Given Video Quality

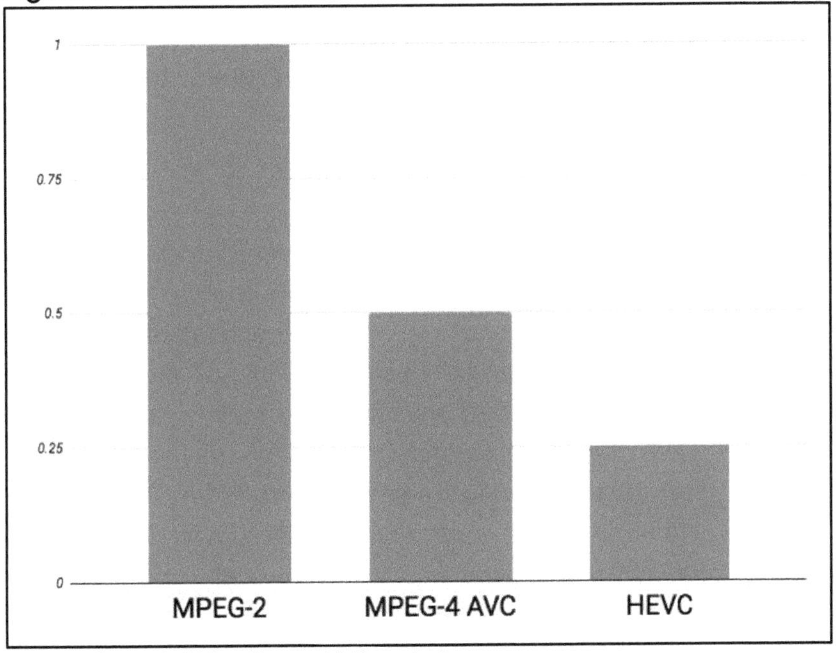

Source: Summit Ridge Group, LLC analysis

C. Multiple-Input Multiple-Output (MIMO)

Multiple-Input Multiple-Output, or MIMO, is a method for multiplying the capacity of a radio link using multiple transmit and receive antennas to exploit multipath propagation.[16] It essentially allows a wireless network to transmit and receive more than one data signal simultaneously over the same radio program stream. This multiplies the capacity of a wireless connection without requiring more spectrum. The more antennas the transmitter or receiver is equipped with, the more signal paths are possible and the better the performance in terms of reliability and data rate.

[MIMO] multiplies the capacity of a wireless connection without requiring more spectrum

MIMO technology has been standardized for 3G and 4G networks. It is in widespread commercial use and is expected to play a crucial part in the 5G networks of the future. MIMO's ability to serve multiple users and multiple devices simultaneously within a condensed area while maintaining fast data rates and consistent performance makes it

---

[16] Multipath propagation is the phenomenon that results in radio signals reaching the receiving antenna by two or more paths.

desirable technology for addressing the needs of the forthcoming 5G era. In particular, new advances in MIMO technology are enabling the use of 24-90 GHz using millimeter wave, or mmW, which are spectrum-using techniques previously thought to be impossible. Since MIMO systems need to pack more antennas into a small area physically, they require the use of higher frequency spectrum because as the carrier frequency gets higher, the antenna elements get smaller.

D. Beamforming

Beamforming uses multiple antennas to control the direction of a wave...and allow for greater signal focus...[and] dramatically increases capacity

Beamforming is a technique used in steerable antenna arrays that allows the transmitter to send data to specific users, among many, by exploiting the channel. A network determines where a device is located and sends a stronger signal in that particular direction. Beamforming uses multiple antennas to control the direction of a wave by appropriately weighing the magnitude and phase of individual antenna signals in an array of multiple antennas. It improves signal reception, reduces interference, and allows for greater signal focusing on specific user devices in high demand areas. [17] Beamforming enables wireless operators to dramatically increase the capacity of a specific amount of spectrum and/or reduce the number of cell sites needed. As discussed in Chapter XIX.A of this *Handbook*, the rate of cell site growth in the U.S. is dramatically lower than traffic growth.

1. High Throughput Satellite Technology

High throughput satellite (HTS) technology is a type of beamforming

High throughput satellite technology (HTS) is a type of beam formation that has increased the capacity of the most advanced GEO satellites - satellites in a geostationary orbit – circling the Earth at the same speed of rotation as the Earth thus maintaining the same location above the ground. HTS increased capacity on advanced new data satellites by approximately two orders of magnitude over the past 5 to 7 years. HTS achieves this dramatic increase in bandwidth capacity through frequency reuse, similar to how cellular operators reuse frequency. This results in each individual satellite being able to offer significantly more bandwidth over the same amount of spectrum. HTS effectively delivers higher performance capabilities at a lower cost. Increasingly, HTS technology is also being incorporated in planned non-geostationary satellites (NGSO).

---

[17]RCR Wireless News, *How Beamforming and Massive-MIMO are Advancing Mobile Networks* (Dec. 4, 2017) https://www.rcrwireless.com/20171204/network-infrastructure/lte/beamforming-massive-mimo-advancing-mobile-networks.

E. 1G Mobile Technologies

1. Time Division Multiplexing (TDM)

Time Division Multiplexing (TDM) is a technique for transmitting a number of separate data, voice, and video signals simultaneously over one program stream by interweaving a piece of each signal one after another. TDM is a technology that allowed 24 circuits to carry voice in one program stream. TDM was used in the legacy telephone network. It was created in the 1870s by Émile Baudot, a French telegraphy engineer, and enabled multiple telegraph signals to be sent on a single wire at the same time. The term "baud" was named after him, which is the modulation rate, or the number of symbols or pulses per second. Modems, for example, are referred to as 600 baud or 1200 baud, meaning that they transmit 600 or 1200 symbols per second. TDM in telecommunications divided up a transmission facility into 24 voice lines, called a T1 in the U.S., or 30 voice lines, called an E1 in Europe. Each of the voice lines has a data bit rate of 64 kbps. Each voice line is referred to as a channel. T1, SONET, and ISDN are all common TDM methods of transmitting data using frequencies in telecommunications.

2. Time Division Multiple Access (TDMA)

TDMA is a channel access method used to facilitate channel sharing without interference

Time division multiple access (TDMA) was an early method of delivering data and voice on mobile phones. TDMA allows multiple stations to share and use the same transmission channel by dividing signals into different time slots and allocating the slots to multiple calls. This enables a single frequency to support multiple, simultaneous data channels.

TDMA is a channel access method used to facilitate channel sharing without interference. It was used in the 2G Global System for Mobile communications (GSM). TDMA was the first digital mobile technology replacing 1G analog cellular service. TDMA was the first platform to enable the use of SMS text messaging, MMS (multimedia messaging), and picture messaging, all of which were encrypted along with voice calls. With TDMA, more users could use the same channel within a frequency. TDMA transmitters divide the single channel into frames, and the frames into time slots. Each mobile user of a base station is a time slot within a channel. There are multiple transmitters, rather than one transmitter for one receiver, for each time slot. The base station directs the mobile phone when to send the signal by assigning it a time slot. When a mobile phone attempts to connect to a base station, a single time slot is allocated to allow all the mobile phones connect to the base station.

The advantage of TDMA over other cellular technologies like CDMA is that once TDMA is connected to a base station and brought into timing on its own dedicated time slot within a frequency, the mobile device does not have to be connected to other frequencies, but needs only to listen and broadcast in its assigned time slot. The mobile device can search and learn of other nearby operating frequencies but does not connect to them. However, when the mobile device is moving the timing with the base station can change because of the distance to the base station changes when the signal arrives. One disadvantage is that the time slot allocated for timing sometimes caused a buzz in nearby speakers. Also, because of the speed of light caused signals to take longer to reach a base station, once the mobile handset went beyond 35 km, the handset could no longer keep its timing correct with the base station, and it would disconnect. TDMA limits bandwidth more than other techniques like CDMA because the time slots require empty slots between them as guard slots, taking up bandwidth. TDMA is also used for satellite and local area wireline transmissions.

3. Frequency Division Multiple Access (FDMA)

Frequency Division Multiple Access, or FDMA, is often used alongside TDMA in GSM. FDMA coordinates channels, or frequency bands, between multiple users. This technique assigns individual frequency slots and reuses these frequency slots throughout the system. To minimize interference from the reuse of frequencies, FDMA allocates different channels for neighboring cell sites. In satellite transmissions, users transmit at a different frequency but share the same frequency channel or transponder. FDMA depends on hardware filters to separate frequencies.

4. Frequency Division Duplexing (FDD)

Frequency division duplex, or FDD, is a technique where a transmitter and receiver operate at different carrier frequencies. FDD is used to slightly separate the send and receive signals in radio transmissions but allow the transmissions to use the same channel of spectrum. By using FDD, base stations do not tie up bandwidth with timing slots such as with TDMA. Many mobile systems use FDD including UMTS, WCDMA, CDMA2000, and WiMAX.

F. 2G Mobile Technologies

1. Code Division Multiple Access (CDMA)

CDMA uses a spread spectrum technique where electromagnetic energy is spread to allow for a signal with wider bandwidth

Code division multiple access, or CDMA, is a multiplexing technique that allows numerous signals to occupy a single transmission channel, optimizing the use of available bandwidth. CDMA opened up the doors for allowing more users to use the same spectrum and for each user to access more data. The CDMA digital standard is a leading communications network standard in North America and parts of Asia.

CDMA technology was initially used by the military in World War II to evade enemy attempts to access radio communication signals. A U.S.S.R. engineer developed CDMA in 1937 and deployed it as a mobile phone weighing 6.5 lbs. in 1957 for Soviet officials. In 1958, the same engineer developed a pocket phone weighing 1.1 lbs. using CDMA. Then, in the early 1990's, Qualcomm introduced the possibility of using the same concept in the context of a cellular network. CDMA is not a government or industry standard like GSM. CDMA technology later became attractive for 3G high-speed mobile use and became the infrastructure on which all 3G networks are based.

CDMA uses a spread spectrum technique where electromagnetic energy is spread to allow for a signal with a wider bandwidth. In CDMA, data and voice packets are separated using codes that are scrambled over a wide frequency spectrum and can only be reconstructed by the intended receiver. CDMA allows several people on different cell phones to be multiplexed over the same channel to share a bandwidth of frequencies. CDMA offers a 6-fold increase in capacity compared to TDMA, and the two technologies are not cross compatible.

Figure 2-4: Different Multiplexing Techniques

Rather than using time division for allocating use of spectrum, CDMA uses codes to spread out the data being sent and received for each user across the same spectrum

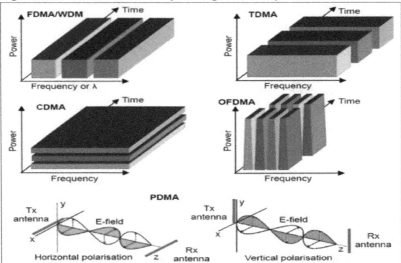

Source: electronicsforu.com[18]

Rather than using time division for allocating use of a spectrum, CDMA uses codes to spread out the data being sent and received for each user across the same spectrum. The CDMA technique is called spread spectrum multiple access. CDMA employs multiple transmitters to send coded data signals to individual mobile devices without causing interference between the users' devices. Each user device is assigned a code, which then correlates only with data sent from the base station using the same code. Other users on the same spectrum in the same system are assigned different codes and can only receive data signals from the base station correlated with their unique codes. The coding technique allows a larger number of users with more data to be sent without causing the same interference that would result with time division multiple access spectrum methods.

CDMA's use of spread spectrum and special coding for multiple transmitters enables it to send signals to individual mobile devices without interference. Each device is able to use the full frequency assigned for all devices. CDMA operates by creating a pseudo-random code that spreads the data uniformly across the transmitted power. Using the pseudorandom code, smaller pulse durations are created to deliver more bits within the signal pulse, thus creating far greater efficiencies for delivering bandwidth and connecting to more users. The spectrum codes for each device allow the devices to receive their unique transmission on the same frequency without

---

[18] Elecgtroncisforu.com, *High-Speed DWDM Technology*,
https://electronicsforu.com/technology-trends/high-speed-dwdm-technology

interfering with other devices.

2. General Packet Radio Service (GPRS)

General packet radio service, or GPRS, was rolled out in 2000 as a packet-switched mobile data service standard by the European Telecommunications Service Institute (ETSI) that worked in tandem with GSM. GPRS delivered data rates from 56 kbps to 114 kbps, similar to dial-up modem service rates. GPRS was a 2G and 3G system for GSM. The GPRS system was sold based on data rates and used a best efforts method. This means the more users on a base station, the lower speeds and quality of service. GPRS delivered the data portion of a user's service, the Internet, while GSM delivered voice and SMS to a user's same device. Some devices that provided data with GPRS would temporarily disable data transmission while voice calls were being delivered with GSM in the same handset, which was a severe flaw in the system as users could not make phone calls while browsing the Internet.

3. Enhanced Data Rates for Global Evolution (EDGE)

The purpose of EDGE was to bridge the data speed gap between 2G and 3G

EDGE, or Enhanced Data Rates for Global Evolution, was first deployed in the U.S. in 2003 by Cingular (part of BellSouth before BellSouth/Cingular were merged with SBC and renamed AT&T). EDGE tripled the data rate compared to GSM. Additionally, EDGE increased the data rate to 236 kbps or four times over that delivered by GPRS. Currently, Evolved EDGE provides a peak rate of 1 Mbps and an average rate of 400 kbps. Its purpose was to bridge the data speed gap between 2G and 3G. This made it a 2.5G technology that delivered backward-compatibility with GSM and GPRS, allowing users to operate on both EDGE and GSM so that mobile carriers were not required to change their base stations. Carriers migrating to EDGE did not have to upgrade their GSM core networks (MAPs), and they only had to make minor equipment changes in their base station radios. Today, edge migration requires just a software upgrade. EDGE is also sometimes referred to as EGPRS (Enhanced GPRS) and also as IMT Single Carrier (IMT-SC). EDGE was made a part of the GSM family by 3GPP (Third Generation Partnership Project)[19] and EDGE is part of the ITU's, or International Telecommunications Union,[20] IMT-

---

[19] Third Generation Partnership Project (3GPP) is a global wireless communications organization that collaboratively develops standards, described in Chapter VII.D of this Handbook.

[20] The ITU specializes in promoting cooperation in the use of international information and communication technologies, including the allocation, standardization and

2000 (or Improved Mobile Telephone Service)[21] family of 3G standards.

4. Global System for Mobile (GSM)

GSM is a 2G mobile standard. It is used on various spectrums in the 900MHz range and the 1800 MHz range, which includes, for example, 25 MHz from 890-915 MHz (the uplink) and 25MHz from 935-960 MHz (the downlink). GSM compresses and digitizes the data signal, then sends the data on a signal channel with two other streams of data for other users for a total of three users per channel. Because each stream has a dedicated time slot, each user receives their unique data transmission from the base station.

G. 3G Mobile Technologies

1. WCDM - Wideband Code Division Multiple Access

WCDMA is used in most 3G mobile networks

Wideband code division multiple access (WCDMA) is used in most third-generation mobile networks such as 3-GSM. WCDMA was an evolution of the 2G network CDMA and was established by NTT Docomo. WCDMA works with 2G GSM and EDGE. WCDMA is compatible with UMTS. WCDMA allowed mobile providers to deliver broadband Internet along with voice, text, SMS, and MMS. WCDMA uses a pair of 5 MHz channels and DS-CDMA, rather than the smaller 1.25 MHz channels, which were used by CDMA2000. WCDMA uses CDMA, which unlike GSM is not a government or industry standard. CDMA was however used in a priority manner by Qualcomm starting in the 1990s.

2. UMTS - Universal Mobile Telecommunication System

Universal Mobile Telecommunications Service (UMTS) is a 3G broadband packet-based transmission of text, digitized voice, video, and multimedia content at rates up to 2 Mbps. UMTS is a 3G technology based on GSM. It was developed by the standards group 3GPP. UMTS was designed as a completed end-to-end mobile system with the radio access network. The complete system was referred to as universal terrestrial RAN, or UTRAN. The core network connected to the RNC, or Radio Network Controllers. The RNCs are

---

regulation of global radio spectrum, described below in Chapter VII.B of this *Handbook*.

[21] Improved Mobile Telephone Service (IMTS) is described below in Chapter VIII.A of this *Handbook*.

connected to the base stations or Node BN's. The validation of user devices requires a SIM or subscriber identity module. The terms WCDMA and UMTS are often used interchangeably. However, WCDMA refers to the radio interface technology used within UTMS, and UTMS refers to the complete system.

3. Evolution Data Optimized (EVDO)

Evolution data optimized (EVDO) combines CDMA and TDM techniques to maximize throughput. However, EVDO does not allow voice and data to be transmitted at the same time. European countries solved the voice-data problem by creating SV-DO or Simultaneous Voice and Data Optimization. SV-DO was not adopted in the U.S., however. 3G-GSM networks in Europe use SV-DO. Carriers introduced CDMA to the U.S. in 1995 because its capacity for both the number of users and data throughput exceeded GSM. GSM was delivered before Qualcomm rolled out CDMA, but because GSM used TDMA, which was limited by time slots and could not provide the same throughput as CDMA, some carriers selected CDMA. 3G GSM adopted a CDMA technology, called WCDMA or Wideband CDMA, which increased its capacity. Ultimately, because 3G GSM was delivered after CDMA, CDMA dominated the market in the U.S.

H. 4G and LTE Mobile Technologies

Long Term Evolution (LTE) is a wireless standard developed by 3GPP and first demonstrated by Ericsson in 2007.[22] It is an upgrade path for carriers with CDMA2000 and GSM/UMTS networks. LTE is a network of base stations without a centralized intelligent controller. This distributed intelligence among the base stations which accelerates handover and connection time.[23] It is important to note that not all LTE networks meet 4G standards specified in 3GPP Releases 8 and 9.

4G is the fourth generation of mobile technology, following 3G. To be considered a 4G, a network must meet the ITU-R's IMT-advanced requirements.[24] These include requirements that the network must be based entirely on IP-packet-switched technology and have peak data

---

[22] *Ericsson Demonstrates Live LTE at 144 Mbps.* Ericsson Press Release (Feb 9, 2007) https://www.ericsson.com/en/press-releases/2007/2/ericsson-demonstrates-live-lte-at-144mbps.

[23] *LTE*, 3GPP http://www.3gpp.org/technologies/keywords-acronyms/98-lte.

[24] Report M.2134-0, *Requirements Related to Technical Performance for IMT-Advanced Radio Interface*, ITU-R (2008) http://www.itu.int/pub/R-REP-M.2134-2008/en.

rates of approximately 100 Mbps for mobile use, as well as meeting a variety of spectrum utilization requirements. Additional aspects of 4G, today's primary mobile technology, are descried throughout this handbook.

I. 5G Mobile Technology

5G is a marketing term to describe the next-generation mobile technology. Standards for 5G have not fully stabilized, but generally, promise large increased in data rates and lower latency. The ITU IMT-2020 standard, for example, allows for downlink speeds as high as 20 Gbps. IMT-2020 set the minimum 5G download at 100 Mbps and minimum upload at 50 Mbps. Maximum latency will be 4ms compared to 4G latency typically in the U.S. at 61ms. 3GPP release 15 covering part of the standard was frozen in June 2018. 3GPP expects Release 16 to be finalized at the end of 2019.[25] Industry observers expect a global launch of 5G services is expected soon after, around 2020.

5G is up to 50% more spectrally efficient than 4G. However, much of increase in data rates in 5G will come from using larger blocks of a higher frequency spectrum, particularly millimeter wave spectrum.

The increase performance of 5G may enable wireless carriers to provide service sufficient to substitute for fixed broadband, and wireline-mobile carriers like Verizon and AT&T may be able to use 5G – particularly with fixed-mobile mmW spectrum and technology as a cost-effective method of adding additional broadband homes to their existing wired broadband base. In home broadband service delivery using wired broadband and mobile broadband using 5G will begin to look similar from a network infrastructure perspective. One of the key components of 5G is the small cell which is located near the home; wireline-mobile operators are deploying fiber into neighborhoods to serve the small cell. Fiber deployment reaching near the homes – resembling fiber-to-the-home -- will be a large cost element of 5G.

Thus, 5G will have many elements of a fixed broadband service to the home. With fiber placed deep into neighborhoods for mobile 5G small cells, mobile carriers could begin to replace slower DSL served by the wireline provider. It is estimated that 28% of the 96 million broadband wired homes are served DSL, 7% by fiber, and 64% cable. Of the 126 million homes in the U.S., 10 million have no access to a wired broadband provider and 46 million have access to just one wired broadband provider. Thus, there are opportunities for a 5G mobile

---

[25] *Release 16*, 3GPP http://www.3gpp.org/release-16.

operator to become the home's new broadband provider. The 5G mobile operator could replace the wired broadband provider much in the way mobile phones have allowed homes to "cut the cord" on voice wireline service. Such a shift in broadband providers from wired to mobile could, possibly, substantially increase mobile operators' revenues while disrupting the cable and wireline businesses even further.

Mobile operators plan to spend billions upgrading to 5G. Many questions remain open about how much will be required to upgrade and where the capital expense will be focused. Typically, the large mobile operators in the U.S. have spent annually between $5-$10 billion per year on network infrastructure. The question remains open whether this capex expenditure will continue in line with previous years or be more, or even less. There are reports that 4G base stations will require only a software upgrade and an antenna change for 5G. The larger network cost could be in building fiber into the neighborhoods to serve new small cells. The other issue is whether customers will be able to experience any real speed or latency quality over what they have been receiving with 4G. Lower band spectrum used for 5G is expected to deliver similar speeds but higher bands like mmW will deliver much higher speeds.

Expected elements of 5G are described throughout this *Handbook*.

III. Network Technologies

A. Multiprotocol Label Switching (MPLS)

[MPLS] gives the network the ability to consistently handle [data] packets with distinct characteristics

Multiprotocol label switching (MPLS) was created in the late 1990s as a more efficient alternative to traditional IP routing. Traditional IP routers required each router to independently determine where the data packet would go next by inspecting the packet's destination IP address before consulting its own routing table. This process consumed time and hardware resources and also resulted in degraded performance for real-time applications such as voice and video. MPLS addressed this problem by establishing pre-determined, efficient routes. The first router a data packet goes to determines the packet's entire route and assigns it to a specific forwarding equivalence class (FEC), indicated by adding a short bit sequence to the packet. Each router in the network uses a table indicating how to handle packets for specific FEC types.

Accordingly, once the packet enters the network, routers no longer need to perform their own individual analysis. Instead, subsequent routers use the bit label as an index into a table that provides them with a new FEC for that packet. This technique gives the network the ability to consistently handle packets with distinct characteristics. Some of the benefits of MPLS are its scalability, performance quality, superior bandwidth utilization, reduction of network connection, and better end user experience. Additionally, it is a virtual private network separate from the public Internet, making it a secure transportation mode. A major drawback of MPLS is the price. MPLS is expensive and must be purchased from a carrier. This makes it far more expensive than sending traffic over the public Internet. Although MPLS is the current standard routing network, software-defined networks may potentially replace it in the future.[26]

The ability to move network elements to software/digital increases flexibility, reduces cost, lowers latency, and extends the life of hardware

B. Software Defined Network (SDN)

Software Defined Networks, or SDN, is a network architecture approach enabling a network to be centrally programmed and updated using external software applications as opposed to having fixed software in the hardware device. SDN helps operators manage an entire network consistently, regardless of the underlying network

---

[26] Neal Weinberg, "*MPLS Explained*," March 16, 2018. https://www.networkworld.com/article/2297171/sd-wan/network-security-mpls-explained.html

technology in order to improve network performance and monitoring. This ability to move network elements to software increases flexibility, reduces cost, lowers latency, and extends the life of hardware. In an age where the number of connected devices is rapidly increasing, network traffic can be alleviated by SDNs, which can help prioritized traffic and conduct analytics on the types of traffic on a network.

4G wireless communication introduced SDN to telecom networks.[27] It was a shift from traditional network devices, such as switches and routers, which have built-in control, data, management, and service planes that operate using protocols to route traffic and manage the network. SDN separates the management of the control plane of network devices from the underlying data plane that forwards network traffic. It effectively converts all the major resources provided by servers, such as computational capacity, memory, storage, and even bandwidth, into abstract network elements. It allows for end-to-end control of a network through application program interfaces (APIs) that are programmed to manipulate these abstract network elements. SDN removes a large portion of what had previously required manual management with virtualized capabilities.

1. SD-WAN Software Defined Wide-Area Network

SD-WAN architecture enables service providers to reduce or eliminate reliance on expensive MPLS

A software-defined wide-area network (SD-WAN) is a specific application of SDN technology. It is applied to wide-area network (WAN) connections which are used to connect enterprise networks over large geographic distances. SD-WAN can route any type of traffic, simplifying the management and operation of a WAN by separating the networking hardware from its control mechanism. SD-WAN uses multiple channels to optimize bandwidth by directing the WAN traffic along the best route. This shifts traffic to links with bandwidth sufficient enough to accommodate each user's needs. SD-WAN uses automatic failover, so if one link fails or becomes congested, traffic is automatically redirected to another link. This further boosts application performance and reduces latency.

Additionally, SD-WAN architecture enables service providers to reduce or eliminate reliance on expensive leased MPLS circuits. It sends lower priority, less-sensitive data over cheaper public Internet connections, reserving private links for mission-critical or latency-sensitive traffic. There has been a debate in recent years over whether

---

[27] ZDNet, Scott Fulton, *What is SDN? How Software-Defined Networking Changed Everything* (May 22, 2018) https://www.zdnet.com/article/software-defined-networking-101-what-sdn-is-and-where-its-going/

SD-WAN could replace MPLS. While MPLS has continued to be a fundamental part of the WAN landscape thus far, SD-WAN technology is becoming more widely used. An increasingly common strategy is to use a hybrid system of MPLS and SD-WAN to offload as much MPLS traffic as possible through SD-WAN. MPLS is used for time-sensitive applications that require guaranteed delivery.

2. Digital Payload

Digital payloads on satellites are a type of SDN. They allow satellite operators to change power allocations, frequency, and beam formation of satellites in orbit. Previously these satellite characteristics were fixed during the manufacturing process and could not be changed during the satellite's entire 15-18-year design life. This technology dramatically improves the satellite's flexibility. As such, satellite operators are increasingly ordering satellites with digital payload elements.

3. ROADM Reconfigurable Optical Add-Drop Multiplier

ROADMs allow operators to access any wavelength from any node at any time

A reconfigurable optical add-drop multiplier (ROADM) is a device for fiber optic cables that can add, block, pass, or redirect modulated beams of various wavelengths in an optical network. A laser tuned to a particular wavelength electronically changes the selected channel routing through the optical network. Like a switch, the ROADM can provide flexibility in rerouting optical streams by bypassing faulty connections, decreasing service disruption, and adapting or upgrading the network. This SDN communications technology increased the amount of bandwidth that can be transported over fiber by more than an order of magnitude. ROADMs allow operators to access any wavelength from any node at any time, which replicates the operational efficiency and flexibility of SDN networks at the wavelength level.

C. Submarine Cable Networking

Submarine networks carry over 95% of the world's electronic communications traffic

Submarine cable networks carry over 95% of the world's intercontinental electronic communications traffic. [28] By contrast, statistics released by the FCC indicate that satellites account for just 0.37% of all U.S. international capacity.[29] Submarine communication cables are hundreds or thousands of miles long and can be as deep

---

[28] Ciena, *Submarine Networking* https://www.ciena.com/insights/submarine/?src=PR.
[29] FCC's Circuit Status Report (Aug. 28, 2015) https://www.fcc.gov/circuit-status-report.

on the ocean floor as Mount Everest is high. The advantage of submarine communication cables is that they have less latency and are less expensive (on a unit of capacity basis) than satellites. The first submarine cable successful operated was laid in 1851 across the English Channel. Submarine networks were traditionally copper but are now always fiber optic cables, which avoids the latency and bit loss issues satellite operators must account for.

Figure 3-1: Submarine Cable Networking

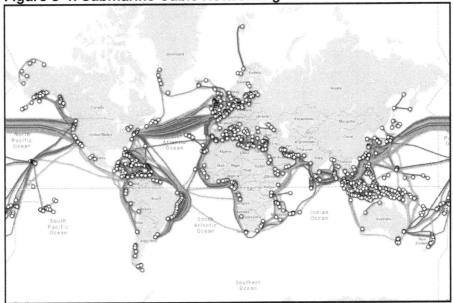

Source: TeleGeography (www.TeleGeorgaphy.com), reprinted with permission

The MAREA cable, a 4,000-mile transatlantic cable between Virginia Beach, VA, and Bilbao, Spain, is capable of carrying 160 terabits per second (Tbps) with eight fibers.[30] MAREA began operation in February 2018 and is the highest-capacity subsea cable to cross the Atlantic. Before 2015, the average submarine network had a capacity of about 16 Tbps and newer post-2015 networks averaging around 97 Tbps, indicating a substantial increase in capacity over the past few years.

1. Trends

Traditionally, subsea cables were owned by telecom carriers, but in the past few years ownership has shifted to major Internet providers such as Google, Facebook, and Microsoft. The reason for this trend change is that the amount of capacity deployed by these content

---

[30] Microsoft, Deborah Bach, *Microsoft, Facebook and Telixus complete the highest-capacity subsea cable to cross the Atlantic* (Sept. 21, 2017) https://news.microsoft.com/features/microsoft-facebook-telxius-complete-highest-capacity-subsea-cable-cross-atlantic/.

providers has outpaced the undersea cable capacity deployed by telecom operators. As of 2018, there are approximately 448 submarine cables in service around the world, a massive increase from the 285 submarine cables in service in 2014. There was more undersea cable laid in 2016 than in the prior five years. This is due to the fact that capacity price is declining at a rate of approximately 20-25% annually[31] while the amount of available capacity has rapidly increased.

Cable rates are falling quickly as a result of the completion of new cable projects, which has provided accelerated shocks to pricing. Submarine pricing has historically been uneven with a wide range of prices with high priced outliers skewing the range. Recently prices have started to converge, probably as a result of more submarine options. Submarine cables have a life expectancy of approximately 25 years in during which they are economically viable from a capacity standpoint. New technologies such as coherent detection modems and ROADMs, however, are extending the viable lifespan of submarine networks.

2. New Technology

Coherent detection modems were originally developed for terrestrial networks. It is a transmission system that consists of a transmitter that allows implementing different modulation formats and a receiver able to detect them. The optical receiver can track the phase of an optical transmitter and extract any phase and frequency information carried by the transmitted signal. Submarine operators' rapid adoption of coherent detection modems by submarine operators has changed how they add capacity to transoceanic corridors, extended the life of existing wet plant assets, and eliminated the closed nature of their networks. This makes it possible for submarine cable operators to choose equipment from a wider variety of vendors. Utilizing coherent modem technology over subsea cables helped to integrate land, sea, and cloud networks.

ROADMs, also originally designed for terrestrial networks, have also been adopted to fit submarine networking. ROADMs greatly simplify and reduce the cost of end-to-end networking. These new technologies allow submarine networks to maximize the efficiency of optical spectrum. This helps them keep up with demand for

---

[31] At the 2018 Pacific Telecommunications Counsel Conference on January 21, 2018, senior analysts from TeleGeographic presented an analysis on the pricing of subsea cable projects.

optical spectrum. This helps them keep up with demand for bandwidth, guaranteeing network availability via software to ensure network faults are handled quickly and effectively. It reduces cost by utilizing optimized network designs to lower the total cost of end-to-end network communication. ROADMS also allows higher data rates of 100 Gbps and higher exceeding the former limit of 10 Gbps allowing much more to be sent over extremely long-haul networks spanning thousands of miles.

3. Submarines and Satellites

Although submarines and satellites differ in capability, their lifecycles are remarkably similar. The first three years of life are dedicated to production and deployment and are without revenue. After production is completed and operation begins there is a steep growth curve in terms of revenue.[32] Traditionally, there is then approximately 36 months at peak profitability before the value begins to decrease at an accelerating rate.

Submarine capacity increases over the past few years also largely mirror the increase in satellite capacity over the same period (See Parts II and III of this *Handbook* for more detailed information about satellite industry dynamics).

D. Network Function Virtualization (NFV)

NFV is designed to consolidate and deliver the networking components needed to support a fully virtualized infrastructure

Network function virtualization or "NFV" is a network architecture that separately packages functions from dedicated hardware into individual virtual network functions (VNFs), which are then run on a virtual server. NFV is designed to consolidate and deliver the networking components needed to support a virtualized infrastructure. This virtualization of network functions reduces dependency on dedicated hardware appliances for network operators and allows for improved scalability and customization across the entire network. NFD and SDN are highly complementary to one another.

1. OpenStack

OpenStack is a form of NFV cloud operating system that controls large pools of computing, storage and networking resources throughout a data center. The data center is managed through a

---

[32] With the entrance of major content providers investing in subsea cables, after operation begins there is a massive leap in earnings because the cable usage is presold, rather than operators having to wait to sell usage until the cable is already operating, which accelerates this process.

resources through a web interface. OpenStack is a combination of open source tools, or projects, that use pooled virtual resources to build and manage private and public clouds. Service providers are using OpenStack as a basis for 5G, Internet of Things (IoT), and NFV. Benefits of OpenStack include reducing software and operational costs, along with giving carriers the flexibility to enhance and update the operating system in real time to meet their specific needs.

2. Network Slicing

The objective of network slicing is to allow a physical mobile operator to partition its network resources to allow for different users to multiplex over a single physical infrastructure. Network slicing is another form of virtualization that allows multiple intelligent networks to run on top of a shared physical network infrastructure. It is enabled by SDN and NFV so that each network slice is its own virtual network that can gather the necessary resources from the other parts of the network to function completely on its own.

The objective of network slicing is to allow a physical mobile operator to partition its network resources to allow for different users to multiplex over a single physical infrastructure.

The ability to partition the physical network at an end-to-end level allows optimum grouping of traffic, isolation from other users to prevent interference, and configuration of resources at a macro level. Network slicing is expected to be heavily employed in new mobile network technologies, Internet of Things (IoT), and very low latency applications. Latency and bandwidth partition decisions must be made by network operators in real time over all of a carrier's spectrum holdings. These decisions can be implemented if the network is software based.

E. WMN Wireless Mesh Networks

A wireless mesh network or "WMN" is a wireless communication network made up of radio nodes organized in a mesh topology. Wireless machine-to-machine (M2M) networks often use WMN. The radio technology can be proprietary, or standards-based like Bluetooth or Zigbee. The WMN network may operate as an IoT network using small inexpensive digital radios that are embedded in consumer electronic devices. The devices can also be networked through smartphones or can be wireless thermostats like Google's Home using Wi-Fi. The mesh network often uses its own router. These devices communicate with each other using low amounts of power, which allows each unit to become a hub in the network, where they pass information along from device to device until the data reaches an Internet-connected node.

WMN is a disruptive technology because it defies the assumption that...every device that wants to communicate over the same spectrum takes capacity away from another device

WMN is a disruptive technology because it defies the assumption that bandwidth is a scarce resource and that every device that attempts to communicate over the same spectrum reduces capacity from another device. In direct contrast to this assumption, under WMN architecture, each new device actually increases the overall last-mile broadband capacity. In WMN, each device in the network both contributes to the network capacity and uses the network capacity. Users add to and share the overall capacity of the network in WMN. Mesh networks dynamically route to mobile nodes to utilize the full range of wireless spectrum available.

F. IoT: The Internet of Things Wireless and Mobile Connected

The Internet of Things, or IoT, was a term that evolved from a technology created in the early 1990's called M2M, or Machine-to-Machine. Prior to 1992, M2M was a wired technology linking mostly sensors used in factories to a central database. In the mid-1990s, as mobile infrastructure was built-out, the M2M industry evolved to using the control channel side on the analog 1G and then 2G digital control channel mobile technology for delivering data from truck containers, train cars, bulldozers, tracking golf carts, sensors in oceans with temperature and pollution data, or electric meters. The mobile operator would transmit the information to and from the M2M service provider's database or control center. Cingular (now AT&T) provided the first mobile network allowing M2M companies to track train cars and truck containers across the country.

Around 2005, the concept rose that the Internet was a way of connecting everything, not just people but machines talking to machines and things talking to things. As mobile connections increased, the Internet moved from an Internet of Any Time connections and Any Place connections to "Any Thing" connections. The term, "Internet of Things," was coined by MIT Auto-ID professor Kevin Ashton in 1999 while working with RFID (Radio-frequency identification) used supply-chain management. M2M became the Internet of Things, or IoT.

IoT devices can be very small, like RFID chips placed on products or in passports and read with low-powered wireless readers, or larger devices that can be connected to the mobile infrastructure such as fixed utility smart-meters, thermostats, or truck meters. The vision for the connected Smart-Home has been around since mid-1980 trials; however, it was not until the cost of mobile devices dropped, the cost of sending mobile data and mobile subscriptions connections fell, and that Wi-Fi became ubiquitous in most broadband wired homes that IoT took off. Digital health has now entered the scene crossing the boundary between mobile smartphones and mobile machines with digital health devices like Fitbit, sleep-tech devices, and home health monitoring devices.

Businesses are building IoT into nearly every aspect of logistics such as putting devices on grocery shelves to track movement of products in real time, counting visitors entering and leaving buildings, tracking at the micro-level temperature in rooms for lowering utility costs, and tracking temperatures in refrigerator truck containers and restaurant coolers to reduce food spoilage costs. In 2022, if the trend continues, U.S. consumers will purchase 520 million connected devices, or almost four devices per home.[33] Gartner Group projects that globally there will be 20.4 billion wired and cellular IoT devices by 2020, doubling the estimated 11.2 billion devices in 2018.[34]

Figure 3-2: Global Total IoT Devices Projected by 2020

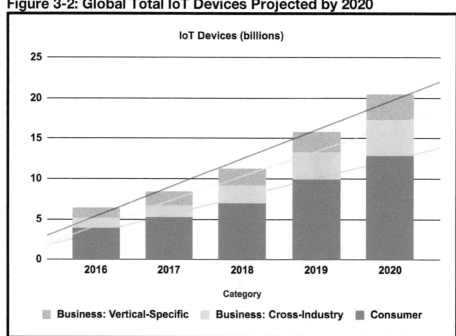

Data Source: Gartner data and Summit Ridge Analysis

IoT devices connect to the Internet using a variety of means, both wired and wireless, and using licensed and unlicensed spectrum. In the home and business, IoT devices often use unlicensed Wi-Fi,

---

[33] Park Associates, *U.S. consumers will buy more than 485 million connected devices in 2021* (May 22, 2018) http://www.parksassociates.com/blog/article/cus-2018-pr16.

[34] Gartner, *Gartner Says 8.4 Billion Connected "Things" Will Be in Use in 2017* (Feb. 7, 2017) https://www.gartner.com/en/newsroom/press-releases/2017-02-07-gartner-says-8-billion-connected-things-will-be-in-use-in-2017-up-31-percent-from-2016.

Bluetooth, and Zigbee. All the major mobile operators have an IoT business which allows IoT providers to connect using the cell network. Mobile operators have the advantage of easily connecting from anywhere that a cell phone will work and low per unit prices because typically IoT is sending narrow-band data, unless it is a video monitor. In 2017, there were a reported 650 million cellular-connected IoT devices globally, equivalent to around 10% of the total global mobile phone market. Ten mobile companies serve about 75% of the 650 million cell-connected IoT devices. In China, mobile IoT service is provided to approximately 230 million by three China operators, Vodafone delivers service to 60 million devices, and AT&T to 36 million devices. Other mobile operators cover the remaining 25% or 170 million devices.[35]

As small-cell growth develops, small-cells will move in closer proximity to the home, giving mobile operators the opportunity to leverage their IoT connectivity businesses and increase ARPU by migrating home IoT devices currently using Wi-Fi. Service and product firms may pay for this mobile connectivity making it transparent to the consumer as a method of keeping the consumer from moving to a competitor. These IoT devices will be in connected refrigerators, washers, dryers, and ovens. Video use — a high-bandwidth service — may burden the 5G mobile carriers but the video demand in the home will increase monitoring sitters, children, elderly, weather, or the pot left on the stove by accident. Computer vision and A.I. will be able to "watch" the home over video for the homeowner. 5G IoT will make use of 3.5 GHz CBRS, which is where small-cells will be used, as well as LTE-U which will aggregate unlicensed 5 GHz with licensed mobile spectrum. Narrow-band use for IoT will be a niche for various bands such as 220 MHz used for PTC - "positive train control." Dish has stated its plans to build-out its AWS-4, 700 MHz E Block, and H Block spectrum for the primary purpose of deploying a narrow band IoT, or NB-IoT, network. Dish explained that their NB-IoT network could deliver IoT services globally.[36]

Summit Ridge Group views IoT as an area that may dramatically grow

---

[35] Berg Insight, "The Global M2M/IoT Communications Market Report" http://www.berginsight.com/ReportPDF/ProductSheet/bi-globaliot3-ps.pdf.

[36] DISH Network, *Ex Parte Presentation in GN Docket No. 17-183, Expanding Flexible Use in Mid-Band Spectrum Between 3.7 and 24 GHz* (May 24, 2018) https://wireless2.fcc.gov/UlsEntry/attachments/attachmentViewRD.jsp?applType=search&fileKey=850740235&attachmentKey=20371372&attachmentInd=licAttach.

Summit Ridge Group views IoT as an area that may dramatically grow from narrowband use to broadband use. Currently, mobile broadband is driven by users downloading by watching YouTube and Netflix video. However, as IoT devices grown in number and capability, bandwidth demand from the average deployed IoT device will grow data demands for both uploading and downloading. Summit Ridge believes that with the dramatic increase in the number of IoT devices projected to pass 20 billion globally (wired, Wi-Fi, and cellular), even a slight growth in video upload will put new bandwidth demands on the networks. IoT devices will be uploading video that computer vision in the cloud will be "looking" at. The demand of IoT video could soon outpace smartphone device demand for downloading video.

G. Cognitive Radio

Cognitive radio or CR is a hybrid technology involving SDR as applied to spread spectrum communications. It is an adaptive, intelligent radio and network technology that can automatically detect available channels in wireless spectrum and accordingly change its transmission or reception parameters to allow more harmonious wireless communication. CR is dynamically configured to use the best wireless channels in its vicinity to avoid user interference and congestion. CRs have the ability to monitor, sense, and detect the conditions of their operating environment and then autonomously adapt their own operating systems to best match those conditions. They can also modify operational parameters such as frequency, modulation schemes, and transmit power.

H. Blockchain

Blockchain is a distributed ledger technology (DLT) that works with peer-to-peer computing nodes that rely upon the Internet to connect the points. It was introduced in October 2008 by pseudonym Satoshi Nakamoto to serve as the public transaction ledger for the cryptocurrency bitcoin. Blockchain was proposed to be a virtual currency system that circumvented a central authority for issuing currency, transferring ownership, and confirming transactions. It also prevents unauthorized changes to the ledger. Blockchain is a distributed database that maintains a shared list of records.

These records are called digital ledger blocks, and each encrypted block of code contains the history of every block before it with time-stamped transaction data down to the second. Blockchain is comprised of two primary components: a decentralized network

network maintains. Every member of the network can view this shared transaction ledger. There is no single point of failure from which records or digital assets can be hacked or corrupted.

Blockchain is an open source software, meaning anyone can examine the code and reuse or improve it. Blockchain is still in its very early stages of adoption.[37] However, while bitcoin is the first application of blockchain technology, it is certainly not the only one. Blockchain has the potential to radically revolutionize the foundation of network structure, similar to the impact of the introduction and adoption of TCP/IP (transmission control protocol/Internet protocol), which laid the foundation for the development of the modern Internet. Blockchain can be used in mobile networks to provide low latency and secure transmissions. It can also secure wireless IoT networks and be used to authenticate users' devices connecting to base stations, or in the reverse, to authenticate base stations to user devices to prevent mobile spoofing.[38] Mobile spoofing is where a base station that looks like the user's carrier but is not, connects a user and takes information from the user, just like when the user is roaming.

PART ONE: BACKGROUND

---

[37] Marco Iansiti and Karim R. Lakhani, Harvard Business Review, *The Truth About Blockchain* (Jan. 2017) https://hbr.org/2017/01/the-truth-about-blockchain.

[38] Mobile spoofing is where a base station that looks like the user's carrier, but is not, connects a user and takes information from the user, just like when the user is roaming.

Figure 3-3: Summary of Network Technologies

Network	What it Does	How it Helps
MPLS	Establishes pre-determined, highly efficient routes for data packets	Superior bandwidth utilization, scalability, and performance quality
SDN	Abstracts network elements and allows for end-to-end control of a network	Increases flexibility, reduces cost, lowers latency, and extends the life of hardware
SD-WAN	Uses multiple channels to optimize bandwidth by direction WAN traffic along the best route	Enables service providers to reduce or eliminate reliance on expensive leased MPLS circuits
ROADM	Allows fiber operators to access any wavelength from any node at any time	Replicates the operational efficiency and flexibility of SDN networks at the wavelength level
NFV	Consolidates and delivers the networking components needed to support a fully virtualized infrastructure	Reduces dependency on dedicated hardware appliances and allows for improved scalability and customization across the entire network
Network Slicing	Allows multiple intelligent networks to run on top of a shared physical network infrastructure	Optimizes traffic management, prevents interference, and allows resources to be configured at a macro level
WMN	Dynamically routes mobile nodes to utilize the full range of wireless spectrum available	Users add to and share the overall capacity of the network in WMN, compared to current wireless networks' Wi-Fi routers, where each new user depletes resources
Cognitive Radio	Automatically detects available channels in wireless spectrum and accordingly changes its own transmission or reception parameters to allow more harmonious wireless communication	Avoids user interference and detection by autonomously adapting an operating system
SAS	Spectrum Access System manages and assigns spectrum on a dynamic, as-needed basis across tiers of priority	Allows high priority users to share spectrum with lower priority users without losing quality of service

Source: Summit Ridge Group, LLC analysis

IV. Television Technology Developments

A. The Transition from Analog to Digital

Analog wireless technology is considered inefficient compared to the digital wireless technology we use today

Every transmission can be divided into two broad categories: analog and digital. Analog is a transmission method where data is translated into a continuous signal of electric pulses with varying amplitude. Digital transmission translates information into a binary format of ones and zeros where every bit is representative of two distinct amplitudes generated by digital modulation. Analog systems do not deliver the required capacity today's systems demand, and analog wireless technology is considered inefficient compared to the digital wireless technology we use today. Since June 13, 2009, full-power U.S. television stations nationwide have been required to broadcast exclusively in a digital format.[39] Most countries have also discontinued analog television transmission.

B. Television Resolution

1. SDTV vs. HDTV

Standard definition television (SDTV) is fairly equivalent with the quality of analog television, but it is transmitted digitally so there is no loss of signal regardless of the distance the signal is traveling, giving it a clear advantage over analog. High definition television (HDTV) is a digital broadcasting format that transmits image resolution that is significantly superior to SDTV, and it is the current standard video format in most broadcasts.

SDTV requires less spectrum to broadcast over the air than HDTV. A TV channel in the U.S. is 6 MHz wide. Originally four SDTV channels using MPEG-2 could use one 6 MHz TV channel for broadcasting. Today, because of software and processing power advances, up to seven SDTV can share one channel. In addition, in the past only one SDTV and one HDTV could occupy the same 6 MHz TV channel. Today, up to three HDTV streams can occupy the same channel. The relocation of UHF TV channels in the repack of 700 MHz and the Broadcast Incentive Auction encouraged different station owners to share channels.[40] Many channels were SDTV and could share. HDTV

---

[39] FCC, Digital Television Transition (Aug. 9, 2016) https://www.fcc.gov/general/digital-television.

[40] *Expanding the Economic and Innovation Opportunities of Spectrum Through Incentive Auctions*, GN Docket No. 12-268, Notice of Proposed Rulemaking, 27 FCC

is a newer technology that began to replace SDTV in the late 1990's. HDTVs took many years to become popular because they were more expensive than SDTVs, but now, in 2018, SDTVs are so rare they are difficult to find in stores.[41]

The main difference between SDTV and HDTV is the resolution. Resolution refers to the quality of the picture, and the higher resolution equals a higher quality picture. Although the benefits of HDTV are abundantly clear, it does come at a cost. High definition transmission requires more capacity than standard definition, and a compressed SDTV signal is five times smaller than a compressed HDTV signal. One of the most often cited reasons for the global explosion in bandwidth demand is the significant rise in video traffic, specifically HD video traffic.[42]

2. Ultra-High Definition Television

A 4k UHD video transmission needs a broadband speed of at least 20 Mbps and an 8k UHD video requires at least 50 Mbps.

Ultra-high definition television (UHD) is a display resolution standard of at least double that of HD (720p and 1020i are the most common standards with 720 and 1020 referring to the number of vertical pixels). UHD is not necessarily a technological breakthrough, as it does not require any new standards for display or do anything new for video processing; it just simply has a higher pixel count, and thus a crisper image. Consumers with 20/20 vision typically cannot distinguish between an HD and a UHD video unless the screen size is larger than 75 inches. Some negative aspects of UHD are that most video content is not broadcasted in UHD resolution, the large size of the media requires massive amounts of bandwidth to broadcast, and the cost to consumers to buy UHS televisions. A 4k UHD video transmission needs a broadband speed of at least 20 megabits per second (Mbps) and an 8k UHD video requires at least 50 Mbps, compared to an HD video, which uses around 5 Mbps.

C. ATSC 3.0

ATSC 3.0 is the latest version of the Advanced Television Systems

---

Rcd 12357 (2012); *Reallocation and Service Rules for the 698-746 MHz Spectrum Band (Television Channels 52-59)*, GN Docket No. 01-74, Report and Order, 17 FCC Rcd 1022 (2002).

[41] Verizon, *HDTV vs. SDTV: What You Should Know* (July 30, 2015) https://fios.verizon.com/beacon/hdtv-vs-sdtv/.

[42] Ciena, Bo Gowan, *How much bandwidth does Broadcast HD video use?* (Sept. 26, 2011) https://www.ciena.com/insights/articles/How-much-bandwidth-does-Broadcast-HD-video-use_prx.html.

Committee [43] standards, which define how television signals are broadcasted and interpreted. In November 2017, the FCC approved ATSC 3.0[44] as the next generation of broadcasting standard on a voluntary, market-driven basis. Over-the-air (antenna-based) television signals currently use version 1.0 of the ATSC standards, which was first introduced in 1996 and initiated the switch from analog to digital transmission. ATSC 3.0 is not backward compatible, so consumers will need to purchase an external converter to use the new standard. ATSC 3.0 offers a more vivid picture and sound quality, including UHD, mobile viewing capabilities, advanced emergency alerts, and better accessibility features. ATSC 3.0 is a hybrid system that can use both over-the-air signals and in-home broadband to deliver an experience closer to cable or satellite television. The audio and video content will be broadcasted over-the-air and other content, such as targeted ads, will be sent over Wi-Fi and integrated into the program. This gives broadcasters more flexibility than they currently have under ATSC 1.0. It may also provide them greater ability to compete with mobile broadband in terms of streaming data and video.

The rollout of ATSC 3.0 and impact on TV broadcasters' business models are still unclear. It will require broadcasters to buy new antennas and exciters and to simulcast during the transition period. Regulations surrounding permitted ATSC 3.0 services under broadcasting regulations are also unsettled. From a broad perspective, on one hand, ATSC 3.0 will give TV broadcasters significantly more capacity that they can sell in innovative ways via consumer subscription. On the other hand, increasing capacity may also increase advertising inventory and lower rates. It is unclear if television broadcasters are prepared to market subscription services to consumers or if consumers are prepared to invest in converters to receive ATSC 3.0 signals.

Major broadcasters with the resources to invest in dedicated groups to exploit ATSC 3.0 technology may be best positioned reap its benefits. Sinclair Broadcasting, Nextstar Media Group, and Univision, for example, have created a consortium, Spectrum Co LLC to focus on ATSC 3.0.[45]

---

[43] Advanced Television Systems Committee, About https://www.atsc.org/about-us/about-atsc/.

[44] *Authorizing Permissive Use of the 'Next Generation' Broadcast Television Standard* GN Docket No. 16-142, 32 FCC Rcd 9930 (2017) https://www.fcc.gov/document/fcc-authorizes-next-gen-tv-broadcast-standard-0.

[45] TVTechnology, Phil Kurtz, *John Hane Joins Spectrum Co as President.* TV Technology (Feb. 1, 2018) https://www.tvtechnology.com/news/john-hane-joins-spectrum-co-as-president.

V. Infrastructure

To meet consumer demands, core infrastructure must evolve along with other new, innovative communications technology. As illustrated in Figure 5-1 below, the shift in end-user behavior is driving new network infrastructure.

A. Copper Cables vs. Fiber Optic Cables

Cables are an important component of telecommunications infrastructure. Cables are used in mobile networks and satellite networks for back-haul from cell towers and satellite dishes. The type of cables a network uses can have a massive impact on network performance, reliability, and profitability. Cables are made either using copper conductors or fiber optic technology, although copper is rarely newly deployed, except for inside Cat 5 or 6 network cabling.

Fiber optic technology allows for far more efficient communication by leveraging high data rates

Copper cables transmit data through twisted pairs of copper wires, while fiber optic cables transmit data in the form of pulses of light through extremely thin strands of glass. Copper cables refer to a wide range of technologies: from twisted pairs, which are commonly found in old homes, to significantly more enhanced Cat (Category) 5, Cat 5e, and Cat 6 Ethernet cables. Two major differentiators between the two types of cables are the distances that they are able to operate over and the data volumes they are able to carry.

Fiber optic technology allows for far more efficient communication by leveraging high data rates with speeds of 10 Gb/s and currently operating over distances farther than 100 kilometers without repeaters, with a maximum cable length of 2000 kilometers. Copper wire cables are still deployed in legacy TDM telecommunications systems and have a much lower bandwidth and range than fiber optic cables. Copper pairs are used to deliver DSL, T-1s, and DS3. As deployed in telephone networks, copper can deliver service for many miles from a central office. Cat 5 indoor copper cables have a 100-meter maximum cable length for delivering local area networks. Two of the most commonly used copper Ethernet cables, the Category (Cat) 5, the Cat 5e and the Cat 6, have data rates of 100 Mb/s, 1 Gb/s, and 10 Gb/s, respectively. A flaw of copper cables is that they are susceptible to noise and pose a spark hazard from generating significant amounts of heat while in use.

Figure 5-1: End User Behavior Is Shifting

Aspect	From	To
Connectivity	Fixed	Mobile
Provisioning	Call Centers	Download Online
Computing	Owned	Sharing Resources

Figure 5-2: End User Behavior Is Also Driving New Networks

Aspect	From	To
Wireline	Copper	Fiber
Voice	TDM	IP
Wireless	3G	4G/5G
Infrastructure	Hardware	Software

Source: Oppenheimer & Co. report and Summit Ridge Group, LLC analysis

B. Fiber Innovation

Fiber can be run in two ways. 1: point-to-point, which is enterprise and carrier-grade fiber, or 2: point-to-multipoint, which is used residentially through passive optical networks, or PONs. PONs uses one fiber to support multiple wavelengths to provide a point-to-multipoint service that can support gigabit type speeds. PONs are less costly than point-to-point systems because a single optic strand can reach dozens of end users. Figure 5-3 describes the next generation of PONs technology to support increasing bandwidth needs.

Figure 5-3: Next Generation PON Technology

Technology	Features
XG-PON	Delivers 10 Gb/s downstream and 2.5 Gb/s upstream using a single fixed wavelength in each direction.
XGS-PON	Delivers 10 Gb/s in both directions and also supports dual rate transmission.
NG-PON2	Supports from 4 to 8 wavelengths of 10 Gb/s each over a single fiber and enables new capabilities like wavelength mobility and channel bonding. It can support more than 40 Gbps.

Source: Oppenheimer & Co. report and Summit Ridge Group, LLC analysis

VI. The Major Regulated Spectrum Bands

Radio spectrum consists of a range of frequencies that can be used to transmit information both by analog and digital methods. This spectrum ranges from approximately 3 kHz to 300 GHz, but the commercially viable spectrum bands range from about 500 kHz (AM Radio) to approximately 30 GHz (Ka-band satellite). The frequencies have different characteristics with respect to the distance they travel, building penetration (indoor reception), antenna sizes needed, and other factors. Consequentially, some spectrum bands are more suitable than others for certain applications. Therefore, the radio spectrum is split into several frequency bands that are assigned particular uses according to the characteristics of the frequencies. In general, lower frequencies have greater distance propagation and better building penetration but require larger antennas and have a lower capacity for data transmission.

Lower frequencies have greater distance propagation qualities and better building penetration but require larger antennas and have lower capacity for data transmission

Most commonly used bands for television, cell phones, pagers, and other devices are between 500 MHz and 3 GHz. Devices requiring limited ranges and small antennas, such as Wi-Fi and Bluetooth, tend to use higher frequencies (2.4 GHz) whereas for long distance communication with underwater submarines, the military uses very low frequencies. When radio technology was starting, the early radios used much lower frequencies than modern radios typically use today. However, technological innovations are increasingly making higher frequencies viable for more common use. This is the historical basis for the somewhat confusing naming convention whereby the High-Frequency band is actually at the lower end of the currently usable spectrum range and the middle of the usable range is called the Ultra High-Frequency band. A description of every radio band is beyond the scope of this *Handbook*, but the FCC's 177-page description can be found on the FCC's website.[46] A concise version is available in Appendix II of this Handbook. A summary of major bands is shown in Figures 6-1 and 6-2 below:

---

[46] FCC Online Table of Frequency Allocations, 47 C.F.R. § 2.106 (June 12, 2018) https://transition.fcc.gov/oet/spectrum/table/fcctable.pdf.

Figure 6-1: Frequency Band Designations (FCC, NTIA & ITU)

ITU Band	Frequency	Band Designation	Abbreviation
4	3 – 30 kHz	Very Low Frequency	VLF
5	30 – 30 kHz	Low Frequency	LF
6	300 – 3,000 kHz	Medium Frequency	MF
7	3 – 30 MHz	High Frequency	HF
8	30 – 300 MHz	Very High Frequency	VHF
9	300 – 3,000 MHz	Ultra-High Frequency	UHF
10	3 – 30 GHz	Super High Frequency	SHF
11	30 – 300 GHz	Extremely High Frequency	EHF
12	300 – 3000 GHz	Tremendously High Frequency	THF

Source: Wikipedia, Summit Ridge Group, LLC analysis

The Institute for Electrical and Electronic Engineers (IEEE) has promulgated separate frequency band designations that use letter-based designations. Unfortunately, the letter-based designations used by regulators typically don't match the IEEE (or any other standard) nomenclature.

Figure 6-2: IEEE Band Designations

Designation	Frequency
HF	3 – 30 MHz
VHF	30 – 300 MHz
UHF	300 – 1,000 MHz
L-band	1 – 2 GHz
S-band	2 – 4 GHz
C-band	4 – 8 GHz
X-band	8 - 12 GHz
Ku-band	12 – 18 GHz
K-band	18 – 27 GHz
Ka-band	27 – 40 GHz
V-band	40 – 75 GHz
W-band	75 – 110 GHz
G-band	110 – 300 GHz

Source: http://www.radioing.com/eengineer/bands.html and Summit Ridge Group, LLC analysis

A. Very Low Frequency (VLF): Under 30 kHz

Due to their long wavelengths (over 10 kilometers), transmissions in this spectrum can "skip" over mountains and generally follow the curvature of the earth. In the early part of the twentieth century, this VLF was used for sending Morse code across the Atlantic. Current commercial uses of this spectrum include clock radios, heart monitors (at very low power levels), and military communication to submarines near the surface (at much higher power levels) and various experimental uses.

B. Low Frequency (LF): 30 kHz to 300 kHz

LF transmissions also follow the curvature of the earth, bounce off the ionosphere and even deflect off mountains. They can also penetrate the ocean to approximately 200 meters. This spectrum is used for time signals, RFID tags, various experimental purposes, submarine communications, aircraft navigation, and some AM radio transmission in parts of Europe, Asia, and Africa.

Position location services in the U.S. were formerly provided near the 100 Hz frequency by the U.S. government using a system named LORAN...

Position location services in the U.S. were formerly provided near the 1 MHz frequency by the U.S. government using a system named LORAN (the former Soviet government used an analogous system called CHAYKA). In recent decades, users left LORAN and CHAYKA in favor of Global Positioning Satellites (GPS). The U.S. Coast Guard and the Russian government terminated transmission on their systems and shuttered Loran operations in 2010. On December 31, 2015, LORAN signals from France, Norway, Denmark, and Germany were terminated; transmission of the United Kingdom's signal continues from their facility at Anthhorn. A similar system is used in Saudi Arabia under the name Saudi Positioning System (SPS).

The DHS funding bill for 2018, passed by the House of Representatives in July 2018, includes the National Timing Resilience and Security Act of 2018 calling for the DHS to fund the construction and maintenance of a new eLoran system "as a complement to, and as a backup for" the GPS system.[47] eLoran is a low-frequency radio navigation system that operates in the 90–110 kHz frequency range. Compared to the original LORAN, it has advanced receiver design and transmission characteristics, which increases its accuracy and usefulness. Additionally, eLoran's powerful low-frequency signals are far less susceptible to jamming or spoofing than GPS signals.[48]

C. Medium Frequency (MF): 300 kHz to 3000 kHz

MF transmissions propagate both in the sky and across the damp earth for up to hundreds of miles. Skyward signals can bounce off the ionosphere extending their distance to even thousands of miles. The ability of signals to bounce off the ionosphere varies by season and

---

[47] Resilient Navigation and Timing Foundation, *Loran Off the Air In Most of Europe* (Jan. 4, 2016) https://rntfnd.org/2016/01/04/loran-off-air-in-most-of-europe-move-to-commercial-possible/

[48] GPS World, Stephen Bartlett, *A Wide-Area Multi-Application PNT Resiliency Solution* (Nov. 23, 2015) http://gpsworld.com/innovation-enhanced-loran/.

by the time of day, generally increasing significantly at night.

This band includes allocations for navigational beacons (in the 190-435 kHz range) and AM radio (535-1705 kHz in the U.S. and 526.5 to 1606.5 kHz in Europe). There are many ship-to-shore radio communications allocations between 1600 and 2850 kHz. The international distress frequency for maritime voice is at 2182 kHz and assigned to channel 16 on the Marine VHF band.

D. High Frequency (HF): 3 to 30 MHz

Despite the name "High Frequency," the frequency is actually quite low, but capable of transmitting signals long distances

Despite the name "High Frequency," the frequency is actually quite low for broadcasting but capable of transmitting signals long distances. By reflecting off the ionosphere, signals in this spectrum range can travel across continents. The primary use of this frequency is for short-wave radio services between 5.950 to 26.100 MHz. These are broadcast services designed to be received by the general public in foreign countries.

High frequency (HF) is the ITU designation for radio frequencies between 3 and 30 megahertz (MHz). It is also known as the decameter band or decameter wave as its wavelengths range from one to ten decameters (ten to one hundred meters).[49]

High Frequency signal propagation is impacted by atmospheric conditions. As atmospheric conditions change significantly with the seasons, the ITU holds a High Frequency Coordination Conference twice a year to coordinate shortwave broadcasting schedules. The changing propagation of the frequency has made it a favorite with amateur radio operators who often experiment to test transmission distances at various times. Spectrum in the High Frequency range is also used for emergency ship to shore communication and aviation communication.

1. Citizen's Band Radio

The Citizen's Band (CB Radio) is allocated the frequency between 26.965 and 27.045 MHz in the U.S. The CB Radio Band is divided into 40 channels of 10 kHz each, which can be used for unlicensed voice communication with approved devices. They are typically used for short-range communication and use is regulated under Title 47, Part 95 of the Code of Federal Regulations (the "CFR").

---

[49] ITU, Rec. ITU-R V.431-7, *Nomenclature of the frequency and wavelength bands used in telecommunications* (2000) https://web.archive.org/web/20131031020427/http://www.itu.int/dms_pubrec/itu-r/rec/v/R-REC-V.431-7-200005-I%21%21PDF-E.pdf

*Unlike the High
Frequency
Spectrum, VHF
signals do not
bounce off the
ionosphere*

2. Extensive Government Use

Approximately two-thirds of the high frequency spectrum is controlled by various government agencies. Recent advancements, particularly automated link establishment (ALE) technology, have made high frequency communication more reliable during changing atmospheric conditions, leading to growth in the use of the frequency by government users. The National Communication Systems (NCS) runs a program called the Shared Resource High Frequency Radio Program (SHARES) that facilitates cooperation between government high frequency users during emergencies. Members agree to relay radio messages from any member who is experiencing an emergency to the intended recipient.

3. Maritime Use Is Slowing

As satellite communication has become less expensive and more reliable, maritime use of HF communication has declined. Several providers, including AT&T, have exited the business. Some of the remaining maritime HF operators have received waivers for secondary terrestrial uses and are seeking to build businesses based on those licenses.

E. Very High Frequency (VHF): 30 to 300 MHz

The VHF spectrum includes a number of services. Frequencies in this spectrum work well for short distances – somewhat longer than range of sight. Unlike the High Frequency spectrum discussed above, VHF signals do not reflect off the ionosphere preventing them from extending their distance via ionospheric "bouncing" like HF transmissions. Common VHF applications include ship-to-shore radio, paging, and certain radio-controlled devices. The 220 MHz band is used for railroad safety, including Position Train Control (PTC) in the U.S., and for a wide range of Internet of things (IoT) applications.

See Chapter XII.C of this *Handbook* for a more detailed description of VHF services.

F. Ultra-High Frequency (UHF): 300 MHz to 3 GHz

Spectrum in the UHF band is the most versatile for many modern communications services. Frequencies in this UHF band range from ten centimeters to one meter in length. UHF radio waves do not bounce off the ionosphere. Hills and large buildings generally block UHF signals but they can penetrate buildings, particularly at the lower

end of the range. Due to their relatively short wavelength, consumer equipment on this frequency band can use small antennas with significant data-carrying capacity. Services in this band include locator beacons, air-ground service, most mobile telecom services (covered in Chapter VIII of this *Handbook*), television, (see Chapter IX of this *Handbook*) and Wi-Fi service.

See Chapter XIII of this *Handbook* for a more detailed description of UHF services.

G. Super High Frequency (SHF): 3 to 30 GHz

SHF frequency is also known as centimeter wave because the wavelengths in SHF range from 1 to 10 centimeters. The spectrum in SHF is also referred to as microwaves.[50] SHF Spectrum in this range has superior capacity to carry data on a bit per MHz basis. But propagation is largely limited to line of sight reception.

Super High Frequency is used primarily by satellite-based systems

Super High Frequency is used primarily by satellite-based systems including IEEE designated frequencies such as C-band (4-8GHz), X-band (7-11.2 GHz), Ku-band (12-18 GHz), K-band (18-27 GHz), and Ka-band (26.5-40 GHz) which are described in detail in Chapter XV. Exceptions include the 4.6 GHz General Wireless Communication Service (GWCS), the 24 GHz band and LMDS (Local Multipoint Distribution Service). In addition to its original primary band at 2.4 GHz, Wi-Fi operates in the 5 GHz band.

Although 3 GHz has historically been considered the upper limit for mobile wireless services, spectrum in the 3-6 GHz range is increasingly coveted by the mobile wireless industry. In the U.S., this includes the CBRS (3.55-3.7 GHz) and the satellite C-band downlink (3.7-4.2 GHz). In February 2013 the FCC announced plans to expand Wi-Fi spectrum to include parts of the 5.9 GHz band, but the FCC is still testing to see if this sharing plan will cause harmful interference to incumbent dedicated short-range communication (DSRC) services. Wireless operators are also currently testing millimeter wave (mmW) frequency technology in the 24-28 GHz bands for 5G services.

See Chapter X of this *Handbook* for a more detailed description of satellite services, most of which are offered in the SHF band.

---

[50] This microwave frequency is contrasted with the widely discussed "millimeter wave" or mmW frequency located from 30-300 GHz. mmW frequency is also called EHF or Extremely High Frequency. It is in the 1 to 10 millimeter range.

H. Extremely High Frequency (EHF): 30-300 GHz

Spectrum at this level and above is sparsely utilized. It is subject to severe rain fade and has poor ability to penetrate buildings and foliage. Nevertheless, portions of the lower end of the range including the Q-band (33-50 GHz) and the V-band (50-75 GHz), which are allocated for satellite and short distance terrestrial broadband, may be increasingly used in the future. In particular, the 39 GHz band is attracting industry attention for terrestrial broadband delivery, with AT&T currently performing 5G trials in the band. The V-band is used in inter-satellite links between the U.S. Milstar 1 and 2 military satellites. As per a Report and Order issued by the FCC on July 14, 2016, the part of the V-band allocated for unlicensed use was expanded to cover 57-71 GHz;[51] Wi-Fi Standard IEEE 802.11ad will operate at 60 GHz and is expected to allow for transfer rates of up to 7 Gb/sec.[52]

PART ONE: BACKGROUND

---

[51] *Use of Spectrum Bands Above 24 GHz For Mobile Radio Use*, Report and Order and Further Notice of Proposed Rulemaking, GN Docket No. 14-177, 31 FCC Rcd 8014 (2016) https://apps.fcc.gov/edocs_public/attachmatch/FCC-16-89A1.pdf.
[52] Radio-Electronics.com, *IEEE 802.11ad Microwave Wi-Fi/WiGig Tutorial* http://www.radio-electronics.com/info/wireless/Wi-Fi/ieee-802-11ad-microwave.php

VII. Overview of Regulatory Process for Spectrum Allocation

Any given frequency band generally cannot be used at the same time by different users or applications without interference or significant coordination requirements to avoid it. And some frequencies are superior to others for certain applications. This creates the need for the enormous regulatory project of efficiently managing spectrum to maximize its value to society. In addition to assigning spectrum, regulators manage spectrum through a two-part process of 1) allocating spectrum bands for the most appropriate applications; and 2) coordinating use between users on a given spectrum band.

A. Background

The first major goal of spectrum regulation is to allocate spectrum to the most technically appropriate applications in proportion to the social need for those applications. This process is very much akin to zoning in a real estate context. If a town decides that it needs more industry, for example, it may expand industrial zoning in areas of the town most suited to industry. Likewise, if more mobile broadband is needed, regulators may allocate additional spectrum for mobile broadband in the most suitable spectrum zones. As with real estate zoning, spectrum regulations may include restrictions to prevent interference with neighboring users.

Intergovernmental treaties proposed by the ITU need governmental approval by the affected countries

The second major goal of spectrum regulation is to coordinate its use among users. Frequently, regulators allocate use by issuing licenses to use portions of spectrum for particular purposes with specific parameters. Alternatively, they may allow spectrum to be used on an unlicensed basis, subject to certain priority rules. This might be similar to a city setting aside some land for a public park or another public use. Regulators also maintain processes for resolving disputes between licensees. Spectrum is allocated and managed through a series of international and national regulatory bodies.

B. ITU International Telecommunications Union

PART ONE: BACKGROUND

The ITU promotes global cooperation in the use of spectrum

Based in Geneva, Switzerland, the International Telecommunications Union (ITU) is a specialized agency of the United Nations. It specializes in promoting cooperation in the use of international information and communication technologies, including the allocation, standardization, and regulation of global radio spectrum. The ITU was founded in Paris in 1865, as the International Telegraph Union. It took its present name in 1934. Currently, the ITU has 193-member nations and 700 private sector entities and academic institutions that have joined the Union as non-voting Sector Members. The ITU rules, including spectrum allocations, are published in its annual report *Radio Regulations.*[53] Individual countries may deviate from ITU rules, including spectrum allocations, so long as those deviations do not interfere with other countries that comply with ITU rules.

Despite its active involvement in international spectrum coordination, the ITU, as in many areas of international law, does not have an effective enforcement mechanism. It largely depends on its member countries to abide by its rules out of their long-term interest in having a coherent international spectrum policy. Entities using spectrum are thus subject to the rules of the national government(s) who issued their license(s), not the ITU. However, many global entities lobby the ITU because ITU rules are likely to be adopted by most counties.

The ITU divides the world into three regions, Regions 1 to 3. Europe and Africa are in Region 1, the Americas are in Region 2, while Asia is in Region 3

The ITU divides the world into three regions, Regions 1, 2, and 3. Europe and Africa are in Region 1, the Americas (North and South) are in Region 2, and Asia is in Region 3. See Appendix I of this Handbook for a map of the ITU Regions.

The ITU also hosts conferences, most recently the World Conference on International Telecommunications 2015 (WCIT-15), where it proposes intergovernmental treaties addressing telecommunication issues such as the global allocation of spectrum and international tariffs. Once adopted, these treaties must pass the national approval processes of the affected countries, although the ITU itself is independent.

The ITU rulemaking process is time-consuming. To effect a change in an ITU policy or standard, one must add the item to the docket a year or so in advance. Frequently no decision is made on an item, which is then carried over to the next conference. Thus, ITU policy change is typically measured in years, sometimes longer.

---

[53] ITU, *Radio Regulations* (2016) https://www.itu.int/pub/R-REG-RR-2016

The ITU has three major divisions: ITU-R, ITU-T, and ITU-D. The Radio Communications Sector (ITU-R) coordinates radio frequency spectrum and satellite orbits. The Standardization Sector (ITU-T) produces and revises technical standards for a variety of communications technologies from IPTV to network communication protocols. The Development Sector (ITU-D) promotes initiatives to expand communications access in underserved areas. It also has a project ITU-EC ACP.

1. ITU-EC-ACP PROJECT

The different Regional Organizations of a Region are often arranged in complex hierarchies of overlapping structures. The Regional Organization pages of the ICT-EC aims to facilitate the work and collaboration with the Regional Organizations by filtering existing reports, and making available new reports according to their specific structures.

ITU rule making process is time- consuming

The ITU and the EC joined forces and signed an agreement aimed at providing "Support for the Establishment of Harmonized Policies for the ICT market in the ACP[54]." This was done as a component of the Programme "ACP-Information and Communication Technologies (ACP)" within the framework of the 9th European Development Fund (EDF). The agreement is in response to both the challenges and the opportunities of information and communication technologies' (ICTs) contribution to political, social, economic and environmental development. The European Union is funding the implementation through three separate sub-projects customized to the specific needs of each region: the Caribbean (HIPCAR), Sub-Saharan Africa (HIPSSA), and the Pacific Islands Countries (ICB4PAC).[55]

2. The Radio Communications Sector (ITU-R)

For spectrum issues, the ITU-R is the most important division of the ITU. Its specific role within the ITU framework is the following:[56]

1. Affect the allocation of spectrum bands, the allotment of radio frequencies, and the registration of radio frequency assignments of any associated orbital position in the geostationary satellite orbit to avoid interference between radio stations of different countries;

---

[54] ITU, ITU-EC-ACP Project, *Support for the Establishment of Harmonized Policies for the ICT Market in the ACP States* https://www.itu.int/en/ITU-D/Projects/ITU-EC-ACP/Pages/default.aspx

[55] Africa, the Caribbean and the Pacific islands.

[56] ITU, *Mission Statement* https://www.itu.int/en/ITU-R/information/Pages/mission-statement.aspx

2. Coordinate efforts to eliminate interference between radio stations of different countries and to improve the use of radio frequencies and the geostationary-satellite orbit for radio communication services.

ITU-R executes its mission by managing five major activities including the following:

*   World Radio Communication conferences (WRC) are held every three or four years. The latest was held in 2015 and the next is scheduled for 2019. The WRC reviews and revises the Radio Regulations - the international treaty governing the use of the radio spectrum and satellite orbits. Revisions are based on an agenda created by the ITU Council, which is set more than a year in advance. The ITU Council, in turn, considers recommendations made by previous WRC conferences. At WRC-19, the member states of the ITU are expected to agree upon new 5G spectrum allocations within the mmWave bands and discuss the need for additional back-haul capacity, along with completing 5G regulations and specifications.

*   Radio Communication Assemblies (RA) manages the structure, the program and the approval of various radio-communication studies.

*   The Radio Regulations Board (RRB) consists of twelve people who are elected at the Plenipotentiary Conference that meets up to four times a year. The RRB approves rules of procedure and addresses issues that the Radio Regulations cannot resolve and advises on a variety of other issues.

*   Study Groups: Over 1,500 specialists from telecommunication organizations and administrations throughout the world participate in the study groups focused on compiling handbooks, drafting technical bases for Radio Communication Conferences, and developing draft recommendations.

*   The Radio Communication Advisory Group (RAG) reviews priorities and strategies of the ITU-R, monitors the progress of and supervises the study groups, and facilitates cooperation and coordination with other organizations along with the other ITU Sectors.

3. ITU-R Priorities

The proliferation and increasing importance of communications devices using different frequencies have increased the importance of spectrum coordination. Consumers expect not only mobile phones but also other devices that use Wi-Fi and Bluetooth technologies to work internationally. Hardware manufacturers need spectrum uniformity to keep production costs low via economies of scale. In recent years, the ITU-R has placed a great deal of emphasis on International Mobile Telecom. It has worked to standardize the 800 MHz band as well as the "digital dividend" spectrum in the 700 MHz range. This digital dividend spectrum was made available when television broadcasting migrated from analog signals to more spectrally efficient digital signals.

In recent years, the ITU-R has placed a great deal of emphasis on International Mobile Telecom

The ITU-R also takes the lead in identifying spectrum band globally that can be used for mobile broadband. It believes such identification can facilitate international harmonization and thus lower-cost devices and global availability.[57]

C. Other International Coordination Entities

While the ITU sets down basic principles for spectrum use worldwide, geographically focused entities handle much of the coordination and details. These entities include:

1. Regional Coordinating Bodies

In addition to official governmental bodies, private standards organizations operate to influence technical standards

Regional coordinating bodies include the European Conference of Postal and Telecommunications Administration (CEPT) in Europe and the Inter-American Telecommunication Commission (CITEL) for the Americas. Europe has another agency, ETSI, which was created by CEPT and is a standards organization for telecom equipment manufacturers and operators. These regional coordinating bodies, as the name suggests, coordinate frequency issues related to a given region. They often focus their efforts on cross-border interference issues and frequency harmonization to allow hardware to travel from one country to another.

2. International Intra-governmental Agreements

In addition to the ITU, regional bodies, national bodies, and individual countries frequently have agreements among themselves for the management of various spectrum issues. The FCC, for example, lists

---

[57] ITU News, Roberto Ercole, *The Future of Mobile* (Dec. 2016)
https://itunews.itu.int/en/2067-The-future-of-mobile.note.aspx

over 50 spectrum-related agreements between the U.S. and Canada alone.[58]

3. Private Groups

In addition to official governmental bodies, private standards organizations operate to influence technical standards for equipment. These groups can be national or international in focus. In the U.S., the Alliance for Telecommunications Industry Solutions (ATIS) focuses on the communications industry. [59] It is accredited by the American National Institute of Standards (ANSI) and is a member of several international bodies.

International umbrella groups, such as the Third Generation Partnership Project (3GPP) have also formed to create greater global influence. 3GPP has three technical specification groups that coordinate with standards development agencies to set international standards in the wireless mobile industry. Member agencies of 3GPP include ARIB (Japan), CCSA (China), TSDSI (India); TTA (Korea), ATIS (USA), ETSI (Europe) and TTC (Japan).[60]

Virtually every country has a national coordinating body to manage spectrum within its borders

D. Third Generation Partnership Project (3GPP)

The Third Generation Partnership Project (3GPP) is a global wireless communications organization that collaboratively develops standards and specifications for cellular telecommunication network technologies. These include radio access, the core transport network, service architecture, and service capabilities. 3GPP was founded in 1998 by several telecommunications standards associations with the purpose of creating a third-generation mobile phone system. The founders were Nortel and AT&T Wireless (when AT&T was a standalone mobile company and before the AT&T name was taken by SBC/Cingular mobile firms). It is located in southern France and housed within the European Technologies Standards Institute (ETSI). ETSI is a European non-profit standards-setting organization recognized by the European Commission. Although the original scope of the collaboration between 3GPP and ETSI was to develop 3G standards, the scope has since widened considerably. The technologies 3GPP has standardized include GSM, GPRS, EDGE, UMTS, HSPA, LTE, LTE-Advanced, and LTE-Advanced Pro.

---

[58] FCC, *Canadian Agreements by Frequency* (Aug. 4, 2003) https://www.fcc.gov/canadian-agreements-frequency

[59] ATIS, *About* http://www.atis.org/.

[60] 3GPP, About, *Partners* http://www.3gpp.org/about-3gpp/partners.

E. Institute of Electrical and Electronics Engineers (IEEE)

IEEE is a large engineering professional organization that publishes an extensive amount of technical literature. It is particularly relevant in telecommunications due to its influence in setting consensus-based technical standards. IEEE standards are not binding on any government or private company. However, they tend to be quite influential due to the telecom industry's need for technically feasible standards to achieve economies of scale and interoperability.[61]

F. National Spectrum Bodies

National spectrum bodies have two primary roles. The first is to administer spectrum policies in their countries and the second is to issue spectrum licenses to users to operate under those policies. As mentioned earlier, countries may deviate from ITU standards so long as the deviation does not cause interference with countries who follow ITU rules. Virtually every country[62] has a national coordinating body to manage spectrum within its borders. In many cases, these are connected with the national postal service, due to historical reasons, and the common relationship both have to communications. These agencies include the Federal Communications Commission (FCC) in the U.S., Ofcom in the United Kingdom, Bundesnetzagentur (BNetzA) in Germany, and the Ministry of Communications and Information in South Korea. Spectrum users must obtain the appropriate permissions/licenses from the national regulatory agencies in the countries in which they operate.

National spectrum bodies also dictate terms for spectrum licenses including length, the method of acquisition (fee, auction, assignment, etc.), qualifications of licensees, and other obligations of licensees. There are three general types of spectrum regulation models:

1) Command and control whereby the government allocates and revokes spectrum usage rights by unilateral decision;
2) Property rights or quasi-property rights whereby the government issues a transferable license to exclusively use spectrum; and
3) The Commons model whereby spectrum is open for use without a license.

---

[61] IEEE, *About IEEE*, https://www.ieee.org/.

[62] The few exceptions include the Vatican, Somalia and a handful of other countries in exceptional circumstances.

These three spectrum regulation models are shown in Figure 7-1 below:

Figure 7-1: Spectrum Allocation Models

Model	Users	Uses
I. Command and Control	• Government Agencies • Maritime industry • Aviation industry	• Military • Aeronautical • Maritime Safety • Emergency Services
II. Property Rights or Quasi-Property Rights	• Commercial entities including: broadcasters, wireless service providers and satellite operators	• Mobile voice and data services • Satellite broadcasting • Fixed wireless
III. Commons	• Individuals • Companies • Government Agencies	• Wi-Fi • Garage door openers • Bluetooth

Source: ITU[63] and Summit Ridge Group, LLC analysis

Most countries now allocate the most valuable spectrum along a property rights model

Most countries now allocate the most valuable spectrum along a property rights model (aside from emergency services and certain government/military uses, which few countries would want sold-off and continue to allocate on a command and control model). However, as discussed in Chapter VII.F of this *Handbook,* there is a growing movement towards the commons approach to maximizing spectrum utilization. In addition to considering physical characteristics of spectrum and its potential uses, most national regulatory bodies also consider international implications when allocating spectrum. The most significant of these is spectrum harmonization – standardization of spectrum band usage. International harmonization facilitates international mobile phone roaming, satellite interference avoidance, access to standardized equipment, and addresses other issues.

---

[63] International Telecommunications Union, Broadband Series, *Exploring the Value and Economic Valuation of Spectrum* (Apr. 2012) http://www.itu.int/ITU-D/treg/broadband/ITU-BB-Reports_SpectrumValue.pdf.

G. The Roles of the FCC and NTIA

1. Background

The FCC …oversees the portion of spectrum in the public domain for private and commercial users

The U.S. maintains two separate agencies to regulate spectrum. First, the Federal Communications Commission (FCC) is an independent agency of the U.S. government that oversees the portion of spectrum in the public domain for private and commercial users. Additionally, the National Telecommunications and Information Administration (NTIA) is the agency within the Commerce Department that regulates and administers the spectrum allocated to government use. The U.S. Government Publishing House *Federal Register* is the legal source for U.S. frequency allocation for both the FCC and the NTIA.

The FCC was created by the Communications Act of 1934 to manage the allocation of all commercial spectrum available in the U.S. for the public good. Five Commissioners can be appointed by the President. Traditionally, the President selects three of the Commissioners and the minority party selects two Commissioners. The Chairman is selected by the President. At the Commission, the Chairman sets the tone and strategy for FCC initiatives, rulemakings, inquiries, and other proceedings. The Chairman's office drafts the proposed orders. The rules governing the FCC are in Title 47 of the CFR. Part 2 of Title 47 of the CFR contains most rules related to radio spectrum allocation. The FCC has allocated spectrum from 9 kHz to 275 GHz to various commercial uses.

The NTIA manages the portion of the spectrum allocated for U.S. government use

Section 305 of the Communications Act of 1934 gives the President the authority to assign all frequencies used by the federal government and in 1978 this power was embedded in the newly created NTIA. Government agencies pay a small below-market fee to the NTIA for a spectrum assignment. NTIA rules can be found within the *Manual of Regulations & Procedures for Federal Radio Frequency Management*, [64] often referred to as the "NTIA Manual" or the "Redbook." An illustration of the relationship between the FCC and the NTIA is shown in Figure 7-2 below.

---

[64] NTIA, *The Manual of Regulation & Procedures for Federal Radio Frequency Management (Redbook* (Sept. 2017)
http://www.ntia.doc.gov/osmhome/redbook/redbook.html

Figure 7-2: Relationship Between the FCC and NTIA

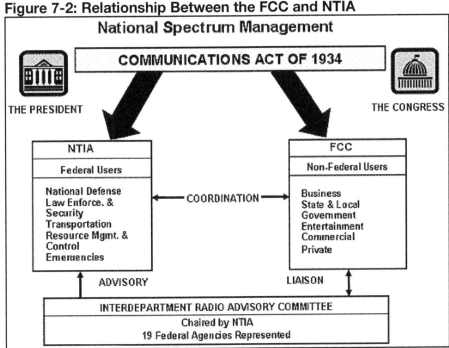

Source: NTIA

The FCC mainly issues primary spectrum licenses to commercial entities, although a secondary market for these licenses has developed

In addition to the NTIA and the FCC, another government agency, the National Communication System (NCS), historically coordinated several emergency communications programs. The NCS was formed in the aftermath of the Cuban missile crisis in 1962 and includes 24 federal government departments and agencies. On July 6, 2012, President Obama signed an executive order[65] to eliminate the NCS and send many of its functions to the Office of Emergency Communication within the Office of Cybersecurity and Communication.

2. Licensing Process

Before issuing licenses, the FCC allocates spectrum for a specific use. 47 C.F.R. 2.1 defines the permissible services for which the FCC can allocate spectrum. The FCC can later issue spectrum licenses for primary use and, to a lesser extent, for secondary use that allow license holders to use the frequency for services within the U.S. spectrum allocation. Primary licensees have the right to use the spectrum within the terms of the license without interference from other users. Secondary licensees are allowed to use spectrum on limited terms that do not interfere with the primary licensee.

---

[65] Administration of Barack Obama, 2012, *Executive Order 13618-Assignment of National Security and Emergency Preparedness Communications Functions* (July 6, 2012) https://www.gpo.gov/fdsys/pkg/DCPD-201200539/pdf/DCPD-201200539.pdf.

Specifically, holders of secondary licenses:

(i) Shall not cause harmful interference to stations of primary services to which frequencies are already assigned or to which frequencies may be assigned at a later date;

(ii) Cannot claim protection from harmful interference from stations of a primary service to which frequencies are already assigned or may be assigned at a later date; and

(iii) Can claim protection, however, from harmful interference from stations of the same or other secondary service(s) to which frequencies may be assigned at a later date.[66]

The licenses' terms dictate the arrangements of the spectrum assignments with respect to the geographic coverage area, the transmission characteristics, and rules of service, to prevent the interference of signals.

Licenses for spectrum for two-way communication are often granted in two separate "paired blocks." For example, LTE-FDD requires separated paired blocks. One of the paired blocks is authorized for uplink and the other for downlink. Regulatory agencies do this because most two-way spectrum transmission technologies work better when the "uplink" (transmission from handset to the base station) is on a separate frequency from the "downlink" (transmission from the base station to a handset).[67] Typically, there is a space of spectrum between the uplink and downlink segments to prevent interference. This space is called the "duplex gap."

FCC licenses explicitly deny the licensees property rights in the terms of their licenses

FCC licenses explicitly deny the licensees property rights in the terms of their licenses. They are for limited periods of time, typically eight years for television broadcasters, ten years for mobile operators and fifteen years for satellite operators. However, the FCC seeks to encourage license holders to invest heavily in both buying spectrum at auction and building their businesses. As a result, spectrum licenses have taken on many of the economic attributes of property including the right to sell.[68] License holders often invest heavily in

---

[66] 47 C.F.R. 2.105(c)(2).

[67] An exception is Time Division Duplexing (TDD) technology which divides the uplink and downlink by time as opposed to frequency. TDD is used by one major operator in the U.S. and it dominant in China with all mobile operators. See Chapter XV.A.7.b of this *Handbook* for an additional discussion of TDD technology.

[68] For a detailed discussion of property rights in FCC spectrum, see: J. Armand Musey, *Broadcasting Licenses: Ownership Rights and the Spectrum Rationalization Challenge*, Columbia Science & Technology Law Review, Vol. 13, 2013 (Sept. 10, 2012). SSRN: http://ssrn.com/abstract=1952138.

acquiring licenses at auctions and building out services. This investment often requires an expectation of long-term control of the spectrum to justify the investment, making it politically difficult to deny renewal absent egregious abuses of the license terms. Spectrum auctions, in theory, serve as a market mechanism for spectrum allocation and a market discipline to ensure that spectrum is used efficiently.

The FCC issues licenses in specific geographical areas...These areas differ depending on the nature of the license and the auction

Despite the fact that the FCC prohibits security interests in licenses, investors in spectrum licensing have been able to circumvent the impact of ownership restrictions. They do this by laying claim to the "economic value" of the license, as opposed to the licenses themselves. Licensees typically affect an economic claim to FCC licenses by putting the license(s) in a holding company and using the stock of the holding company as collateral. In this case, security investors have a stake in the "economic value" and proceeds of licenses when sold. Bankruptcy courts have generally upheld this strategy when done properly.[69]

3. Licensing Areas Vary

The FCC issues licenses for specific geographical areas.[70] FCC divides the country into geographical units for the auctions. These areas differ depending on the nature of the license and the auction. License areas can range from the whole country to one of 734 Cellular Market Areas (CMAs). The upcoming 3.55 GHz CBRS auction is expected to be held on the basis of census tracts. There are over 74,000 census tracts in the U.S.[71] By creating different geographies for different licenses, operators and investors have a difficult task of determining the value of the spectrum using different size geographies for comparison, as it creates a confusing system of geographical units of license areas. These licensing areas are described in Appendix III.

4. Current Emphasis of FCC

In recent years, the FCC's focus has largely been to keep its regulations current with the communications sector's rapidly changing technology and business plans. New technology often undermines the

---

[69] Id. at 327-330.

[70] In addition to geographical territory license areas described in this chapter, the FCC also issues certain licenses for discrete locations and point-to-point links.

[71] U.S. Census Bureau, Geography, *2000 Tallies of Census Tracts, Block Groups, and Tabulation Blocks* https://www.census.gov/geo/maps-data/data/tallies/tabgeo2k.html

The FCC, unlike other spectrum regulatory agencies in other countries, has focused almost entirely on transmission requirements

logic behind previous rules. This unnecessarily limits choices available to consumers, service providers, and equipment manufacturers. New technology can also create new spectrum needs. The corollary is also true – regulatory restrictions can drive technological development. However, the prevailing view of U.S. regulators is that society is generally best served when market demand drives technological development. Consequently, the FCC seeks to update the regulatory framework to accommodate that demand. Currently, the FCC's biggest priority is allocating additional bandwidth to mobile broadband as part of the National Broadband Plan,[72] Mobile Now, along with other initiatives discussed in Chapter XVI of this *Handbook*. In addition to the National Broadband Plan, the FCC has issued 13 broadband progress reports.

The FCC, unlike other spectrum regulatory agencies in different countries, has focused its efforts almost entirely on transmission requirements as opposed to requirements for receivers of transmissions. If receivers work beyond their allocated spectrum band into a neighboring band, a licensed operator in that neighboring frequency band often cannot use its spectrum without interfering with the non-compliant receivers. Once they reach a critical mass, it is often politically hard to move these non-compliant receivers. In the case of GPS, the widespread availability of receivers that received signals outside of their spectrum limited LightSquared's (now Ligado) ability to use adjacent spectrum.[73] Going forward, Summit Ridge Group expects the FCC to place additional emphasis on receiver equipment compliance.[74]

In 2018, the FCC defined four major objectives in their Fiscal Year 2018-2022 Strategic Plan:[75]

- Closing the digital divide
- Promoting innovation
- Protecting consumers and public safety
- Reforming the FCC's processes

---

[72] FCC *2010 National Broadband Plan* (Mar. 17, 2010) http://www.broadband.gov/plan

[73] Wikipedia, Lightsquared/GPS, *Interference issue* http://en.wikipedia.org/wiki/LightSquared

[74] U.S. General Accounting Office, *Spectrum Management: Further Considerations of Options to Improve Receiver Performance* (Feb. 2013) http://www.gao.gov/assets/660/652284.pdf

[75] FCC. *Strategic Plan 2018-2022* (Feb 12, 2018) https://www.fcc.gov/document/strategic-plan-2018-2022

5. Government Spectrum Use Questioned

Sixty percent of the most valuable U.S. spectrum has either exclusive or primary allocation to government users such as the Department of Defense.[76] According to a report released by the U.S. Government Accountability Office (GAO) in 2011, however, the NTIA had shown limited ability to effectively manage federal spectrum use or to evaluate the actual federal needs for spectrum. The NTIA had instead focused on preventing interference between spectrum allocated to different government agencies. Most observers believe the spectrum used by government entities is underutilized in many areas. However, due to lenient reporting requirements for the government regarding its spectrum use, the actual figures on available or underutilized spectrum remain opaque.[77] On June 14th, 2013, a presidential memo, among other things, directed the NTIA to assess the actual uses of spectrum assigned to federal agencies.[78]

The NTIA has shown limited ability to effectively manage federal spectrum use or to evaluate the actual federal needs for spectrum

In order to address the nation's growing interest in and demand for radio spectrum, the NTIA, in consultation with federal agencies, has developed a compendium[79] of detailed reports describing federal spectrum uses from 225 MHz to 6 GHz.

The NTIA reports and datasets provide information for each frequency band in this range in which the Federal Government used significantly. In the bands they use, the federal agencies generally have an exclusive or shared allocation in the U.S. Table of Allocations.[80] However, these agencies also operate in some bands allocated on an exclusive basis for non-federal operations in order to perform coordinated operations with non-federal entities or to use commercial

---

[76] President's Council of Advisors on Science and Technology (PCAST), *Realizing the Full Potential of Government-Held Spectrum to Spur Economic Growth* (July 2012) https://obamawhitehouse.archives.gov/sites/default/files/microsites/ostp/pcast_spectrum_report_final_july_20_2012.pdf (*PCAST Report*).

[77] United States Government Accountability Office, *SPECTRUM MANAGEMENT: NTIA Planning Processes Need Strengthening to Promote the Efficient Use of Spectrum by Federal Agencies*, GAO-11-352 (Apr. 2012) https://www.gao.gov/products/GAO-11-352.

[78] The White House, *Presidential Memorandum – Expanding America's Leadership in Wireless Innovation* (Jun, 14, 2013) https://obamawhitehouse.archives.gov/the-press-office/2013/06/14/presidential-memorandum-expanding-americas-leadership-wireless-innovatio (*Presidential Memo*)

[79] NTIA, *Federal Government Spectrum Compendium* (Aug. 21, 2017) https://www.ntia.doc.gov/other-publication/2017/federal-government-spectrum-compendium

[80] FCC OET, Policy and Rules Division, *Online Table of Frequency Allocations* (June 12, 2018) https://transition.fcc.gov/oet/spectrum/table/fcctable.pdf

services. Summary information on federal spectrum use of other bands may be found in NTIA's Federal Spectrum Use Summary. The Federal Government Spectrum Use Reports from 225 MHz to 5 GHz are updated as of December 1, 2015, while the 5-6 GHz bands are updated as of January 2017.[81]

6. Information on Non-Federal Spectrum Use

Information and data on non-federal services and uses that are authorized by the FCC is available from the FCC's Spectrum Dashboard[82] (from 225 MHz to 3.7 GHz) and licensing databases.

H. Regulators Are Making Solid Headway with Reallocation of Spectrum

1. The FCC Delivered Spectrum in Response to Congress and Industry's Fear of a Spectrum Crunch

In the past, delays in government spectrum allocated created inefficiencies that led the mobile industry to believe, or at least advocate, that there was a shortage of spectrum in the U.S. wireless industry commonly referred to as the wireless "spectrum crunch." Inefficiencies emerge when the market demand for spectrum changes, as recently evidenced by the increased demand for wireless broadband. FCC license policies, however, have not permitted licensees in the past to change their use to accommodate market changes. Once market changes indicate a higher value use for spectrum, licensees often had wait for years until the FCC allowed them to use the spectrum for that new use. These regulatory delays have been a frequent source of frustration among service providers. However, in the U.S., the FCC is generally considered more rapid in its policy changing process than its international counterparts.

Since 1994, the FCC has issued licenses almost entirely through auctions

Licensing for primary (priority) use accounts for the most significant portion of licenses are issued by the FCC. Historically, spectrum licenses have been distributed either through applications or auctions. For example, the FCC provided spectrum allocations at no cost for AM, FM, television, and the first entrants of cell phone service. In recent years, governments around the world have increasingly turned to auctions to allocate spectrum licenses. This trend has likely been

---

[81] NTIA, Federal Spectrum Use Summary, *Federal Government Spectrum Use Reports 225 MHz – 7.125 GHz* (Aug. 2017) https://www.ntia.doc.gov/page/federal-government-spectrum-use-reports-225-mhz-7125-ghz

[82] FCC's *Spectrum Dashboard* (July 7, 2014) http://reboot.fcc.gov/reform/systems/spectrum-dashboard

driven by the desire to avoid the perception of bias on the part of those judging applications and has improved the chances that licenses go to their highest use. Since 1994, the FCC has issued licenses almost entirely through auctions. This method of distributing spectrum rights has limited access to spectrum for many service providers because auctions are infrequent and time-consuming. Accordingly, many service providers bid for spectrum in excess of their current needs to ensure a sufficient amount for future needs. Moreover, incumbent service providers are typically in a position to pay the most at auctions, thus limiting new competition. These characteristics result in heavy centralization and underutilization of the available spectrum, which most economists agree is worth many times what the government raises at auction in terms of economic benefit to society.[83]

Another problem with auctions is that entities needing smaller, more tailored licenses may not be able to justify bidding enough for the large license packages.[84] In the U.S., this problem is mitigated by the fact that most terrestrial licenses are allocated in small regions as opposed to nationally as in many other countries.[85]

2. Solutions Are Politically Difficult

One solution to eliminating spectrum inefficiencies has been for the FCC to reclaim the spectrum that was demonstrably underutilized or not utilized at all by the licensee and then to reallocate it for higher value uses. Unfortunately, this process typically takes many years, depriving the public of the most efficient use of the spectrum in the interim. Examples of the time required for the FCC to reallocate spectrum through administrative processes are shown in Figure 7-3 below. Another manner to eliminate these efficiencies would be to simply allow existing license holders the flexibility to use the spectrum for new, more valuable uses. However, governments often find this

This process of reclaiming and reallocating spectrum] typically takes many years, depriving the public of the most efficient use in the interim

---

[83] *See,* Thomas W. Hazlett & Roberto E. Munoz, *A Welfare Analysis of Spectrum Allocation Policies,* Geo. Mason L. & Econ. Res. Paper No. 06-28 at 2 (Jan.19, 2008), http://ssrn.com/abstract=908717 (arguing that total social welfare benefits produced in public spectrum auctions are dominant over auction revenues).

[84] *See,* William Lehr and J. Armand Musey, *Right-Sizing Spectrum Auction Licenses: The Case for Smaller Geographic License Areas in the TV Broadcast Incentive Auction* (2013). Hastings Communications and Entertainment Law Journal, Vol. 37, (2014-2015) SSRN: https://ssrn.com/abstract=2357792 or http://dx.doi.org/10.2139/ssrn.2357792

[85] *See,* Thomas W. Hazlett, Roberto E. Muñoz, and Diego B. Avanzini, *What Really Matters in Spectrum Allocation Design,* 10 NW J TECH & INTELL Prop. 93 (2012), http://scholarlycommons.law.northwestern.edu/njtip/vol10/iss3/2

solution to be impracticable. For instance, an existing licensee who may have received a license at little or no cost would be allowed to have the rights to use it for a more valuable new service without paying for the "upgrade." This distorts the market because the upgraded license holder is free to compete against companies who may have paid billions of dollars for their licenses. Mobile wireless companies, for example, complained when certain satellite telephony companies were given permission to use their spectrum terrestrially at no additional cost.[86]

Figure 7-3: Time Historically Required to Reallocate Spectrum

Band	First Step	Available for Use	~ Lag Time
Cellular (AMPS)	1970	1981	11 years
PCS	1989	1995	6 years
EBS/BRS	1996	2006	10 years
700 MHz	1996	2009	13 years
AWS-1	2000	2006	6 years

Source: *FCC and Summit Ridge Group, LLC analysis*

3. Secondary Spectrum Market Improves Efficiency

Over the past 15 to 20 years, the FCC has gradually eased barriers for buying and selling spectrum rights. In 2000 the FCC revised its spectrum policy in the report *"Principles for Promoting the Efficient Use of Spectrum by Encouraging the Development of Secondary Markets."*[87] This new market-based policy, which was further defined and extended in subsequent reports in 2002 and 2004,[88] suggested establishing a secondary market for licenses to create a more efficient and dynamic market for spectrum licenses.

This secondary market serves as a platform for breaking the larger

Over the past 10-15 years, the FCC has gradually eased barriers to buying and selling spectrum rights

---

[86] Initially via Ancillary Terrestrial Component ("ATC") rules in the US or Complementary Ground Component ("CGC") in Europe, and later wholesale conversion to terrestrial rights in the case of DISH's AWS-4 spectrum. A similar debate is occurring now as the satellite industry seeks to be able to sell its satellite c-band spectrum for use as mobile broadband spectrum.

[87] *Principles for Promoting the Efficient Use of Spectrum by Encouraging the Development of Secondary Markets*, Policy Statement, FCC-00-401, 5 FCC Rcd 124178 (2000) https://www.fcc.gov/document/principles-promoting-efficient-use-spectrum-encouraging-development-secondary-markets.

[88] For a list of FCC documents related to its secondary market policies, see FCC *The Secondary Markets Initiative* (May 20, 2016) https://www.fcc.gov/wireless/bureau-divisions/technologies-systems-and-innovation-division/spectrum-leasing/secondary.

frequency licenses acquired on the primary market into smaller, more differentiated licenses that are then subleased to smaller entities. This reduces inefficiencies by creating cheaper licenses that can be better tailored to the needs of a secondary buyer. These subleases determine the rights under which the primary spectrum holder (the lessor) can provide another entity (the lessee) access to certain parts of its spectrum in accordance with the FCC's determined standards. Despite the regulatory progress, the lack of available hardware capable of dynamically changing frequency presents a major challenge to spectrum leasing. Nonetheless, recently developed smart radio technology, operable on a wide range of bands, may ameliorate this problem.

4. Spectrum Transfer Approval Process More Streamlined

Despite the liberalization of the rules for buying and selling spectrum, the FCC has not conceded the ultimate government ownership of spectrum

Spectrum transfers in the secondary market generally occur in one of two forms: a de facto transfer or a spectrum manager lease. De facto transfers are FCC approved arrangements in which the spectrum holder (licensee) effectively transfers the control of part of the spectrum to the lessee for a specified period (short-term leases for under 360 days, long-term leases for over 360 days). Meanwhile, de jure (rightful) control of the spectrum remains with the licensee. The second form of transfer, the spectrum manager lease, is an arrangement that allows the licensee to provide the lessee with a certain range of frequencies as long as de facto and de jure control over that particular spectrum remain with the original spectrum holder. Since de facto control is not transferred, no approval from the FCC is needed in this process.

The processes of acquiring spectrum licenses were defined and streamlined by the reports the FCC published in 2000, 2002 and 2004.[89] However, there currently is no existing market-making intermediary that facilitates the trading of the licenses between spectrum holders (licensees) and spectrum users (lessees), and the FCC has not determined what entity would act as such. However, the FCC did state that the agency itself would not act in this role. The role

---

[89] The net effect of these reports is that the acquisition process has been streamlined. The general review process has been reduced from 30 to 21 days, while certain de facto transfer proposals could be reviewed as fast as within a single business day. *See Promoting Efficient Use of Spectrum Through Elimination of Barriers to the Development of Secondary Markets*, Second Report and Order, Order on Reconsideration, and Second Further Notice of Proposed Rulemaking, FCC 04-167, WT Docket No. 00-230 (2004).

would be most effectively filled by independent parties who compete with one another.[90]

Despite the liberalization of rules for buying and selling spectrum rights and a streamlined approval process, the FCC has not conceded ultimate government ownership of spectrum. As such, until the government gives up this ultimate power, any change of control will require its approval.

5. Economists Support Arguments for Privatization

Advocates of the market-based approach of allocating spectrum have campaigned for the privatization and free sale of spectrum, without the need for any license. One of the most notable advocates was Nobel Prize-winning economist Ronald Coase. In 1959, he argued that privatizing spectrum ownership would result in a rapid reallocation to the most productive use for society.[91] However, governments around the world have ignored Coase's theory and resisted selling spectrum, viewing it as a public good rather than an exchangeable commodity. Additionally, some academic research points to problems that can arise from unrestricted market trading of spectrum. These include spectrum warehousing and excessive fragmentation of spectrum, which impedes the formation of useful units.[92] Nevertheless, the licensing regimes of many countries, including the U.S., go a long way towards mimicking property rights without explicitly granting them.

6. The FCC is Opening Up New Uses for Prime Spectrum

The FCC, the President, and Congress have recognized that spectrum has been underutilized, and have since addressed many bands of spectrum with innovative mechanisms. The FCC has recognized in the 3.5 GHz CBRS proceeding and has created a method of using the spectrum (the CBRS proceeding is discussed in detail Chapter VIII.K of this *Handbook*) that in congested urban areas prime spectrum below 3.7 GHz has been used at less than 20% of capacity.[93] The

In 1959, the economist Ronald Coase argued that privatizing spectrum ownership would result in a rapid reallocation to the most productive use for society

The FCC, the President, and Congress have recognized that spectrum has been underutilized, and has since addressed many bands of spectrum with innovative mechanisms.

---

[90] Commercial TVWS database vendors include Google and Microsoft.

[91] Ronald Coase, "*The Federal Communications Commission*," 2 J Law & Econ (1959).

[92] For a detailed academic discussion of the potential challenges related to unregulated spectrum markets, see Patrick Xavier & Dimitri Ypsilanti, *Policy Issues in Spectrum Trading*, The Journal of Policy, Regulation and Strategy for Telecommunications, Information and Media, Vol. 8 Issue 2 (2006), p. 34-61. http://www.emeraldinsight.com/journals.htm?articleid=1546218&show=abstract .

[93] R.B. Bacchus K.J. Zdunek, & D.A. Roberson, *Long-term Spectrum Occupancy Findings in Chicago* (2011), IEEE Symposium: New Frontiers in Dynamic Spectrum Access Networks http://www.ece.iit.edu/~taher/dyspan11.pdf; Mark McHenry, *NSF*

FCC has now created incentives for efficient use of the 3.5 GHz spectrum to encourage spectrum sharing among commercial users.[94]

7. Creating Unlicensed Spectrum Through Reallocation

Because of the success of Wi-Fi (discussed in Chapter XV, C. 1), there has been an increasingly large movement towards the use of unlicensed spectrum. Unlicensed spectrum has been in use since 1985 for devices like microwave ovens, TV remote controls, cordless phones, garage door openers, and wireless local area networks. However, the massive success of Wi-Fi and the development of "smart radios" that can change frequencies as needed to avoid interference have increasingly caused industry observers to see unlicensed spectrum as an alternative to licensed spectrum. As detailed in Chapter XV.A of this *Handbook*, the FCC and the NTIA evaluated a significant expansion of unlicensed spectrum use, including the current processes at 3.5 GHz and 5 GHz. In 2015, the FCC established the new CBRS proceeding for shared broadband use of the 3.5 GHz CBRS band.[95] Users sharing spectrum will have general authorized access (GAA) to the spectrum through an innovative "license by rule" at no cost to the user. Other users will be able to purchase at auction exclusive licensed, priority rights to 10 MHz bands of the CBRS spectrum in small size geographies. However, as long as those 10 MHz bands are not operational, the 10 MHz will be considered GAA and will be available for any GAA user at no cost.

In the 5 GHz band, the FCC voted to make 100 MHz of spectrum available for unlicensed Wi-Fi use. Unlicensed spectrum in the 5 GHz band is likely to be used by mobile carriers for LTE-U (described in Part II Chapter VIII.M of this *Handbook*) to deliver 700 Mbps and

Users sharing spectrum will have access to no-cost CBRS spectrum. Other users will have rights to exclusive spectrum when it is not used by the government or those who liked the exclusive license users purchased licenses at auctions.

Spectrum Occupancy Measurements: Project Summary, Shared Spectrum Company (2005) http://www.sharedspectrum.com/wp-content/uploads/NSF_Chicago_2005-11_measurements_v12.pdf; The New America Foundation and The Shared Spectrum Company, *Dupont Circle Spectrum Utilization During Peak Hours: a Collaborative Effort of the New America Foundation and the Shared Spectrum Company*, A New America Foundation Issue Brief. https://vilimpoc.org/research/policy/NAF-SSC-Spectrum-Measurement-Results.pdf.

[94] International approaches to developing efficiencies in government spectrum vary. In the U.K., for example, the military was required to value the spectrum that it uses. If private entities are willing and able to meet this price, the military is required to move from the spectrum, presumably using the funds from the private sector to do so.

[95] *See*, FCC *3.5 GHz CBRS, 3.5 GHz Band / Citizens Broadband Radio Service*, https://www.fcc.gov/wireless/bureau-divisions/broadband-division/35-ghz-band/35-ghz-band-citizens-broadband-radio

above speeds using aggregated licensed and unlicensed spectrum - the unlicensed spectrum will be used with a special LTE that does not interfere with Wi-Fi. Mobile carriers operating in the 3.5 GHz band will initially have a combination of a possible 120 to 150 MHz, depending on the area and what is sold, of auctioned licensed and no-cost spectrum. Large portions of the C-band spectrum, occupying 500 MHz from 3.7 to 4.2 GHz, is reallocated from satellite providers as expected in the new C-band proceeding. If this happens, the 2013 fear heard constantly from industry leaders and regulators of the "Spectrum Crunch" will likely be rendered just a fear.

Various proposals, including the U.S. PCAST Report, have encouraged other governments to implement systems to share unused spectrum between government and commercial users. Some European countries have begun implementing these initiatives. These will significantly expand available spectrum and allow for growth of new mobile and fixed wireless services. One example is the new mmW fixed service using 24 to 26 GHz that can deliver fixed wireless into homes that equals, and even exceeds, Mbps speeds now delivered by cable companies using wired networks. New startups are using this application and major mobile companies are testing it. The advantage over wired cable is the cost of delivering the wireless network to the end-user is much lower than the cost of building HFC cable or fiber into the homes. From a valuation perspective, the new influx of the massive new quantities of licensed and unlicensed spectrum is expected to put downward pressure on the value of spectrum. Many new beachfront spectrum bands have opened since 2012, and supply appears about to pass demand. Chapter XXVI.H of this *Handbook* discusses this valuation point in greater depth.

The wireless industry invests roughly $30 billion annually in capital expenditures to build-out networks

8. Effect of Lobbying Efforts

The wireless industry invests roughly $30 billion annually in capital expenditures to build-out networks.[96] The major carriers average $5 billion to $10 billion in capital expenditures each. Given that the industry is heavily regulated, it would be irresponsible for them to not protect their investment with appropriate political lobbying efforts. Lobbying expenditures by the Telecom Services industry totaled $86.1 million in 2016 according to OpenSecrets.org. Of this amount, the CTIA spent $11.0 million. Lobbying expenditures in 2016 by parent companies of the Big-4 wireless companies are shown in Figure 7-4 below:

---

[96] CTIA, *State of the Wireless 2018* (July 10, 2018) https://www.ctia.org/news/the-state-of-wireless-2018.

Figure 7-4: U.S. Telecom Lobbying Expenditures in 2016

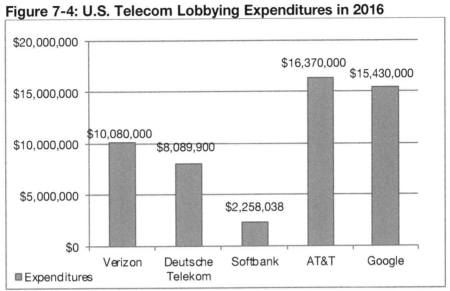

Source: Open Secrets and Summit Ridge Group, LLC analysis

The wireless industry uses its lobbying budget to maintain constant vigilance on pending legislation and FCC policy changes...

The lobbying budget by the telecom services industry reflects the industry's regulatory intensiveness. The wireless industry uses its lobbying budget to maintain constant vigilance on pending legislation and FCC policy changes and to submit comments on almost every docket (e.g., in the broadcast inventive auction process alone, AT&T filed 11 comments). This gives the wireless industry significant access to members of Congress, affording it influence over spectrum policy. For example, when the FCC attempted to prevent AT&T and Verizon's participation in the broadcast incentive auctions, Congress quickly responded with legislation instructing the FCC not to prevent any qualified bidder from participating.[97]

The largest industry players often set the narrative of how an issue is explained. These corporations have stressed the "spectrum crunch," with little supporting information, as the basis for their need for significant amounts of additional spectrum. Only recently have opponents challenged the data and assumptions behind the spectrum crunch hypothesis, a delay that's potentially due to their funding disadvantage.

---

[97] The FCC is able to set spectrum caps and other limits on auction participants. AT&T and Verizon lobbied to prevent this from being part of the FCC's final auction rules.

PART TWO: U.S. SPECTRUM BAND DESCRIPTIONS AND ANALYSIS

VIII. Mobile Wireless Service Band Descriptions

Mobile wireless technology advances in handset chips, base station technology, and spectrum reallocation and efficient methods of spectrum use, like spectrum sharing, many new bands are in the starting gate for mobile use.

For the last 30 years, mobile wireless services have operated in multiple portions of the radio spectrum between 470 MHz and 2690 MHz.[98] Recently, a convergence of various factors has led the FCC and mobile carriers to work together to allocate and utilize spectrum previously not considered usable for mobile uses. These factors include:

- Innovative radio access network ("RAN") mobile technologies in base-stations and handsets, incoming innovative 5G technologies

- Advanced antenna techniques

- Increases in last mile fiber and cable penetration delivering closer to ubiquitous high-speed unlicensed Wi-Fi for smartphones at home and work

- Soaring smartphone penetration increasing customer expectations for faster Internet speeds away from home and in rural areas

- New spectrum sharing methods enabling the reallocation of previously used government spectrum for commercial mobile use

These factors have led to the FCC considering opening and approving new mobile spectrum bands from 470 MHz to 80 GHz.

The use of spectrum that was not previously considered mobile phone spectrum began in 2009 when the FCC opened 18 TV channels for mobile use by requiring TV stations to transition from analog transmission to digital. Then, that same year, the FCC authorized the newly freed TV spectrum for unlicensed "TV White Space" use. This required innovative software-driven broadband base stations' radios to select channels and was managed by spectrum sharing databases. In 2012, Congress passed groundbreaking legislation authorizing an auction for the sale of TV channels that would be reallocated for

---

[98] Additionally, the FCC will be auctioning spectrum in the mmWave bands (24 GHz and 28 GHz) for mobile use in the fall, the 3.5 GHz CBRS spectrum is expected to be in use by the end of 2018, and there is currently an FCC rulemaking for 3.7-4.2 GHz C-Band spectrum for mobile use.

Public Safety LTE mobile use.[99]

Also, in 2012, President Obama issued a report prepared by Internet executives, including Google and Microsoft, ordering federal agencies to work towards making inefficiently used federal spectrum available for commercial uses.[100] The FCC followed the guidance of the PCAST report and used pioneering spectrum sharing databases and software driven base-band radio technology developed for unlicensed use for the newly available TV spectrum. The FCC continued its pace of releasing new spectrum for mobile use when in December 2012, the FCC opened an innovative spectrum sharing proceeding for the 3.5 GHz CBRS band freeing up 150 MHz of spectrum for mobile small cell and fixed wireless base station use. Using a database connected to the mobile and fixed base stations, the FCC created a method of protecting Navy radar that occasionally used the band. The database instructs small cells to stop transmitting when a Navy radar is turned on, which also allows for spectrum efficiencies. This concept led the FCC to create an auction for new smaller license areas based on the size of state counties. The use of a database directing base stations to turn off, or lower power, in small areas now allowed for sharing of unlicensed, licensed, and incumbent spectrum use without interference.

In 2016, the FCC, leveraging technologies developed by the cellular industry,[101] started considering the implementation of a method to dramatically increase the Mbps throughput for LTE, LTE-Unlicensed (LTE-U).[102] It combined unlicensed spectrum in the 5 GHz range with licensed mobile spectrum, and the following year saw the first LTE-U device approved.[103] LTE-U has the potential to deliver dramatically fast 5G speeds surpassing 700 Mbps.[104] The same year, the FCC opened the Spectrum Frontiers, proceeding to auction even more spectrum in the millimeter waves. This included 28 GHz, 37 GHz, and 39 GHz, for mobile, fixed, and unlicensed use. The FCC is also considering 24 GHz, 26 GHz, 42 GHz, and 50 GHz bands for mobile

Using a database connected to the small cell base stations, the FCC created a method of protecting Navy radar that occasionally used the band

---

[99] Middle Class Tax Relief and Job Creation Act of 2012.

[100] *PCAST Report, supra* note 76.

[101] Including LTE-U, LTE-LAA and MuLTEFire.

[102] FCC, "OET Authorizes First LTE-U Devices" (February 22, 2017) https://www.fcc.gov/news-events/blog/2017/02/22/oet-authorizes-first-lte-u-devices

[103] FCC, "OET Authorizes First LTE-U Devices" (February 22, 2017) https://www.fcc.gov/news-events/blog/2017/02/22/oet-authorizes-first-lte-u-devices

[104] Corbin Davenport, "T-Mobile's LTE-U Network is Rolling Out in Select Cities," Android Police (June 26, 2017). https://www.androidpolice.com/2017/06/26/t-mobiles-lte-u-network-rolling-select-cities/

In 2018, the FCC opened a new proceeding that would potentially reallocate large portions of 500 MHz of satellite spectrum in the C-band (3.7-4.2 GHz) for mobile use

use. [105] The FCC approved the use of 14,000 MHz in the 60/70 GHz band for unlicensed fixed Wi-Fi-like service called WiGig. In 2017, the FCC began to consider using millimeter wave in the 70/80 GHz band as a possibility for shared spectrum. [106] They thought using the database method developed for the TV spectrum would allow for licensed and unlicensed high-throughput mobile, and fixed service could share the spectrum with smart beam-forming antennas and handset advances. For now, though, the FCC will continue to keep this 70/80 GHz band for fixed-only service.[107] Finally, in 2018, the FCC opened a new proceeding that would potentially reallocate large portions of 500 MHz of satellite spectrum in the C-band (3.7-4.2 GHz), for mobile use. The FCC is also considering applying the 3.5 GHz database sharing method to significant portions of this band.

The new spectrum that the FCC is allocating for mobile use is in addition to many existing bands supplying the mobile industry today. Unlicensed Wi-Fi available in the 2.4 GHz and 5 GHz bands also plays, and will continue to play, a large role in delivering significant quantities of bandwidth to the same smartphones using licensed spectrum. Today, smartphone users depend primarily on Wi-Fi for transmitting data traffic that is not delivered over license holders' wireless networks, but instead delivered over the users' home and work Wi-Fi networks.

Mobile carriers plan to use the newly available licensed spectrum to enable their customers to experience Internet speeds outside the home equal to speeds delivered by Wi-Fi in the home. Carriers hope to purchase licenses for this newly available spectrum, such as the 600 MHz and 3.5 GHz bands, in an auction because the range of spectrum will allow the carriers to penetrate building walls with the spectrum far better than spectrum currently licensed. In addition, the carriers have plans to create outdoor networks in urban and rural areas that will give their customers the same experience while traveling as they do at home while using Wi-Fi that is provided by their cable company or wired telecom provider. The newly reallocated spectrum could also help mobile carriers to replace the fixed wireline

---

[105] FCC, "2016 Report and Order" (WT Docket No. 10-112) https://transition.fcc.gov/Daily_Releases/Daily_Business/2016/db0728/FCC-16-89A1.pdf

[106] FCC, "2016 Report and Order" (WT Docket No. 10-112) https://transition.fcc.gov/Daily_Releases/Daily_Business/2016/db0728/FCC-16-89A1.pdf

[107] FCC, "2016 Report and Order" (WT Docket No. 10-112) https://transition.fcc.gov/Daily_Releases/Daily_Business/2016/db0728/FCC-16-89A1.pdf

carriers in the home, increasing the mobile carriers' average revenue per user (ARPU), which is currently divided between the mobile carriers and the fixed home Internet providers.

The table in Figure 8-1 below shows spectrum previously open and opening up by 2020 targeted primarily for mobile use. Spectrum allocated to individual US wireless carriers is shown in the Allnet Insights and Analytics charts in Appendix A of this *Handbook*.

Figure 8-1: Spectrum Allocated For Mobile Use

Band	Frequency	Bandwidth	Auction Date	Database Sharing?
Cellular	850 MHz	50 MHz	1981	No
PCS	1900 MHz	120 MHz	1994	No
SMR	900 MHz	14 MHz	2007	No
600 MHz	600 MHz	70 MHz	2017	Yes
700 MHz	700 MHz	70 MHz	2008	No
Add'l PCS	1900 MHz	10 MHz	2009[108]	No
AWS-1	1710 MHz	90 MHz	2006	
AWS-3	1700 MHz	65 MHz	2015	
AWS-4	2000 MHz	40 MHz	2012	
WCS	2400 MHz	20 MHz	2010	
EBS/BRS	2500 MHz	194 MHz	2013	
CBRS	3.5 GHz	150 MHz	2018	Yes
C-band	3.7 GHz	100 MHz	2018 NPRM	Yes
24 GHz	24 GHz	700 MHz	2018 Auction 102	No
28 GHz	28 GHz	850 MHz	2019 Auction 101	No
Total MHz: 2,543 MHz				

Source: Summit Ridge Group, LLC Analysis

---

[108] This is the PCS G Block (1910-1915 and 1990-1995 MHz), previously unlicensed, became available for licensed use after the FCC issued a rule change in 2004. Sprint was granted a license for this spectrum in 2009.

A. In the Beginning: No Cost 800 MHz Licenses

The first commercial mobile service was introduced in 1965.

The first commercial mobile service was introduced in 1965 by AT&T and called Improved Mobile Telephone Service (IMTS). The spectrum assigned for the service was VHF (Very High Frequency) 35 MHz and 43 MHz, located below TV channel 2,152 MHz and 148 MHz, located below TV Channel 7, and UHF (Ultra High Frequency) 454 MHz and 459 MHz, located below TV Channel 14. Demand for new IMTS was strong and AT&T limited the service to 40,000 users nationwide. High demand caused users to sometimes wait for 30 minutes to obtain one of the 12 available channels. The IMTS antennas were placed up to 500 feet high, which is much higher than the average 150 to 200-foot macro cells used today, and allowed one antenna to deliver service on the 12 channels within a 120-mile diameter circle. IMTS was not cell phone service and was delivered much like a two-way TV or radio service with one antenna. The IMTS service is still today in use in some rural areas.

B. Advanced Mobile Phone Systems: 800 MHz

IMTS mobile service was followed in 1983 by the introduction of Advanced

IMTS mobile service was followed in 1983 by the introduction of Advanced Mobile Phone Systems (AMPS). AMPS was the first "cell" 1G service deployed. The FCC allocated 40 MHz of spectrum for AMPS, located at 824-849 MHz for the uplink to the base station and 869-894 MHz for the downlink to the handset. The FCC divided the AMPS band into two blocks, the A block and the B block, in each of the 734 Cellular Market Areas (CMAs) across the country. Each block originally contained 333 channels but was expanded in the late 1980s to 416 channels after spectrum was reallocated from UHF TV channels 70-83, for a total of 84 MHz from 806-890 MHz.[109]

The FCC allocated the B block, at no cost, to the local Bell operating companies. To create a competitive market, they allocated the A Block, also at no cost, to non-wireline businesses, such as operating paging companies, in a comparative hearing of applicants. In most CMAs, the B Block licenses went to the local wireline telephone companies, such as BellSouth, Southwestern Bell, PacBell, Mountain Bell, NYNEX, and Bell Atlantic. Later, Bell Atlantic and NYNEX completed a merger and became Verizon, and BellSouth/Cingular and SBC completed a merger and became AT&T. In 1988, the FCC relaxed the requirement for new cell phone providers use AMPS, which opened the door for carriers to use more advanced digital

---

[109] Includes 6 MHz of spectrum for public safety, 806-909 MHz and 851-854 MHz.

technologies using the same AMPS spectrum.[110]

To create the 734 CMAs, the FCC used a 1950's mapping system for 306 urban metropolitan statistical areas (MSAs), drawn around urban areas, and 428 rural statistical areas (RSAs). These new areas did not follow state boundaries or the seven regional Bell operating companies' territories.

The FCC auctioned 25 MHz licenses for several remaining unserved RSAs and CMAs. These two auctions included FCC Auction No. 45[111] in 2002 (A Block licenses in 3 rural RSAs) and FCC Auction No. 77[112] in 2008 (A Block licenses in 2 unserved CMAs). A summary of the frequency allocations is in Figure 8-2 below:

Figure 8-2: Former 800 MHz Cellular Channel License Blocks

A Block		B Block	
Spectrum	Amount	Spectrum	Amount
824.0 to 835.0	11.0 MHz	835.0 to 845.0	10.0 MHz
845.0 to 846.5	1.5 MHz	846.5 to 849.0	2.5 MHz
869.0 to 880.0	11.0 MHz	880.0 to 890.0	10.0 MHz
890.0 to 891.5	1.5 MHz	891.5 to 894.0	2.5 MHz
25 MHz total		25 MHz total	

Source: FCC and Summit Ridge Group, LLC analysis

As of 2008, the AMPS cellular providers were allowed to terminate their analog services and switch entirely to more spectrum-efficient digital services

As of 2008, the AMPS cellular providers were allowed to terminate their analog services and switch entirely to more spectrum-efficient digital services. All major cell phone providers now use this spectrum to provide services using digital technologies.

The FCC paired the 804 to 824 MHz section with the 851 to 869 MHz section of the band and allocated it for various public safety radio systems now used by police and emergency responders.

---

[110] Gustav Barth, "Cellular Phones: Is There Really Competition?" Incidental Paper, Program on Information Resources Policy, Center for Information Policy Research, Harvard University (p.6). http://www.pirp.harvard.edu/pubs_pdf/barth/barth-i94-3.pdf

[111] FCC, Fact Sheet - Auction 45: Cellular RSA. https://www.fcc.gov/auction/45/factsheet#Licenses%20Offered

[112] FCC, Fact Sheet - Auction 77: Closed Cellular Unserved. https://www.fcc.gov/auction/77/factsheet Note: This was a very small auction, raising a total of only $25,002

See Figure 8-3 below for a graphic description of the 800 MHz band:

Figure 8-3: 800 MHz Plan – Post Reconfiguration

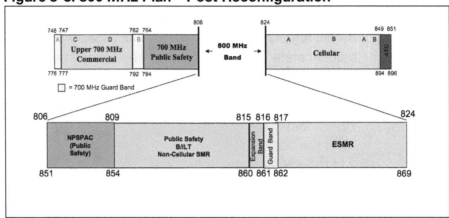

Source: FCC

Figure 8-4 shows the allocation of the 800 MHz band for public safety used following guidelines developed by the National Public Safety Planning Advisory Committee (NPSPAC).

Figure 8-4: Allocation of 800 MHz Band for Public Safety Use

Allocation	Bandwidth (MHz)	Frequencies
Public Safety	6 MHz	806–809 MHz, 851-864 MHz
Public Safety/ non-cellular SMR	12 MHz	809-815 MHz, 854-860 MHz
Expansion Band	2 MHz	815-815 MHz, 860-861 MHz
Guard Band	2 MHz	816-817 MHz, 661-862 MHz
ESMR	14 MHz	817-824 MHz, 862-869 MHz
Cellular	50 MHz	824-849 MHz, 869-894 MHz

Source: FCC and Summit Ridge Group, LLC analysis

C. Personal Communications Service (PCS): 1.8 GHz and 1.9 GHz

In 1993, after the initial frequency bands used for AMPS mobile services (806 to 902 MHz) were exhausted, the FCC allocated a higher spectrum range to a new cellular phone service called Personal Communication Services (PCS), which used only new digital transmissions.[113] As early as 1989, the first petition to the FCC from commercial mobile service providers appeared requesting additional spectrum to use for a new mobile technology. Similar arguments for allocating new spectrum for more advanced mobile technology continued to be made from that time through today.

The FCC assigned PCS to a new spectrum allocation that contains the 130 MHz from 1850 to 1915 MHz, for uplink, and 1930 to 1995 MHz, for downlink. PCS spectrum was divided into seven frequency blocks (A-G), each of which has between 10 to 30 MHz of bandwidth. The PCS spectrum can be used for a variety of technologies including GSM, 3G, and 4G technologies. It is divided into two spectrums: narrowband PCS and broadband PCS. The narrowband PCS spectrum is allocated to relatively simple two-way text-based services, while broadband PCS spectrum is for more complex two-way wireless data and voice services on both mobile and fixed technologies PCS operators were divided into broadband PCS and narrowband PCS, which included paging companies.

The PCS spectrum is divided into narrowband PCS and broadband PCS licenses

The PCS spectrum was auctioned across the country in 51 geographical units called Major Trading Areas (MTAs), 493 Basic Trading Areas BTAs), and 175 Economic Areas (EAs).

SprintPCS was an example of an early PCS new mobile entrant. Note in Figure 8-5 below that the FCC originally create 30 MHz C Block licenses but then split the C Blocks into multiple licenses: C-1 and C-2 with 15 MHz each; and C-3, C-4, and C-5 with 10 MHz each.

The PCS Band plan is illustrated in Figure 8-5 below.

[113] FCC Website, Personal Communication Services (PCS) page.
https://www.fcc.gov/wireless/bureau-divisions/mobility-division/broadband-personal-communications-service-pcs

PART TWO: U.S. SPECTRUM

Figure 8-5: PCS Band Plan

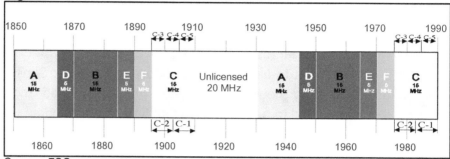

Source: FCC

Channel Block	Frequencies (MHz)	Bandwidth (MHz)	Pairing
A	1850-1865, 1930-1945	30	2 x 15 MHz
B	1870-1885, 1950-1965	30	2 x 15 MHz
C	1895-1910, 1975-1990	30	2 x 15 MHz
D	1865-1870, 1945-1950	10	2 x 5 MHz
E	1885-1890, 1965-1970	10	2 x 5 MHz
F	1890-1895, 1970-1975	10	2 x 5 MHz
Duplex Gap	1910-1930	20	NA

Source: FCC and Summit Ridge Group, LLC analysis

D. L-Band (1.6 GHz) and S-Band (2.0 GHz)

The FCC introduced MSS licenses in 1997, which currently occupy a total of 90 MHz of spectrum in the L-band and S-band

Mobile Satellite Services (MSS) operate in the 1.6 GHz L-band and 2.0 GHz S-band frequency bands. The also FCC allocated MSS licenses in 1997, covering a total of 90 MHz of spectrum.

As discussed in Chapter XVI.A.5, the FCC is seeking to free parts of the L-band and S-band spectrum for dual satellite and terrestrial authorization.

E. Advanced Wireless Spectrum (AWS): 1.7 GHz and 2.1 GHz

AWS spectrum is intended for fixed and mobile voice and data services. Current service rules for these bands can be found at 47 C.F.R Part 27. The AWS spectrum contains multiple sections. A band plan for AWS-1 spectrum and for the 2 GHz AWS 2, 3 and 4 spectrum as a whole, is illustrated in Figure 8-6 and 8-7 respectively below.

Figure 8-6: AWS 1 Band Plan Detail (90 MHz total)

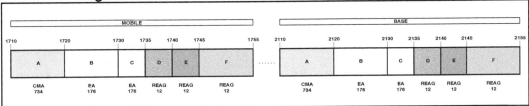

Channel Block	Frequencies (MHz)	Bandwidth (MHz)	Pairing
A	1850-1865, 1930-1945	30	2 x 15 MHz
B	1870-1885, 1950-1965	30	2 x 15 MHz
C	1895-1910, 1975-1990	30	2 x 15 MHz
D	1865-1870, 1945-1950	10	2 x 5 MHz
E	1885-1890, 1965-1970	10	2 x 5 MHz
F	1890-1895, 1970-1975	10	2 x 5 MHz
Duplex Gap	1910-1930	20	NA

Source: FCC[114] and Summit Ridge Group, LLC analysis

AWS-2 spectrum contains the frequency ranges 1915-1920 MHz and 1995-2000 MHz (H block – paired), 2020-2025 MHz and 2175-2180 MHz (J-block – paired). In 2014, Dish Network acquired the AWS-2 H Block for $1.564 billion in FCC Auction No. 96.

AWS-3 spectrum runs from 2155-2175 MHz and is paired with the 1755-1780 MHz band. In 2015 it was sold in FCC Auction No. 97, which had a record $44.9 billion in proceeds. The auction was for a total of 65 MHz. Block A1 (1695-1700 MHz) and Block B1 (1700-1710 MHz) were unpaired, and G Block (1755-1760/2155-2160 MHz), H Block (1760-1765/2160-2165 MHz), I Block (1765-1770/2165-2170 MHz), and J Block (1770-1780MHz and 2170-2180 MHz) were paired. The G Block is licensed in 734 CMAs and the other paired spectrum blocks are licensed in 176 geographically larger EAs. AT&T, Verizon,

---

[114] http://wireless.fcc.gov/services/aws/data/awsbandplan.pdf.

and Dish accounted for 93% of the total proceeds.

AWS-4 spectrum runs from 2000-2020 MHz and 2180-2200 MHz.[115] This spectrum is currently licensed to Dish Network.

Figure 8-7: 2 GHz AWS-2, 3 & 4 Band Plan (125 MHz total)

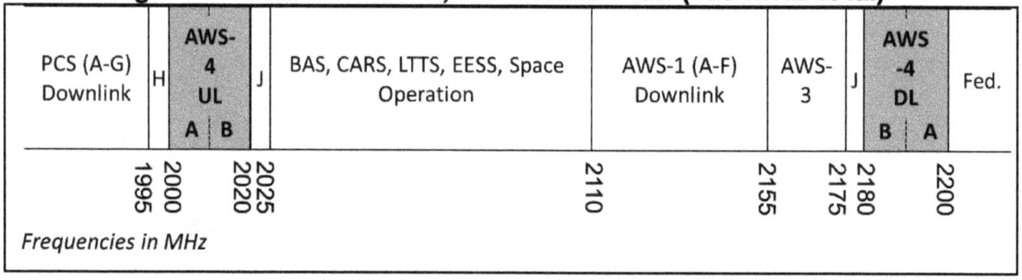

Frequencies in MHz

Application	Frequencies (MHz)	Bandwidth	Pairing
AWS- 2 H Block	1915-1920 1995-2000	10 MHz	2 x 10 MHz
AWS- 2 J Block	2020-2025, 2175-2180	10 MHz	2 x 5 MHz
20 MHz total			
AWS-3 A1 Block	1695-1700 MHz	5 MHz	Unpaired
AWS-3 B1 Block	1700-1710 MHz	10 MHz	Unpaired
AWS- 3 G Block	1755-1760, 2155 – 2160	10 MHZ	2 x 5 MHz
AWS- 3 H Block	1760-1765 2160-2165	10 MHz	2 x 5 MHz
AWS- 3 I Block	1765-1770, 2165-2170	10 MHz	2 x 5 MHz
AWS- 3 J Block	1770-1780, 2170-2180	20 MHz	2 x 10 MHz
65 MHz total			
AWS-4 A Block	2000-2010, 2190-2200	20 MHz	2 x 10 MHz
AWS-4 B Block	2010-2020, 2180-2190	20 MHz	2 x 10 MHz
40 MHz total			

Source: FCC and Summit Ridge Group, LLC analysis

---

[115] FCC website. See: https://www.fcc.gov/wireless/bureau-divisions/mobility-division/advanced-wireless-services-aws/advanced-wireless-0

Federal government agencies currently use much of the AWS-1 uplink spectrum

AWS-1 spectrum contains the frequency ranges 1710-1755 MHz (45 MHz) for uplink and 2110-2155 MHz (45 MHz) for downlink.[116] It is divided into six frequency blocks (A-F). Federal government agencies currently use much of the uplink spectrum and will need to be moved to new spectrum allocations to allow for commercial uses. There is much uncertainty over the cost and timing of this move. The licenses for AWS Block A are issued for the 734 Cellular Market Areas, Blocks B and C are issued for the 176 Economic Areas, while blocks D, E, and F are issued for each of the 12 Regional Economic Groups. There have been two AWS-1 auctions: FCC Auction No. 66 in 2006 where average prices ranged from $0.40 to $0.72 per Mhz/Pop, depending on the spectrum block sold. Auction No. 78 in 2008 was a much smaller auction for licenses that did not sell in Auction No. 66 and realized much lower prices.

AWS-2 spectrum contains the frequency ranges 1915-1920 MHz and 1995-2000 MHz (H block – paired), 2020-2025 MHz and 2175-2180 MHz (J-block – paired). In 2014, Dish Network acquired the AWS-2 H Block for $1.564 billion in FCC Auction No. 96.

AWS-3...sold in FCC Auction No. 97, which had a record $44.9 billion in proceeds

AWS-3 spectrum runs from 2155-2175 MHz and is paired with the 1755-1780 MHz band. In 2015 it was sold in FCC Auction No. 97, which had a record $44.9 billion in proceeds. The auction was for a total of 65 MHz. Block A1 (1695-1700 MHz) and Block B1 (1700-1710 MHz) were unpaired, and G Block (1755-1760/2155-2160 MHz), H Block (1760-1765/2160-2165 MHz), I Block (1765-1770/2165-2170 MHz), and J Block (1770-1780MHz and 2170-2180 MHz) were paired. The G Block is licensed in 734 CMAs and the other paired spectrum blocks are licensed in 176 geographically larger EAs. AT&T, Verizon, and Dish accounted for 93% of the total proceeds.

AWS-4 spectrum runs from 2000-2020 MHz and 2180-2200 MHz.[117] This spectrum is currently licensed to Dish Network. While it was originally subject to ATC requirements (see Chapter XVI.A.5 for background on ATC), the FCC eliminated the ATC requirements for this band in 2013, allowing it to be used with terrestrial-only handsets. This significantly increased the value of the spectrum by lowering the cost of the handsets.

---

[116] FCC Website. See: https://www.fcc.gov/wireless/bureau-divisions/mobility-division/advanced-wireless-services-aws

[117] FCC website. See: https://www.fcc.gov/wireless/bureau-divisions/mobility-division/advanced-wireless-services-aws/advanced-wireless-0

F. Wireless Communication Service (WCS): 2.3 GHz

The WCS band consists of 30 MHz in the frequency range 2305-2320 MHz and 2345-2360 MHz. The FCC intends for the WCS band to be used for wireless broadband, by dividing it into two 10 MHz blocs (paired 5 MHz blocks) and two unpaired 5 MHz blocks. The satellite radio provider SiriusXM Satellite Radio controls the 25 MHz between the two blocks for its two separate satellite networks. An illustrated description of the WCS band is in Figure 8-8 below.

Figure 8-8: WCS Band Plan

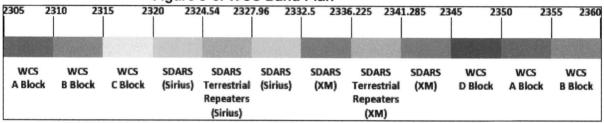

SiriusXM Satellite Radio controls 25 MHz between the two WCS blocks for its satellite radio service

Application	Frequency (MHz)	Bandwidth (MHz)	Pairing
WCS – A Block	2305-2310, 2350-2355	10 MHz	2 x 5 MHz
WCS – B Block	2310-2315, 2355-2360	10 MHz	2 x 5 MHz
WCS – C Block	2315-2320	5 MHz	Unpaired
SDARS (Sirius)	2320-2324.54, 2327.96-2332.5	9.08 MHz	2 x 4.54 MHz
SDARS Repeaters (Sirius)	2324.54-2327.96	3.42 MHz	Unpaired
SDARS (XM)	2332.5-2336.225, 2342.285-2345	7.430 MHz	3.725 MHz
			3.715 MHz
SDARD Repeaters (XM)	2336.225-2341.285	5.060 MHz	Unpaired
WCS – D Block	2345-2350	5 MHz	Unpaired

Source: FCC and Summit Ridge Group, LLC analysis

One significant technical issue that the WCS band faces is interference with DARS (Digital Audio Radio Service) spectrum, which abuts the frequency ranges used for WCS.

AT&T and SiriusXM entered into a voluntary agreement in the summer of 2012 to solve this issue. On October 17, 2012, the FCC effectively approved this agreement by adopting its key terms as service rules to enable WCS and satellite radio to operate without interference.[118] These service rules allow 20 MHz to be used for mobile broadband service and 10 MHz for fixed broadband service. The FCC has indicated that some portion of the fixed allocation may be used for mobile services in the future.

WCS licenses are issued via auction, but only one has taken place, which was FCC Auction No. 14 in 1997.[119] The A and the B blocks were issued for the 52 Major Economic Areas (MEAs) while the C and D blocks were issued for the 12 Regional Economic Area Groupings (REAGs).

WCS spectrum use is subject to FCC service rules under 47 C.F.R. Part 27.

G. BRS/EBS (2.5 GHz)

The 2.5GHz Educational Broadband Services (EBS) spectrum – 194 MHz from 2495-2690 MHz -- is the largest contiguous band of spectrum

The 2.5GHz Educational Broadband Services (EBS) spectrum – 194 MHz from 2495-2690 MHz -- is the largest contiguous band of spectrum below 3 GHz. In 1963, the spectrum was allocated for educational TV and was assigned to various universities, high schools, and religious institutions including Catholic schools. Currently, 2,190 EBS licenses are owned by 1,300 licenses. The FCC allocated 114 MHz to EBS and 80 MHz to Broadband Radio Service, or BRS. In two auctions, the FCC sold 493 BTA (Basic Trading Area) BRS licenses to 191 small businesses. But approximately half of the EBS spectrum remained unused. EBS spectrum could be sublicensed to non-EBS entities, but not transferred. Sprint, through its 2013 acquisition of Clearwire, controls approximately 133 MHz subleased to it from BRS/EBS licensees.[120] In May 2018, the FCC adopted a rulemaking to allow for the more efficient use of BRS/EBS which would give

---

[118] 47 C.F.R. Part 27. See also, AT&T Public Policy Blog, FCC Approves AT&T, Sirius XM WCS Spectrum Band Proposal, October 17, 2013, http://attpublicpolicy.com/fcc/fcc-approves-att-sirius-xm-wcs-spectrum-band-proposal.

[119] More information about FCC Auction No. 14 can be found at: https://www.fcc.gov/auction/14/factsheet

[120] Commission's Rules to Facilitate the Provision of Fixed and Mobile Broadband Access, Educational and Other Advanced Services in the 2150-2162 and 2500-2690 MHz Bands, WT Docket No. 03-66, et al., Order on Reconsideration and Fifth Memorandum Opinion and Order and Third Memorandum Opinion and Order and Second Report and Order, 21 FCC Rcd 5606 (2006).

mobile carriers an opportunity to own the licenses.[121] The proposed changes include: 1) enlarging the geographic size of the BTAs which could increase the value; 2) allowing BRS/EBS licensees to fully transfer their licenses to other entities and allowing entities physically located in an unused EBS spectrum areas to license the spectrum; and 3) establishing an auction for non-EBS entities to purchase the remaining spectrum. The EBS/BRS Band is below in Figure 8-9.

Figure 8-9: EBS/BRS Band Plan

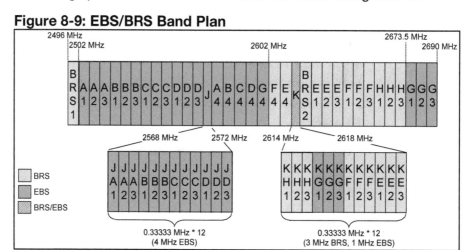

Type	Frequency (MHz)	Amount	Type
BRS	2496-2502	6 MHz	Unpaired
EBS	2502-2602	100 MHz	Unpaired
BRS	2602-2615	13 MHz	Unpaired
EBS	2615-2616	1 MHz	Unpaired
BRS	2616-2673.5	57.7 MHz	Unpaired
EBS	2673.5-2690	16.5 MHz	Unpaired

Source: FCC and Summit Ridge Group, LLC analysis

The 700 MHz band promises to be a band that can be used to deliver ubiquitous mobile service in rural areas in through building walls because of its excellent propagation characteristics.

H. 700 MHz Upper and Lower Bands

In 1997, the FCC began to implement the Congressional mandate in the Telecommunications Act of 1996 to create digital television service, or DTV, and to reallocate the former analog TV spectrum into two 12 MHz channels for public safety and the remaining 36 MHz for commercial uses via auction.[122] That same year, the FCC allocated portions of the Upper 700 MHz band from 764-776 MHz (Channels 63

---

[121] FCC website. See: https://www.fcc.gov/wireless/bureau-divisions/broadband-division/broadband-radio-service-education-broadband-service#block-menu-block-4

[122] Telecommunications Act of 1996, § 201; Balanced Budget Act of 1997 § 3004.

and 64) and 794-806 MHz (Channels 68 and 69) for public safety. The FCC allocated 746-764 MHz (Channels 60-62) and 776-794 MHz (Channels 65-67) for fixed, mobile, and broadcast services.[123]

Following Congress's mandate to reclaim and organize the TV spectrum, the FCC determined that all new DTV digital channels could occupy the spectrum previously occupied between channels 2-51, post DTV.[124] Relocating TV channels located in the 700 MHz spectrum enabled the FCC to reallocate the vacated spectrum for public safety, mobile, fixed, and advanced broadcast use.

Figure 8-10: 700 MHz Upper and Lower Band Plan

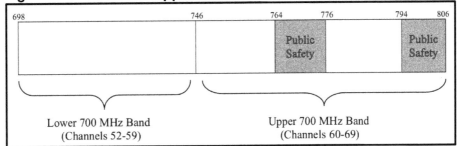

Source: FCC WT Docket No. 06-150[125]

The Lower 700 MHz band – the 48 MHz from 698-746 MHz, (TV channels 52-69) - was auctioned for mobile broadband in 2002 and 2003. The TV channels operating in the band were required to relocate to other channels by 2006. In the Upper 700 MHz band, 36 MHz were allocated for auction and 24 MHz were reserved for public safety (TV channels 70-83).[126]

The 700 MHz spectrum has been called the "Beachfront Spectrum" for mobile service because of the propagation advantages it has over higher cellular spectrum. The 700 MHz spectrum is a relatively low frequency for mobile service with a correspondingly high wavelength. The larger the wavelength of the radio wave the more the wavelength can pass through materials like brick walls or other radio wave

---

[123] *Reallocation of Television Channels 60-69, the 746-806 MHz Band*, ET Docket No. 97-157, Report and Order, 12 FCC Rcd 22953 (1998), recon., 13 FCC Rcd 21578 (1998) (Upper 700 MHz Reallocation Order).

[124] 47 U.S.C. 309(j)(14); *Reallocation and Service Rules for the 698-746 MHz Spectrum Band (Television Channels 52-59)*, GN Docket No. 01-74, Memorandum Opinion and Order, 17 FCC Rcd 11613 (2002) (Lower 700 MHz).

[125] *Service Rules for the 698-746, 747-762, and 777-792 MHz Bands* Report and Order, page 7. https://www.fcc.gov/document/service-rules-698-746-747-762-and-777-792-mhz-bands-et-al-0

[126] The Lower 700 MHz Band Auction No. 44 and Auction No. 49 were held in August 2002 and May 2003, respectively.

The larger the wavelength of the radio wave the more the wavelength can pass through materials like brick walls or other radio wave blocking materials. A 700 MHz radio wave is 0.42 meters in length, while the 2 GHz wavelength is almost three times smaller at 0.15 meters. As such, a 700 MHz radio wave is capable of overcoming obstacles in the environment better than higher frequencies. TV stations occupied the 700 MHz spectrum to be able to penetrate through foliage and brick walls and into living rooms. Moreover, the longer propagation range of 700 MHz spectrum (as well as 800 MHz spectrum described below) is ideal for providing wireless service in rural areas where fewer base stations per square mile are needed.

Due to the long propagation range of the frequency, service providers need fewer base stations and towers to build a network, making the cost of building the network less expensive overall than compared to those with higher frequencies and shorter propagation ranges. The build-out cost per user, however, could be similar in urban and rural areas because there are fewer users in rural areas per square mile than in urban areas. Because the population density is lower in rural areas, the highest demand for 700 MHz spectrum may be for mobile services in rural areas with lower traffic volume or for indoor IoT services in urban areas with less bandwidth-intensive applications.

On the other hand, there may be strong demand for 700 MHz and lower spectrum in urban areas because the spectrum penetrates foliage, buildings, and most importantly, building walls. In-building mobile service has been one of the most troubling problems for mobile carriers to solve because higher frequency spectrum has more difficulty penetrating brick and concrete walls. When deployed in an urban area, the new 700 MHz bandwidth could give a carrier a major marketing and user experience advantage over a carrier not using the spectrum because of the ability to receive better service inside buildings. Carriers using 700 MHz in urban areas could also lower the network costs required for delivering effective in-building coverage per user by decreasing the need to build indoor DAS antenna systems or indoor small cells.

Many other countries around the world are in the process of a reallocation of the 700 MHz band from television to mobile services

Another attractive feature of the 700 MHz spectrum band is that because of advances in smartphone antennas, the longer antennas needed for this lower frequency range are now small enough to fit into phones. Lower spectrum frequencies require larger antennas, which is why VHF antennas are larger than UHF antennas. Before these smaller, newer technologies, mobile phones were not able to accommodate the longer antennas required. The innovations in

1. FCC 700 MHz Allocation

Until 2002, the Lower 700 MHz band spectrum, from 698-746 MHz, was used for UHF television channels 52 to 59. Each analog TV channel occupied 6 MHz. Figure 8-11 below illustrates the Lower 700 MHz band plan. The Upper 700 MHz band, from 746-806 MHz, was previously used for UHF channels 60 to 69 (Figure 8-12). In the U.S., the Upper and Lower 700 MHz bands have been available for mobile wireless service since 2008 when the FCC completed the DTV repacking of UHF channels 52 to 69 down below channel 51. These lower channels are referred to as the 600 MHz band. Spectrum regulators in many other countries around the world have instituted a similar reutilization of this band from TV to mobile services.

The DTV repacking of the 700 MHz band UHF channels is referred to as the "digital dividend" spectrum (a reference to the large swath of spectrum freed up by digitizing TV signals). Digital channels did not require a large number of guard bands between channels like analog TV technology required. Therefore, guard bands were free to be used for mobile, fixed broadband, and other uses. Parts of the 700 MHz band, previously occupied by television channels 62-64 and 67-69 (Band 14), were allocated for a nationwide public safety mobile network dubbed "FirstNet."[127]

In 2012, the U.S. Congress authorized $7 billion from the proceeds of a series of spectrum auctions to construct the FirstNet system

In 2012, the U.S. Congress authorized $7 billion from the proceeds of a series of spectrum auctions to construct the FirstNet system in 24 MHz of Upper 700 MHz spectrum.[128] Although the spectrum had already been allocated to public safety, it had not received funding for a network. FirstNet's mission was to develop, build, and operate a nationwide broadband network that would equip first responders with interoperable equipment using LTE. In 2017, the FirstNet organization entered into an agreement with AT&T, after an RFP process, for AT&T to use the spectrum and provide the FirstNet service. AT&T has exclusive rights to the 24 MHz of FirstNet spectrum and will receive $6.5 billion for the build-out and then $15 billion more for network upgrades from FirstNet over the next 25 years. Having ownership of the 24 MHz will ensure that AT&T maintains the FirstNet business.

---

[127] For information about FirstNet, see FirstNet page of the National Telecommunications & Information Administration Website. https://www.firstnet.gov/.

[128] Middle Class Tax Relief and Job Act of 2012. See: https://www.congress.gov/112/plaws/publ96/PLAW-112publ96.pdf

Figure 8-11: U.S. Lower 700 MHz Band Plan

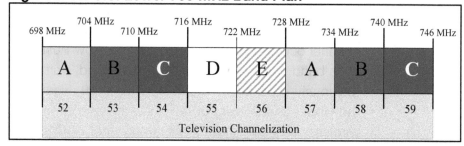

Block	Frequencies (MHz)	Bandwidth	Paring	Geographical Area Type	No. of Licenses
A	698- 704, 728-734	12 MHz	2 x 6 MHz	EA	176
B	704-710, 734-740	12 MHz	2 x 6 MHz	CMA	734
C	710-716, 740-746	12 MHz	2 x 6 MHz	CMA	734
D	716-722	6 MHz	Unpaired	EAG	6
E	722-728	6 MHz	Unpaired	EA	176

Source: FCC and Summit Ridge Group, LLC analysis

Figure 8-12: U.S. Upper 700 MHz Plan

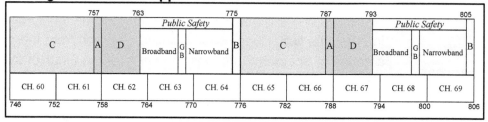

The FCC's proposed band plan for 700 MHz faces several criticisms

Block	Frequencies (MHz)	Bandwidth	Paring	Geographical Area Type	No. of Licenses
C	746-757, 776-787	22 MHz	2 x 11 MHz	REAG	12
A	757-758, 787-788	2 MHZ	2 x 1 MHz	MEA	52
D	758-763, 788-793	10 MHz	2 x 5 MHz	Nationwide	1*
B	755-776, 805-806	2 MHz	2 x 1 MHz	MEA	52

*Subject to sharing with adjacent public safety network band

Source: FCC and Summit Ridge Group, LLC analysis

2. Criticisms of the U.S. Band Plan

Although the U.S. was at the forefront of developing the 700 MHz band for mobile use, the FCC's proposed band plan for 700 MHz faced several criticisms. First, the 700 MHz band is highly fragmented so operators could not acquire the large 15 to 20 MHz blocks needed for efficient use available from LTE. For example, the A Block in the lower portion of the band is separated from Channel 51 of the television band by only a 1 MHz gap, potentially causing interference that could severely limit its use. In the 2008 auction, the A Block sold, on average, for approximately 60% less than the B Block, which experiences no such potential interference.[129] Moreover, because of the lower quality of the band, much of the A Block was auctioned to second-tier service providers. The larger service providers have resisted ordering handsets that operate in the A Block.[130] The lack of affordable handsets that function in the A Block makes it harder for the second-tier players to operate in the A Block and helps to reinforce the dominant position of the larger players. Ultimately, the FCC implemented its 700 MHz interoperability plan requiring carriers using the lower 700 MHz band to offer handsets that work on all of the frequency blocks.[131]

3. APT 700 MHZ band Plan

The leading alternative to the U.S. band plan for the 700 MHz spectrum is a plan proposed by the Asian Pacific Telecommunity (APT). The APT band plan calls for either 90 MHz of paired frequency-division duplex (FDD) spectrum (two 45 MHz bands) with a 10 MHz duplex gap in the center as a guard band for LTE, or 108 MHz of time-division duplex (TDD) spectrum. FDD is a system of dividing the send and receive signals into different frequencies. TDD, by contrast, uses the same frequencies for sending and receiving, but alternates using them at different times to avoid interference. The APT plan is illustrated in Figure 8-13 below.

---

[129] More information on FCC Auction 73 can be found at: https://www.fcc.gov/auction/73/factsheet

[130] Sam Churchill, "FCC Orders Lower 700 MHz Interoperability" DailyWireless.org (October 29, 2013). http://www.dailywireless.org/2013/10/29/fcc-orders-lower-700-mhz-interoperability/

[131] Dan Meyer, "FCC Implements Lower 700 MHz Interoperability Plan," RCR Wireless (January 17, 2014). https://www.rcrwireless.com/20140117/carriers/fcc-implements-lower-700-mhz-interoperability-plan

Figure 8-13: APT 700 MHz Band Plan

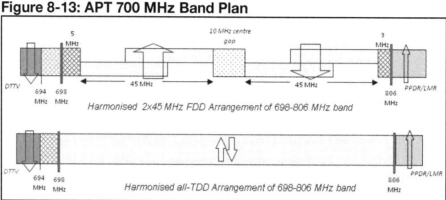

Source: FCC

Type	Frequency Range	Amount	Use
APT - FDD	698 to 703 MHz	5 MHz	Guard Band
APT – FDD	703 to 748 MHz	45 MHz	Uplink
APT – FDD	748 to 758 MHz	10 MHz	Centre Gap
APT – FDD	758 to 803 MHz	45 MHz	Downlink
APT – TDD	803 to 806 MHz	3 MHz	Guard Band
APT – TDD	694 to 698 MHz	4 MHz	Guard Band
APT – TDD	698 to 806 MHz	108 MHz	Two-way TDD

Source: 4G Americas and Summit Ridge Group, LLC analysis.

The original wireless system, AMPS, is a spectrum band located at 824 to 849 MHz and 869 to 894 MHz

The APT plan has become popular in Asia and Latin America as it avoids the fragmentation inherent in the U.S. plan. However, using TDD and FDD on the same frequency is problematic since TDD uses the same frequency on the uplink and downlink, which interferes with FDD. Because few government regulators seem prepared to choose one or the other, Summit Ridge Group believes that both will be used in adjacent regions, causing additional fragmentation.

I. 600 MHz TV Broadcast Incentive Auction

In 2012, Congress ordered the FCC to conduct the most complex auction ever attempted for spectrum licensing. This was done to pay for the public safety FirstNet 700 MHz LTE network and gain funds for the U.S. Treasury. The auction would raise money to compensate TV

Local over-the-air TV businesses have reached their nadir and are not likely to improve.

stations for giving up the 600 MHz channel by shutting down or relocating to a lower 6 MHz wide UHF channel. By 2012, only 10% of U.S. homes watched TV using over-the-air broadcasting. TV stations were suffering from station values dropping as advertising dollars moved to the Internet, chasing viewers who spent more time on the Internet than watching local TV stations.[132] Many stations were relieved to be able to exit the market by selling off their spectrum rights. Some stations received bids that exceeded their over-the-air business value. For some of the TV stations auction was equivalent to a declining business in a beach district selling the beachfront property to a buyer wanting only the property, not the business, for a repurposed use such as a new resort. Summit Ridge Group's view is that local over-the-air TV businesses have likely reached their nadir, and improvement likely depends on the successful rollout of new business models based on enhanced technology such as ATSC 3.0. Also, mobile carriers desired the excellent propagation characteristics of the 600 MHz UHF spectrum for LTE, just as they had been for the Lower and Upper 700 MHz bands in the 2013 auctions.

Following Congress's direction, the FCC prepared a complex incentive auction for the closing down or relocation of the 600MHz UHF TV stations.[133] If the TV stations did not wish to shut down, relocate, or share a channel, the station channels could be ordered by the FCC to relocate (moving below channel 37 or elsewhere within the sub-channel 37 range so that all stations can "fit" their original coverage patterns as close as possible). Over 800 of the remaining TV stations were required to repack. The FCC's goal was to clear up to 126 MHz for the newly designated 600 MHz band. Channel 37, which was used for radio astronomy would be maintained. The FCC planned the auction in different scenarios based on potential demand.

---

[132]In 2018, YouTube reported that their viewers were watching 180 million hours per day on TV screens, or 11 minutes per day per average YouTube viewer), and that 50% of the users watched YouTube on mobile devices. Cable cord cutting increased to 33 million homes in 2018, up from 25 million in 2017, a 44% increase. These figures demonstrate that not only is the TV screen being lost to over the air broadcasting, but to cable TV as well. The dramatic growth of TV screens lost to Internet only, dramatizes the many good reasons that local TV stations were supportive of having the opportunity to exit the business by selling not based on a valuation of their financials to media consolidator or other buyer looking to grow the business but based on the value of their licensed spectrum (which was given to the station at zero-cost by the FCC) to a mobile carrier seeking beach front spectrum.

[133] *Expanding the Economic and Innovation Opportunities of Spectrum Through Incentive Auctions*, GN Docket No. 12-268, Notice of Proposed Rulemaking, 27 FCC Rcd 12357 (2012) (NPRM).

The Incentive Auction resulted in repurposing a total 70 MHz for licensed LTE use.

On March 29, 2016, the FCC began the Incentive Auction with Reverse Auction 1001, where the TV stations bid for the lowest price they would accept for their spectrum licenses, followed by Forward Auction 1002, where the bidders offered bids of the highest prices they would pay for the spectrum channels. On March 30, 2017, one year later, the FCC closed the auction. The Incentive Auction resulted in repurposing a total 70 MHz for licensed LTE use. The total amount raised from the mobile carriers was $19.3 billion. Of this amount, $10.5 billion was paid to the TV broadcasters with winning bids (for shutting down or relocating) and $7 billion was put in the U.S. Treasury. The FCC reserved $1.75 billion to reimburse TV stations for the cost of relocating antennas and purchasing new equipment.[134] Of the possible plans, the FCC had lower demand by mobile carriers than expected and cleared, through the auction process, a total of 84 MHz of seven 6 MHz paired blocks. The highest amount the FCC hoped to clear was 126 MHz of ten 6 MHz paired blocks. The final cleared band consisted of seven 10 MHz blocks, or 70 MHz total, for $19.5 billion. The results left an 11 MHz duplex gap guard band separating the up and downlinks, and two 3 MHz guard bands on either side of channel 37 to protect the radio astronomy transmissions. A 14 MHz guard band separated the new license owners use from the relocated TV stations.

The TV Incentive Auction was successful, even though it was the most complex spectrum auction conducted. Due to similar propagation characteristics, mobile carriers valued the spectrum at similar levels they paid in the 700 MHz auction.

TV stations were given 36 months to move from their channels to their new channels starting from April 13, 2017. The FCC is requiring 957 of the stations that did not bid, or did not submit winning bids, to relocate to different frequencies. Of the 176 stations who won in the bidding, 30 stations will relocate to VHF channels and 146 TV stations will stop broadcasting or enter into a channel sharing agreement with a remaining station.[135] One station received $309 million for its spectrum, a non-commercial station received $190 million, and a cable company sold two local stations for $482 million. There were 50 winning mobile bidders and 2776 licenses sold. Licenses were sold based on Partial Economic Areas ("PEA") which are 416 subdivisions

---

[134] *See*, FCC *Reimbursement of Relocation Costs* https://www.fcc.gov/about-fcc/fcc-initiatives/incentive-auctions/reimbursement.

[135] FCC, *FCC Broadcast Television Spectrum Incentive Auction, Auction 1001, Winning Bids* (April 4, 2017) https://docs.fcc.gov/public/attachments/DA-17-314A2.pdf

of Economic Areas. PEAs could be aggregated by bidders into EAs or REAs.[136] The two largest bidders were T-Mobile ($7.9 billion for 414 PEAs) NS Dish ($6.2 billion for 416 PEAs). AT&T bid only $910 million. Two major carriers, Verizon and Sprint, did not participate in the 600 MHz auction.[137] The bidding TV stations at the end of the auction received only $10 billion rather than $86 billion originally bid.

There was great speculation about why three of the major carriers did not participate as expected. One possibility was the complexity of the auction, which had many moving targets. Summit Ridge Group believes that the auction may have simply taken place too soon after the highly successful 2015 AWS 3, FCC Auction 97, which raised $41 billion, far more than the $10 billion reserve amount set by the FCC before the bidding, or the roughly $15 to $25 billion expected by most industry observers. FCC Chairman Wheeler noted that AWS-3 was "by far the highest-earning spectrum auction the U.S. has ever seen." Commissioner Clyburn called it "phenomenal," and suggested that because the AWS-3 bands were near the AWS-1 bands, which was already populated with active base stations, turn up costs were low and turn up time was fast, making the AWS-3 very desirable to carriers.

FCC Chairman Wheeler noted that AWS-3 was "by far the highest-earning spectrum auction the U.S. has ever seen"

Summit Ridge Group believes that there may be three reasons for the underperformance of Incentive Auction:

1. Allocated Spectrum Capital Expended on AWS-3: The cash reserved by the mobile carriers for Incentive Auction purchases may have been spent in the vigorously bid AWS-3 auction.

2. Mid-Band and mmWave spectrum: The opportunity to bid on the 150 MHz of 3.5 GHz PAL spectrum and the 24 GHz and 28 GHz mmWave opportunities may have shifted the carriers away from the advantages of the lower 700 MHz. The higher throughput of LTE-U and mmW of 500+ Mbps combined with the densification of 3.5 GHz small cells, may have been viewed as a better overall network strategy than using 700 MHz, which could deliver strong propagation in rural areas and into buildings but offered lower throughput, by the 2016 Incentive

---

[136] *Incentive Auction Closing and Channel Reassignment*, Public Notice, Report & Order, DA 17-314, 32 FCC Rcd 2786 (2017) https://www.fcc.gov/document/fcc-announces-results-worlds-first-broadcast-incentive-auction-0

[137] FCC *TV Incentive Forward Auction Bid Summary* https://docs.fcc.gov/public/attachments/DA-17-314A3.pdf

Auction. Summit Ridge believes that for U.S. wireless carriers, capacity is becoming more important than coverage. The U.S. mobile market, is shifting from a focus on building nationwide networks to the race to speeds of 1 Gbps.

3. Verizon and AT&T already owned sufficient amounts of low band spectrum at 700 MHz and 800 MHz (AMPS). Sprint was highly leveraged and did not have enough cash.

Figure 8-14: 600 MHz TV Band After Transition Band Plan

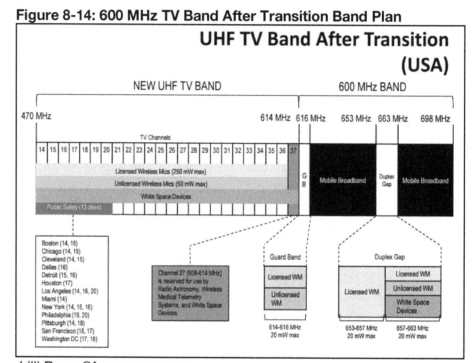

Lilli.Burns@freemanxp.com

Source: Shure Americas

J. Spectrum Sharing: Future of Spectrum Efficiency

In 2008, as the TV stations were completing their DTV move and freeing up the Digital Dividend spectrum, the FCC presented a new concept previously not considered: spectrum sharing, which was urged by Internet firms like Google and Microsoft. The technology for spectrum sharing was developed within DARPA for use by the military. Commissioner Chairman Michael Powell first introduced the concept of spectrum sharing in 2004. In 2008, Google and Microsoft promoted, with the FCC, the DARPA concept of using a cloud database for spectrum sharing to create more unlicensed spectrum similar to Wi-Fi from newly available DTV spectrum. It is notable that this was one of the first FCC proceedings driven by Internet companies for the main purpose of delivering more unlicensed spectrum. That same year the FCC opened the TV White Spaces (TVWS) proceeding and in 2010 issued the final rulemaking order amending Part 15, the unlicensed spectrum rules, to create unlicensed spectrum sharing.[138] White spaces are the white areas in spectrum charts where the spectrum was either a guard band or was vacant. With TV White Space, a new era of spectrum efficiency was rolled out for the wireless world.

The base station could move from channel to channel using the information provided by the database depending on the location of the base station.

In the 2010 TVWS order, the FCC allowed the UHF vacant white space channels to be used for fixed, but not mobile, unlicensed spectrum. However, because TV channels used different channel spectrum in different geographies, meaning that white space channels varied from one geography to another, an online database connected to the radios would be needed to prevent interference with TV broadcasts. With this online database method, the TVWS base station makes channel selections from information received from the database – which is in turn fed with data from the FCC about available spectrum. The TVWS database, which knows the base station's location, uses an algorithm to calculate the precise area covered by a TV station channel, giving the TVWS base station information about what spectrum is free in that specific location for unlicensed use in that specific location. The information also allows the base station to move from channel to channel as needed to avoid interference from other white space users.

The databases were provided by approved commercial providers, including Google, Microsoft, and iconectiv (former Telcordia). The base stations delivered broadband to customer equipment located within the station's reach. Using the 6 MHz TV channels and the 600 MHz band, the TVWS delivered 12-20 Mbps. The 500-698 MHz spectrum available is ideal for delivering broadband to homes and businesses located in rural areas with dense foliage and hilly terrain.

The TV White Space FCC database system was the first spectrum sharing method

This TV White Space FCC database system was the first "spectrum sharing" method devised. The FCC TV White Space orders and the TV White Space industry paved the way for a new era of spectrum sharing using databases.

The 3.5 GHz CBRS FCC orders that followed in 2012 (described below in Chapter VIII.K of this *Handbook*), applied a database similar

---

[138] *FCC Unlicensed Operation in the TV Broadcast Bands*, Second Memorandum Opinion and Order, ET Docket No. 04-186, 25 FCC Rcd 18661 (2010);47 C.F.R. § 15.711.

spectrum sharing system for a more complex system of spectrum. The FCC is also considering applying the database technology to the mmW 30-80 GHz bands, and other bands to deliver greater efficiencies from federally allocated spectrum - from licensed spectrum that is fallow, or spectrum not being efficiently used. The spectrum sharing method also allowed the FCC for the first time to offer very small license areas because the database can direct base stations to use certain power levels and antenna direction to deliver spectrum to small, highly-defined geographies contained in the database.

K. 3.5 GHz CBRS Spectrum Sharing

In 2012, the FCC issued its first order implementing the directive of President's PCAST spectrum report, which required federal government agencies to find and share inefficiently used spectrum.[139] When opening the 3.5 GHz CBRS proceeding, the FCC renamed the TV White Space database the Spectrum Access System (SAS) and created a tiered, priority licensing system.[140]

The CBRS system is complex but will allow many different types of users to take advantage of the SAS' computing power and the Internet to share available spectrum. The FCC Commissioners' unanimously support CBRS. Industry leaders are enthusiastic about the possibilities of the spectrum sharing method being developed for CBRS that could create a dramatic shift in delivering large amounts of inefficiently utilized spectrum. Many suggest that the CBRS spectrum sharing system could be the future for most bands. As a baseline moving forward, if the spectrum is fallow – meaning it is exclusively licensed but not built out – SAS-based spectrum sharing will allow others to make use of the spectrum until the licensee is actually operating. The SAS system will incentivize both spectrum owners and non-owners to start building out and using all spectrum quickly as possible.

The CBRS spectrum sharing system is similar to the TVWS system.

CBRS small cell base stations receive authorization to use particular bands of spectrum from an Internet-connected SAS database.

---

[139] *Amendment of the Commission's Rules with Regard to Commercial Operations in the 3550-3650 MHz Band*, Notice of Proposed Rulemaking, GN Docket No. 12-354, 27 FCC Rcd 15594 (2012).

[140] *Amendment of the Commission's Rules with Regard to Commercial Operations in the 3550-3650 Band*, GN Docket No. 12-354, Report and Order and Second Further Notice of Proposed Rulemaking, 30 FCC Rcd 3959 (2015). *Promoting Investment in the 3550-3700 MHz Band*, Notice of Proposed Rulemaking and Order Terminating Petitions, GN Docket No. 17-258 (2017). Note that originally the proceeding was for 3550-3650 MHz, but the FCC increased the upper part of the band to 3700 MHz.

CBRS base stations receive authorization to use particular bands of spectrum from an Internet-connected SAS database. The SAS authorizes the use of the spectrum for particular times in certain locations and at designated power levels. spectrum and licensed commercial mobile spectrum, not unlicensed spectrum. In 2014, the FCC issue moved the 3.5 GHz proceeding forward with its Further Notice of Proposed Rulemaking, which was then followed by Second Further Notice of Proposed Rulemaking in 2015, creating new rules for 3.5 GHz CBRS spectrum sharing in Part 96.[141]

The Navy has had exclusive use of portions of the lower 3.5 GHz band spectrum for radars. The FCC determined that when the radar is not being used, the spectrum could be used for licensed and unlicensed use. To protect Navy radar, the FCC created three levels of users for the spectrum: i) incumbent access (IA), ii) priority access licenses (PALs), and iii) general authorized access (GAA) licenses.

Incumbent access users are the federal government (i.e. the Department of Defense Navy radar), satellite users, and grandfathered, fixed wireless licensees. IA users receive interference protection from second-tier PAL and third-tier GAA licensees.[142] Each of the PAL licenses will be auctioned and give the PAL licensee priority use of a 10 MHz channel in a never-attempted before "county" size area. The CBRS small cells can densify spectrum capacity within urban areas. Ten CBRS small cells covering the same area as a single microcell could deliver a tenfold increase in capacity using the same quantity of spectrum. A portion of the PAL can be sublicensed.

In addition to mobile service, CBRS is designed for fixed wireless broadband service

The FCC created two categories of CBRS radios: Category A which is a base station for indoor low power and Category B for outdoor higher power. The end user devices (EUD) are low powered devices, like mobile phones, that communicate with the Category A and B base stations. The FCC limited Category A CBRS power output for low-powered, indoor use. Category B CBRS radios operate only outdoors, with increased power for non-rural areas and more for rural

---

[141] *Amendment of the Commission's Rules with Regard to Commercial Operations in the 3550-3650 MHz Band*, GN Docket No. 12-354, FCC 14-49, Further Notice of Proposed Rulemaking, 29 FCC Rcd 4273 (2014); *Amendment of the Commission's Rules with Regard to Commercial Operations in the 3550-3650 MHz Band*, GN Docket No. 12-354, FCC 14-49, Report and Order and Further Notice of Proposed Rulemaking, 30 FCC Rcd 3959 (2015).

[142] The fixed wireless Part 90 rule licensees, operating in the spectrum before the new spectrum sharing order, will be grandfathered in the new CBRS regime. The fixed licensees will slowly be migrated off the spectrum, or upgraded to CBRS to meet the requirements of Part 96 spectrum sharing.

areas.[143] Information about the Category B put into the SAS database includes antenna gain, beam width, azimuth, down tilt angle, and antenna height. The SAS uses this information to lessen interference. The Category A and B requirements are in Figure 8-15 below.

Figure 8-15: CBRS Radio Requirements

CBRS	Max Conducted Power dBm/10 MHz	Max EIRP Power dBm/10 Mhz	Max Conducted PSD dBm/10 MHz	Installation
Category A Indoor	24	30	14	Indoor
Category B Urban	24	40	14	Outdoor Prof Install
Category B Rural	30	47	20	Outdoor Prof Install

Source: FCC and Summit Ridge Group, LLC analysis

Depending on the area, CBRS mobile operators can use from 120 to 150 MHz of licensed and unlicensed spectrum. There are a maximum of seven PAL 10 MHz licenses in each census tract. One PAL user can own only four licenses, totaling 40 MHz, in a single PAL census tract. The four PAL licenses will be auctioned in more than 74,000 census tracts. PAL licenses will have a three-year term, and then be subject to re-auction. The short three-year PAL term is the subject of dispute by some of the mobile carriers who would prefer a more typical ten-year spectrum license.

GAA users are required to use the spectrum on an opportunistic basis with other GAA users.

GAA, the CBRS third-tier, is a licensed service that resembles an unlicensed service because it is free for users. GAA users are required to use the spectrum on an opportunistic basis with other GAA users. There are eight 10 MHz GAA channels for a total of 80 MHz of GAA spectrum from 3620-3700 MHz. Because GAA is not licensed, like the PAL census tract, the channels are available in all geographies. This means that a mobile carrier could potentially use 120 MHz of

---

[143] Power limits compare to unlicensed Wi-Fi.

spectrum in the CBRS, or 80 MHz GAA plus 40 MHz PAL. If the three other potential PAL licenses were not taken, or in operation, the CBRS operator would have access to 150 MHz. With 120 MHz of spectrum available, it is possible that data rates could reach 800 Mbps.[144]

The CBRS spectrum sharing is complex for many reasons. For example, if a Navy radar turns on in a census tract licensed to the PAL, CBRS Environment Sensing Capability (ESC) sensor will signal the SAS database serving the PAL, and the SAS will automatically shut down the PAL to protect the radar. In a second example, in some areas, there are fixed satellite downlink receivers. The SAS is fed with data about the satellite dish and its location and will ensure that no CBRS base station interferes with the satellite spectrum. CBRS spectrum sharing is illustrated in Figure 8-16.

Figure 8-16: CBRS Spectrum Sharing

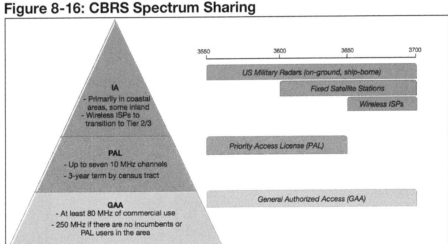

Source: Summit Ridge Group, LLC analysis

The small PAL census tract solves the issue of license holders not fully building out large licensed areas, like PEAs. If a PAL is incompletely built out, GAA users can operate in any part of the census tract not built out. If the spectrum is available, the SAS will enable its free GAA use. Thus, CBRS will dramatically lessen the competitive incentive for spectrum warehousing. CBRS warehoused spectrum will not have the same monetary value as other warehoused spectrum and, indeed, will enable competitors to use the spectrum without cost.

The spectrum sharing technology and regulations enabling the use of

---

[144] Amitava Ghosh, *5G New Radio- Technology and Performance* (July 20, 2017) http://mmwrcn.ece.wisc.edu/wp-uploads/2017/05/5G-NR-Ghosh-Nokia-Keynote.pdf.

PART TWO: U.S. SPECTRUM

3.5 GHz is sweeping through other countries. The European Conference of Postal and Telecommunications Administrations (CEPT) is examining the 3.4-3.8 GHz band for the first use of 5G.[145] It is anticipated the CBRS will be GAA approved by FCC in late 2018.

L. 3.7 GHz C Band Reallocation for Mobile

In 2017, the FCC opened a notice of inquiry for increasing wireless broadband in the mid-band spectrum 3.7-4.2 GHz, in 5.925-6.425 GHz, and in 6.425-7.125 GHz at the request of a few satellite providers.[146] In July 2018, the FCC moved the proceeding forward by issuing a Notice of Proposed Rule Making.[147] The satellite providers' spectrum is the C-band. The C-band technically covers the frequencies from 4-8 GHz but satellite providers use 3.7-4.2 GHz for downlinks – just above the 3.5 GHz spectrum sharing proceeding – and 5.925-6425 GHz for uplinks. The satellite providers viewed this time as an excellent opportunity to sell their spectrum licenses directly to mobile operators who valued it more. The 2018 Mobile Now Act148 required the FCC to identify 255 MHz of federal and non-federal spectrum available for mobile and fixed wireless service and to conduct a feasibility study of the C-band for "commercial wireless services" by 2020.

The 3.7-4.2 GHz [C-band] could potentially add 500 MHz of additional spectrum

The 3.7-4.2 GHz spectrum could add potentially up from 100 to 500 MHz of additional spectrum for the 3.5 GHz CBRS users.[149] Summit Ridge Group views this as an opportune time for satellite operators because a) mobile carriers are hungry for mid-band spectrum that would increase the 3.5 GHz spectrum sharing from 150 MHz by at least 100 MHz (potentially as much as 500 MHz), and b) satellite

---

[145] European Commission Directorate-General for Communications Networks, Content and Technology, Radio Spectrum Policy Group, *Strategic Spectrum Roadmap Towards 5G for Europe: RSPG* Second Opinion on 5G Networks (2018) https://circabc.europa.eu/sd/a/fe1a3338-b751-43e3-9ed8-a5632f051d1f/RSPG18-005final2nd_opinion_on_5G.pdf.

[146] *Expanding Flexible Use of the 3.7 to 4.2 GHz Band, Petition for Rulemaking to Amend and Modernize Parts 25 and 101 of the Commission's Rules; Fixed Wireless Communications Coalition, Request for Modified Coordination Procedures,* Notice of Inquiry, 32 FCC Rcd 6373 (2017).

[147] *Expanding Flexible Use of the 3.7 to 4.2 GHz Band, Petition for Rulemaking to Amend and Modernize Parts 25 and 101 of the Commission's Rules; Fixed Wireless Communications Coalition, Request for Modified Coordination Procedures,* Order and Notice of Proposed Rule Making, GN Docket No. 18-122, RM-11791, RM-11778, 5 FCC Rcd 24075 (Jul 12, 2018) (*Mid-Band NPRM*).

[148] MOBILE NOW Act, Section 603(a)(1) of the Act.

[149] "Intelsat-SESIntel believe that consortium members could make approximately 100 megahertz of spectrum available … via privately negotiated agreements" *Mid-Band NPRM,* para. 81.

providers are currently facing a decline in their customer use of this spectrum. Satellite providers may view this as a once in a business-cycle opportunity to sell off their spectrum for terrestrial uses. The process is different from the TV inventive auction, as that was run by the FCC and the government kept roughly 50% of the proceeds. The C-band proposal, on the other hand, is for the incumbent licensees to run a private process and keep all of the proceeds. In return, the satellite industry promised to have the spectrum reallocated in an expedient manner, potentially accelerating the process by years.

Other countries, such as the European Commission through the CEPT, Australia, and Japan, are looking at reallocating the C-band as the "first primary band for 5G." [150] Methods of reallocating the spectrum from satellite to mobile use could include FCC led auctions or an innovative alternative to allow satellite providers to voluntarily sell spectrum through a secondary market method using an independent third party "Transition Facilitator" to manage the valuation of the satellite spectrum and the sale of licenses to mobile carriers. The Transition Facilitator would be a cooperative entity with expert knowledge of satellite spectrum valuation and the satellite operators. It would be created by the relevant satellite operators to coordinate negotiations, clearing, and repacking the band. A Transition Facilitator would be more efficient and faster than an FCC auction and create a more coordinated market than satellite vendors selling on their own spectrum with the potential for holdouts creating gaps in the available spectrum. On the other hand, the satellite auction process could be directed by the FCC using an auction process similar to the Broadcast Incentive Auction process.

M. 5 GHz for 5G Aggregated 700 Mbps Throughput

Unlicensed spectrum is governed by Part 15 of the FCC rules. Part 15 requires radios to prevent harmful interference to other services by limiting transmitter power, accepting harmful interference, and not allowing unapproved emissions. Industry associations have developed standards for unlicensed spectrum including Wi-Fi, Bluetooth, and Zigbee. In 2016 3GPP developed a standard for LTE to use unlicensed spectrum called LAA or Licensed Assisted Access. LAA allows unlicensed smartphones with an advanced LTE version

---

[150] *Mid-Band NPRM*, para. 6.

that follows Part 15 rules for unlicensed 5 GHz spectrum. In order to prevent harmful interference, LAA includes listen-before-talk to helps ensure that the communications of other unlicensed devices are not impacted. Normally, LTE is always transmitting, looking for a signal, and could interfere with the band. Part 15 requires listen-before-talk in order to minimize interference.

The LTE-U Forum proposed using LTE-U or "LTE for unlicensed" (developed by Qualcomm) which created a proposal to allow LTE to be used in the Wi-Fi space. LTE devices will be aggregated licensed spectrum with 20 MHz of unlicensed 5 GHz. In 2016, the FCC Office of Engineering and Technology, or OET, approved an inter-industry agreement to determine if coexistence and sharing between LTE-U and Wi-Fi would work. In 2017, the OET approved LTE-U devices for operation in the 5 GHz band.

T-Mobile announced in 2017 that using "carrier aggregation" that its LTE-U / LAA tests resulted in 741 Mbps download speeds using 80 MHz of aggregated spectrum.[151] New smartphones now include 4 - 5 component carriers for downlink carrier aggregation, and 2 - 3 component carriers for uplink carrier aggregation, with various channel bandwidth combinations and carrier aggregation configurations being used for both downlinks and uplinks.

N. 24 GHz – 80 GHz Millimeter Wave for Mobile

In 2016, the FCC the concluded the first Report and Order on the Spectrum Frontiers proceeding to clear more spectrum in the high millimeter wave (mmWave) band for mobile broadband use.[152] The mmWave frequency is located from 30-300 GHz and is also called EHF or Extremely High Frequency. Millimeter wave frequencies, which are in the 1 to 10-millimeter range contrasts with "microwave" frequencies, which are located in the 1 to 10-centimeter wave range. Figure 8-17 below illustrates the mmWave national weighted average spectrum depth by frequency block.

---

[151] T-Mobile, *T-Mobile Completes Nation's First Live Commercial Network Test of License Assisted Access (LAA)* https://www.t-mobile.com/news/lte-u.

[152] *In the Matter of Use of Spectrum Bands Above 24 GHz for Mobile Radio Services*, Notice of Proposed Rulemaking, 30 FCC Rcd 11878 (2015); *Use of Spectrum Bands Above 24 GHz For Mobile Radio Services*, Report and Order and Further Notice of Proposed Rulemaking, 31 FCC Rcd 8014 (2016); *Use of Spectrum Bands Above 24 GHz for Mobile Radio Services*, Second Report and Order and Second Further Notice of Proposed Rulemaking, Order on Reconsideration, and Memorandum Opinion and Order, 32 FCC Rcd 10988 (2017) (*Spectrum Frontiers Orders*).

Figure 8-17: National mmWave Spectrum Holdings

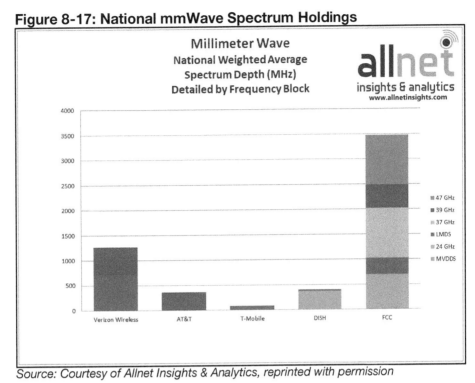

Source: *Courtesy of Allnet Insights & Analytics, reprinted with permission*

As a result of [the Spectrum Frontiers], the FCC will auction 1.55 GHz of spectrum from the 24 GHz band and 28 GHz band in November 2018.

From 2016 to date, the FCC has been exploring proposals by commercial mobile and fixed licensed and unlicensed providers to make more efficient use of the mmWave spectrum. As a result of these proposals, the FCC will auction 1.55 GHz of spectrum from the 24 GHz band and the 28 GHz band in November 2018. The 28 GHz Band (27.5 – 28.35 GHz), which contains 850 MHz of newly reallocated spectrum, will be licensed for mobile use on a countywide basis. The 28 GHz licenses are for Upper Microwave Flexible Use Service (UMFUS).[153]

On November 14, 2018, Auction 101 will allow bidding to take place on 3,074 countywide licenses of UMFUS in the 28 GHz band from 27.5 - 27.925 GHz (425 MHz) and 27.925-28.350 GHz (425 MHz). Auction 102 will follow with the 24 GHz band auction of 2,912 PEA size licenses in 7 blocks from 24.25–24.45 (two 100 MHz blocks in each PEA) GHz and 24.75–25.25 GHz (five 100 MHz blocks in each PEA).

---

[153] *Use of Spectrum Bands Above 24 GHz For Mobile Radio Services*, Report and Order and Further Notice of Proposed Rulemaking, GN Docket No. 14-177, 31 FCC Rcd 8014 (2016) https://docs.fcc.gov/public/attachments/FCC-15-138A1.pdf.

PART TWO: U.S. SPECTRUM

The 28 GHz band has been occupied by LMDS licensees for fixed wireless service covering 493 large basic trading areas, which will be broken up into county-sized areas. The LMDS licensees will be authorized to use the 28 GHz for mobile service. For the 39 GHz band, with 1400 MHz of spectrum, the FCC created PEA-sized license areas.

Figure 8-18: Spectrum Frontiers Proposed Spectrum Bands

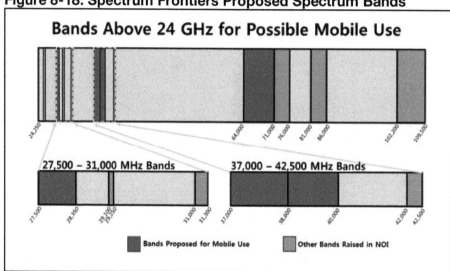

Source: FCC[154]

The FCC decided in 2016 to allocate 14,000 MHz for unlicensed use in the 57-71 GHz band

From 37 to 38.6 GHz, consisting of 1600 MHz of spectrum, the FCC will create a spectrum sharing mechanism for federal military use and for commercial use, including fixed broadband.

The FCC decided in 2016 to allocate 14,000 MHz for unlicensed use in the 57-71 GHz band. The 64-71 GHz band was authorized created as an unlicensed Part 15 band for use as unlicensed Wireless Gigabit or "WiGig" and interactive motion sensing. WiGig is an IEEE standard 802.11ad. It has the potential to deliver 7 Gbps rates, some of the fastest wireless rates obtained. WiGig products are being used internationally and opening up the spectrum will allow for multi-gig throughput and the FCC determined the spectrum should be used now that unlicensed radios, both for mobile and fixed, were already on the market. The FCC declined mobile carriers' requests to designate the 64-17 GHz band for licensed mobile use.

---

[154] *Id.*

Figure 8-19: LTE Networks

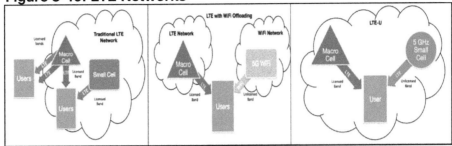

Source: Summit Ridge Group, LLC analysis

Figure 8-20: Frequency Dynamic Selection for 5.15-5.925 GHz

Frequency Band	Type	Frequency Dynamic Selection Required?	Unlicensed Amount
5.15-5.25 GHz	UNII-1	No	2x20 MHz
5.25-5.35 GHz	UNII-2	Yes	2x20 MHz
5.35-5.47 GHz	UNII-2B	Yes- not yet available	Possible 120 MHz
5.47-5.725 GHz	UNII-2C	Yes	2x20 MHz
5.725-5.85 GHz	UNII-3	No	2x20 MHz
5.85-5.925 GHz	UNII-4 (DSRC)	No	2x20 MHz

Source: FCC and Summit Ridge Group, LLC analysis

The 70/80 GHz band includes various subsections. In 2017, the FCC considered but did not agree to allow UMFUS mobile use for 70 and 80 GHz. The reason for not allowing mobile use was that mobile carriers could not agree on an appropriate spectrum sharing method to protect the fixed use in the band. In 2003, the FCC permitted fixed license use of the 70/80 band, and in 2017, the FCC determined that even indoor unlicensed used could be harmful for fixed license outdoor use. The fixed, licensed use with point-to-point short distance radios could be leveraged for more growing back-haul demand use for small cells.[155]

---

[155] *Use of Spectrum Bands Above 24 GHz For Mobile Radio Services*, Second Report and Order, Second, Further Notice of Proposed Rulemaking, and Memorandum Opinion and Order, 32 FCC Rcd 10988 (2017).

PART TWO: U.S. SPECTRUM

IX. Radio and Television Broadcasting Band Descriptions

The spectrum allocated to radio (AM and FM) and television (VHF and UHF) services lies between 540 kHz and 698 MHz. For both radio and television broadcasting, these frequency bands are divided into different stations that operate at specified maximum power levels and are spaced apart appropriately for the purpose of preventing interference with different stations. In 2009, radio and television broadcasting have transitioned from traditional analog transmission to digital transmission, which uses binary signals that are significantly more efficient.

Radio broadcasting has maintained its analog broadcasts alongside digital broadcasting while television broadcasting eliminated analog signals in 2009

Radio broadcasting has maintained its analog broadcasts alongside digital broadcasting, while television broadcasting eliminated analog signals in 2009. This allowed stations to add additional services or reduce their spectrum needs. Television licenses are 6 MHz each. Currently, 210 MHz is allocated to television broadcasting, after the FCC incentive auction, which repurposed 84 MHz previously used for broadcasting. See Chapter XV.D and XVI.A for additional information about the FCC's television incentive auction.

A. AM Radio: 540 kHz to 1700 kHz

AM (amplitude modulation) radio, varies the amplitude (height) of the radio waves while keeping the wavelength or frequency constant to transmit and receive audio signals. It is the simplest radio technology. AM Radio frequencies are issued in three categories: Clear, Regional and Local. Additionally, there are four classes (A-D) of AM licenses – each station has two classes, one local and the other regional. These overlapping groupings determine the permitted power and hours of station operation. AM radio licenses typically are issued for a period of eight years and licensees are subject to rules of service under 47 C.F.R. 73 Subpart A. AM stations are allowed a maximum transmission bandwidth of 10.2 kHz.

FM radio spectrum modulation is more complex than AM radio spectrum modulation

B. FM Radio: 92.1 to 107.9 MHz

FM radio spectrum modulation is more complex than AM radio spectrum modulation. It uses frequency modulation (FM), which varies the frequency of the carrier wave (keeping the height [amplitude] of the radio wave constant) to broadcast audio signals. FM Radio stations are subject to rules of service under 47 C.F.R. Subpart B. FM stations in the U.S. are 200 kHz apart. They typically broadcast using a 15 kHz signal and a 38 kHz stereo subcarrier. This allows nearly 75 kHz of signal deviation with adjacent channel interference. There are seven types of FM radio station licenses. Their power limits are described in Figure 9-1 below.

Figure 9-1: FM Radio Licenses

Station Class	Maximum ERP	Reference HAAT in meters (ft.)	Class contour distance in kilometers
A	6 kW (7.8 dBk)	100 (328)	28
B1	25 kW (14.0 dBk)	100 (328)	39
B	50 kW (17.0 dBk)	150 (492)	52
C3	25 kW (14.0 dBk)	100 (328)	39
C2	50 kW (17.0 dBk)	150 (492)	52
C1	100 kW (20.0 dBk)	299 (981)	72
C0	100 kW (20.0 dBk)	450 (1476)	83
C	100 kW (20.0 dBk)	600 (1968)	92

Source: FCC and Summit Ridge Group, LLC Analysis

In addition to the categories above, noncommercial educational, public safety, and transportation entities may be eligible for low power (100 watts maximum) FM licenses that have a range of approximately 3.5 miles (5.6 kilometers). Low Power FM licensees are subject to rules contained in 47 C.F.R. Part 73 Subpart G.

C. VHF Television: 54 to 88 MHz and 174 to 216 MHz

VHF signal propagation is superior [to UHF], but only by a small margin

The lower portion of this band (54 to 88 MHz) includes channels 2 through 6 while channels 7 through 13 are in the upper portion (174 to 216 MHz). Due to its lower frequency range relative to UHF television, VHF signal propagation qualities provide a slightly longer range. This partially accounts for why stations that carry VHF television were

traditionally more valuable than their UHF counterparts. Today, the high data rates achieved by UHF makes them more valuable.

D. UHF Television: 470 to 698 MHz

Ultra High Frequency (UHF) television broadcasting includes channels 14 through 51 except channel 37 (608 to 614 MHz), which is allocated to radio astronomy in the U.S., Canada, and a few other countries. The UHF band was reduced in 2009 to the current 470-698 MHz band by moving channels 52-69 into lower channels during the digital transition. Before this reduction, the UHF television band occupied 470 to 806 MHz. The FCC had previously eliminated channels 70 to 83 (806-890 MHz) to create the original cell phone and public safety bands. This progressive reduction of television broadcast spectrum and reallocation to mobile services is an international trend in most economically developed countries.

Progressive reduction of television broadcast spectrum and reallocation to mobile services is an international trend in most economically developed countries

Television licenses are available in three categories: Full Power, Class A, and Low Power. Full power stations may broadcast in television market areas and have rights against interference in their areas. Low power stations are required to broadcast at low power so as to not interfere with either Full Power or higher priority low power broadcasters known as Class A stations and have no rights against interference from them.

Full power television broadcast licensees, both VHF and UHF, are subject to rules in 47 C.F.R. Subpart E. Class A television broadcast licensees are subject service rules in 47 C.F.R. 73 Subparts J. Low power televisions broadcasters are subject to service rules in 47 C.F.E. 73 Subpart L.

X. Satellite Frequency Band Descriptions

Most satellites are positioned over the equator in a geostationary position so they rotate at the same rate as the earth

Most satellites are positioned over the equator in a geostationary position so that they rotate in synchronicity with the earth, thus appearing stationary from earth. To avoid interference, regulations require operators of satellites using the same frequencies to position them two degrees of longitude apart. This creates 180 possible locations in each band of spectrum. There are exceptions, such as DBS (satellite television) in the U.S., where the high power levels and small user equipment require nine degrees of spacing. To put a satellite in an orbital slot, the operators require permission from the country with rights to that orbital slot. Most countries also require satellite operators to obtain licenses to send signals to customers in that country. While the FCC generally assigns orbital slots by auction, the International Telecommunication Union (ITU) rules prevent countries from auctioning orbital slots that it considers international – those serving multiple countries. Despite the ban on auctioning licenses for using such slots, they are effectively sold on the secondary market.

A minority of satellites are not in geostationary orbit, but rather in Middle Earth Orbit (MEO) or Low Earth Orbits (LEO). These satellites move faster than the earth so a fleet of them is needed for constant coverage of a given area. Among these are the Iridium and Globalstar satellite fleets, each with dozens of satellites, using a low earth orbit to minimize latency (delay) on calls. The orbits and spectrum for non-geostationary satellites are coordinated through the ITU. However, these service providers must negotiate rights to sell their services and the royalty rights for their customers to use their equipment in each country that they operate. This can be a daunting task.

C-band is used primarily for satellite transmission and is desirable in tropical areas due to its resistance to rain fade

Satellite communication is less sensitive to differences in frequency than terrestrial communication because the power levels from the satellite are so low that a constant line of sight is generally necessary regardless of spectrum, and there are no ionospheric bouncing issues to contend with. However, as with terrestrial communication, lower frequencies face less interference, in the case of satellites primarily by rain and light foliage. But with increased congestion in the lower frequencies, satellite service providers have increasingly turned to higher frequencies, which is enabled by higher power satellites that can penetrate weather-related blockage. Until the late 1980s, C-band

With increased congestion in the lower frequencies, satellite service provides have increasingly turned to higher frequencies - enabled by higher power satellites

was the dominant satellite frequency band; the Ku-band and Ka-band were considered unusable. Nearly a decade later, higher-powered satellites have allowed Ku-band to become popular. Now, Ka-band is becoming increasingly popular as improved solar panel technologies make the construction of even higher-powered satellites possible. Support is also growing for satellites in the V-band. If such a satellite could be built, it would have significantly greater data capacity, which could make satellite broadband more competitive with terrestrial alternatives. Descriptions of satellite bands follow. Note that satellite frequency bands deviate slightly from the traditional IEEE Band descriptions in Figure 2-2 in Chapter II of this *Handbook*.

A. L-Band: 1.4 GHz and 1.6 GHz

The term L-band and S-band originated from the IEEE nomenclature describing spectrum used for radar. "L" means "long wave" from 1-2GHz, and "S" means "short waves" covering 2–4 GHz. The L and S bands are at the boundary of UHF and SHF. Satellite broadcasters are allocated the 1482.352 to 1490.624 MHz and 1525 to 1646.5 MHz bands. The former is used primarily for satellite radio and related services; the latter for satellite telephony (MSS) services. The middle part of the band is reserved primarily for radio astronomy, military and global positioning systems such as the European Galileo and the Russian GLONASS systems. The L-band frequency plan is illustrated in Figure 10-1 below.

Figure 10-1: L-Band Frequency Plan

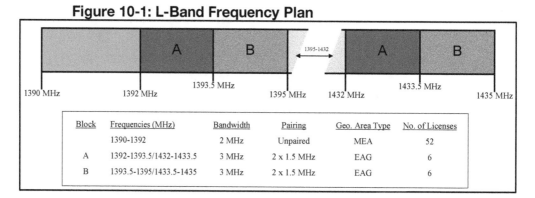

Block	Frequencies (MHz)	Bandwidth	Pairing	Geo. Area Type	No. of Licenses
	1390-1392	2 MHz	Unpaired	MEA	52
A	1392-1393.5/1432-1433.5	3 MHz	2 x 1.5 MHz	EAG	6
B	1393.5-1395/1433.5-1435	3 MHz	2 x 1.5 MHz	EAG	6

Block	Frequency (MHz)	Bandwidth	Pairing	Area	Licenses
	1390-1392	2 MHz	Unpaired	MEA	52
A	1392-1393, 1432-1433.5	3 MHz	2 x 1.5	EAG	6
B	1393.5-1395, 1433.5-1435	3 MHz	2 x 1.5	EAG	6

Source: FCC and Summit Ridge Group, LLC analysis

B. S-band: 2.0 to 2.7 GHz

The S-band is used primarily for satellite radio services (2.31 to 2.36 GHz) as well as mobile satellite services (portions between 2.0 and 2.2 GHz) and the AWS mobile services. The 2.4 to 2.483 GHz segment is allocated for unlicensed use such as Wi-Fi, Bluetooth, and cordless telephones. Non-radio equipment such as microwave ovens use this band and, unlike radios, utilize the entire band while operating but have short distances thus mitigating interference issues.

C. C-band: 3.4 to 6.725 GHz

Many countries are considering reallocation of the lower portion of the C-band receive band for terrestrial Wi-Fi use

The standard C-band is from 3.625 to 4.2 GHz (downlink) and 5.85 to 6.425 GHz (uplink). The extended version of the C-band uses 3.4 to 3.65 GHz (downlink) and 6.425 to 6.725 GHz (uplink). The Indian National Satellite Systems have a super extended version of this band that includes 4.5 to 4.8 GHz (downlink) and 6.725 to 7.025 GHz (uplink). C-band is used primarily for satellite transmission and is desirable in tropical areas due to its resistance to rain fade. Regulators in many countries are considering reallocating the lower portion of the receive band for terrestrial Wi-Fi use. Fixed Satellite Service (FSS) operators are the main users. A disadvantage of C-band is that it requires larger antennas to receive signals, making them harder to install and more expensive. This limits widespread C-band use by satellite television consumers. As previously discussed, C-band is the target of potential reallocation to terrestrial. Mobile use consideration is particularly advanced in the U.S.

D. Ku-band: 10.7 to 18 GHz

Ku-band is used primarily in satellite communications. Most commercial satellite television signals in the U.S. and Europe are

Most commercial satellite television signals in the United States and Europe are transmitted in Ku-band

transmitted in Ku-band. Although not as resistant to rain fade as C-band, its higher frequency allows consumers to use much smaller reception antennas. The Ku-band allocation is more complex than the C-band. In ITU Region 2 (the Americas), this band is used for FSS (11.7 to 12.2 GHz for downlink and to 14.0 to 14.5 GHz for uplink) DBS (12.2 to 12.7 GHz for downlink and 17.3 to 17.8 GHz for uplink) services.

In ITU region 1 (Europe and Africa), the frequencies are slightly different: FSS uses 10.7 to 11.7 GHz for downlink and 14.0 to 14.8 GHz for uplink while DBS uses 11.7 to 12.5 GHz for downlink and 17.3 to 18.1 GHz for uplink. In Australia (ITU Region 3), the Ka-band downlink is 12.25 to 12.75 GHz and uplink is from 14.0 to 14.5 GHz.

E. X-Band: 7 to 11.2 GHz

Military communication satellites primarily use X-band at 7.25 to 7.75 GHz (downlink) and 7.9 to 8.4 GHz (uplink). It is also used for radar applications, deep space applications, and amateur radio. Some motion detectors use the 10.525 GHz frequency.

F. Ka-band: 26.5 to 40.0 GHz

The newest addition to the commercial FSS bands is the Ka-band. Ka-band satellites have historically suffered from significant weather-related interference, which made it less valuable than the C-band and Ku-band. However, new higher-powered satellites over the past 10 to 15 years have largely overcome this problem. This band is heavily used in state-of-the-art satellite broadband systems. A list of Ka-band frequencies is in Figure 10-2 below.

Figure 10-2: Authorized U.S. Satellite Ka-band Frequencies

Frequency	Amount
18.3 to 18.8 GHz	500 MHz
19.7 to 20.2 GHz	500 MHz
28.35 to 28.6 GHz	250 MHz
29.25 to 30.0 GHz	750 MHz
Total	**2,000 MHz**

Source: FCC and Summit Ridge Group, LLC analysis

Local Multipoint Distribution Service (LMDS) is another technology that operates in the Ka-band at 28 to 31 GHz, transmitting signals from a single point to multiple points or a single point (LMDS is described in greater detail in Chapter XIV.A.4 of this *Handbook*). It requires line of sight between the reception and transmission antennas and a range of approximately 1.5 miles (2.4 km). In the U.S., LMDS intended use was for "wireless cable" but most video providers abandoned it in favor of other technologies. Today LMDS is used to back-haul mobile traffic from cell phone towers, particularly in Europe. There is some discussion of using LMDS for residential broadband in rural areas.

G. V-band: 50-75 GHz

The upcoming Wi-Fi standard 802.11ad will use frequency in the 60 GHz range

The V-band is used as a link between certain military satellites. Otherwise, it is lightly used, mostly for research purposes. This band may become developed for commercial satellite communications as the Ka-band becomes more congested. Satellite companies have already filed applications for NGSO networks using 37.5 – 42.0 GHz for downlink and 50.4 – 52.4 GHz for uplink.[156] The upcoming Wi-Fi standard 802.11ad will also use frequency in the 60 GHz range.[157]

One advantage of high frequencies is their significantly increased capacity to carry data. Satellites in this band could increase their data capacity to the point that they are competitive with terrestrial broadband options. However, they must overcome the obstacles of blockage from atmospheric conditions. This will require the development of higher-powered satellites, which in turn require improvements in solar panel technologies for power.

---

[156] Calab Henry, *FCC Gets Five New Applications for Non-geostationary Satellite Constellations*, Space News (Mar. 2, 2017) https://spacenews.com/fcc-gets-five-new-applications-for-non-geostationary-satellite-constellations/

[157] Edward Chester, *4.6Gbps Wi-Fi: How 60 GHz Wireless Works-and Should You Use It?* ArsTechnica (Dec. 15, 2016). https://arstechnica.com/gadgets/2016/12/802-11ad-Wi-Fi-guide-review/

XI. Government/Military Frequency Use Descriptions

A. U.S. Federal Agencies Uses Large Amounts of Spectrum

60% of spectrum is controlled primarily by federal government agencies

Almost 60 percent of available spectrum is allocated for government use in the U.S.[158] The spectrum controlled by the federal government is among the most desirable, located in all major bands. Figure 11-1 illustrates the spectrum bands used by the federal government.

Figure 11-1: U.S. Government Spectrum Usage

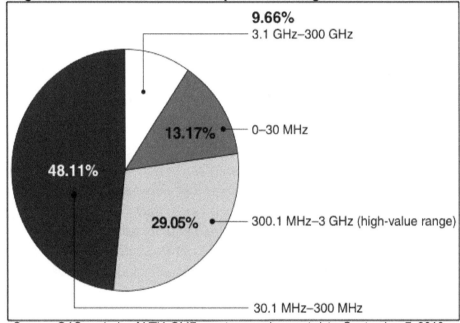

Source: GAO analysis of NTIA GMF spectrum assignment data, September 7, 2010

B. Defense Is Largest Government User

The largest portion of the spectrum used by the Federal government is for national defense, followed by law enforcement. Figure 11-2 below illustrates the use of spectrum by federal agencies.

---

[158] *PCAST Report, supra* note 76, at 8.

Figure 11-2: U.S. Government Agencies with the Most Spectrum

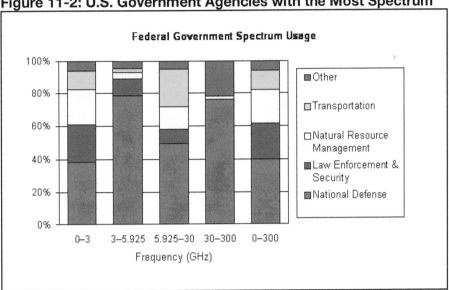

Source: NTIA

C. Government Spectrum Trends

As mentioned previously, U.S. federal government agencies have been heavily criticized for not efficiently using their spectrum. This criticism culminated in the PCAST Report. On June 14, 2013, the White House released a presidential memorandum ordering the creation of a Spectrum Policy Team ("Spectrum Team"). The Spectrum Team is ordered to:

1) Produce a report within one year detailing the FCC and NTIA's spectrum sharing initiatives and include recommendations for improvement.

2) Facilitate current plans to for federal agencies sharing or returning spectrum in the 1697 - 1710 MHz band, the 1755 – 1850 MHz band, the 5350 – 5470 band and the 5850 –5925 MHz band. They are also directed to facilitate sharing of other spectrum under 6 GHz.

3) Publish an inventory of test facilities for sharing spectrum and a standard for sharing within 6 months.

4) Evaluate each federal agency's use of its spectrum and each agency is directed to submit its own assessment. Each agency that uses spectrum between 400 MHz and 6 GHz is directed to only keep the minimum spectrum needed for its mission.

5) Expansion of testing of federal agency's use of their spectrum.

6) Development of performance criteria for receivers using shared spectrum.

7) Propose market-based incentives for agencies to encourage them to relinquish or share their spectrum.

8) Encourage the Spectrum Team to identify ways to redeploy any returned spectrum for commercial broadband use.

The assessment's purpose is to be used as an intermediate stage for identifying and prioritizing strategic options for the potential repurposing of spectrum bands

In 2016, the NTIA published a summary of the results of its quantitative assessment of spectrum usage in response to the 2013 Presidential Memorandum "Expanding America's Leadership in Wireless Innovation." The assessment's purpose is to be used as an intermediate stage in a process for identifying and prioritizing strategic options for the potential repurposing of bands and the extent to which frequencies assigned to these agencies could be further evaluated for sharing with commercial users. The NTIA's assessment analyzed 960 MHz of spectrum in the 1300-1390 MHz, 1675-1695 MHz, 2700-2900 MHz, 2900-3100 MHz, and 3100-3550 MHz frequency bands. The agencies using this spectrum worked with the NTIA to supply or verify information regarding the characteristics of the systems utilizing these bands, with parameters for the spectrum utilized (frequency and bandwidth), geographic area, and estimated time usage. The results of the report are as follows:

- In the 1300-1350 MHz band, the report concludes that opportunities for frequency and geographic sharing are extremely limited. It finds there will be no opportunities for time sharing while the government's long-range radars remain in place. The report does note however, that there is an initiative to explore the feasibility of relocating the Federal Aviation Administration's radars to the 2700-3100 MHz band, which would significantly improve the potential for sharing.

- In the 1350-1390 MHz band, there are no opportunities for frequency sharing and the opportunities for geographic sharing are limited. There are, however, opportunities for time sharing with terrestrial and airborne systems operating in this sub-band.

- In the 1675-1695 MHz band, the NTIA found there are no opportunities for frequency sharing, but there may be geographic sharing opportunities with federal reserve stations, contingent on the successful completion of a feasibility study.

- In the 2700-2900 MHz band, NTIA found that there were no opportunities for any type of sharing due to Air Traffic Control and Next Generation Radar systems supporting safety of life functions that are operating nearly 24/7.

- In the 2900-3100 MHz band, the report finds that there are no opportunities for frequency sharing and that opportunities for time-sharing are extremely limited. Geographic sharing opportunities may exist contingent upon the successful completion of a sharing feasibility study. The report also notes that there would be a significant change in the results of the quantitative assessment frequency and geographic usage data if the FAA's radars are relocated to this band.

- In the 3100-3500 MHz band, the NTIA found that there are potential opportunities for frequency sharing, particularly in the 3505-3550 MHz portion of the band. Additionally, geographic sharing opportunities may exist, specifically in the upper 45 MHz portion of the band, contingent upon the successful completion of a feasibility study.[159]

PART TWO: U.S. SPECTRUM

---

[159]Wiley Rein LLP, *NTIA Releases Report on Quantitative Assessments of Federal Spectrum Candidates for Commercial* (Nov. 21, 2016) https://www.wileyrein.com/newsroom-articles-NTIA_Releases_Report_on_Quantitative_Assessments_of_Federal_Spectrum_Candidates_for_Commercial_Use.html

XII. Very High Frequency (VHF) Services

Frequencies in the VHF frequency band work well for short distances – somewhat longer than the range of sight. Unlike the High Frequency spectrum discussed above, VHF transmissions do not extend their range by "bouncing" off the ionosphere. The VHF spectrum band includes a number of services. Some common VHF applications are discussed below.

VHF frequencies work well for short distances – somewhat longer than the range of sight

A. Lower Paging: 35, 43, 152 & 158/159 and 454 MHz

The lower paging band occupies several blocks of frequencies. The 35, 43, 152 and 158 MHz blocks are not paired. However, part of the 152 block is paired with 159 MHz band and the 454 MHz band is paired within the 454 MHz block. The paging industry has largely been in decline as mobile phones with greater functionality have dropped in price. An illustration of the lower paging band plan is shown in Figure 12-1 below.

Figure 12-1: Lower Paging Band Plan

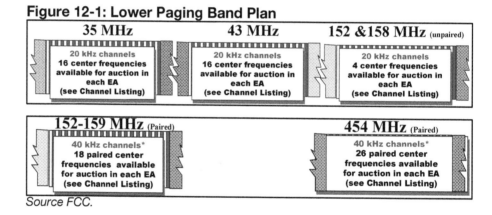

35 MHz	43 MHz	152 &158 MHz (unpaired)
20 kHz channels 16 center frequencies available for auction in each EA (see Channel Listing)	20 kHz channels 16 center frequencies available for auction in each EA (see Channel Listing)	20 kHz channels 4 center frequencies available for auction in each EA (see Channel Listing)

152-159 MHz (Paired)	454 MHz (Paired)
40 kHz channels* 18 paired center frequencies available for auction in each EA (see Channel Listing)	40 kHz channels* 26 paired center frequencies available for auction in each EA (see Channel Listing)

Source FCC.

B. Radio Control Service: 72 to 73 MHz and 75.4 to 76 MHz

Located in the 72.0 to 73.0 MHz and 75.4 to 76.0 MHz spectrum ranges, radio control spectrum is commonly used for short-distance, one-way communications for operating devices that have an on/off switch located at a place distant from the operator. This includes devices such as model aircraft and cars. Service rules for this frequency band are located at 47 C.F.R. Part 95.

C. VHF Public Coast: 150.8 to 162.025 MHz

Channel 16 of the VHF Public Coast Band is the international calling and distress channel

This band is divided into two parts, a marine mobile services portion, and a land mobile services portion. Marine VHF is installed on virtually all large ships as well as most small craft. It is used for safety purposes including collision avoidance. Channel 16 of the VHF Public Coast Band is the international calling and distress channel. Power levels range from 1 to 25 watts, giving a maximum range of 60 nautical miles with an antenna mounted on a tall ship or 5 nautical miles when using small antennas mounted at sea level.

On land, the 151 to 154 MHz is used for short-distance, two-way communication, usually via small handheld devices. The spectrum is divided into five channels of 11.25 or 20 kHz each. An illustration of the band plan for the VHF Public Coast band is shown in Figure 12-2 below. Service rules for this frequency band are located at 47 C.F.R. Part 95.

Figure 12-2: VHF Public Coast Band Plan

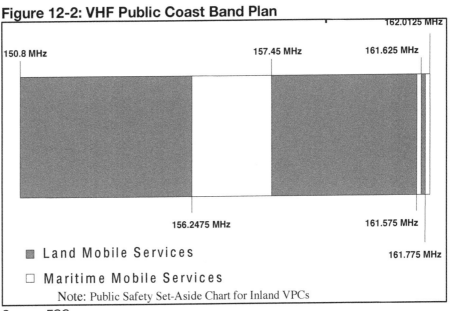

Source: FCC

continued on next page

Application	Frequencies (MHz)	Bandwidth	Type
Land Mobile Services	150.8-156.2475	5.4475 MHz	Unpaired
Maritime Mobile Services	156.2475-157.45	1.1925 MHz	Unpaired
Land Mobile Services	157.45-161.575	4.125 MHz	Unpaired
Maritime Mobile Services	161.575-161.625	0.050 MHz	Unpaired
Land Mobile Services	161.625-161.775	0.150 MHz	Unpaired
Maritime Mobile Services	161.775-162.0125	0.2375 MHz	Unpaired

Source: FCC and Summit Ridge Group, LLC analysis

D. Basic Exchange Telephone Radio Service (BETRS)

BETRS frequencies are allocated to provide basic telephone service... where traditional wireline service is not feasible

BETRS operates in the 152 to 159 MHz, 454 to 460 MHz, 816 to 820 MHz, and 861 to 865 MHz spectrum bands. Note: the latter two frequency blocks for this service fall outside the VHF spectrum range and into the UHF spectrum discussed in Chapter V.D of this *Handbook*. The frequency blocks are broken down into 94 channels of 20 kHz each. This group of frequencies is allocated for basic telephone service in remote locations where traditional wireline service is not feasible. This spectrum is licensed on a site-by-site basis and is available to buy or lease on the secondary market. A similar service called the Rural Radiotelephone Service also operates in the 152 to 150 MHZ and the 454 to 460 MHz bands. Service rules are located at 47 C.F.R. Part 22.

E. Automated Marine Telecommunication System (AMTS)

AMTS use is limited to 12 nautical miles off the Unites States coast

The automated marine telecommunication system is a commercial system that offers both voice and data to marine customers in coastal areas and inland waterways. Use is limited to 12 nautical miles off the U.S. coast. AMTS spectrum may also be used in Land Mobile Radio systems subject to interference restrictions with the adjacent television channels 10 and 13 or the Air Force Space Surveillance System operating at 216.880-217.080 MHz. It consists of 20 channels of 25 kHz each. Users with geographical area licenses can also use

12.5 kHz or 6.25 kHz channels to increase the number of channels. Uses include equipment monitoring and positive train control. An illustration of the AMTS band plan is shown in Figure 12-3 below.

Figure 12-3: Automated Marine Telecommunication System

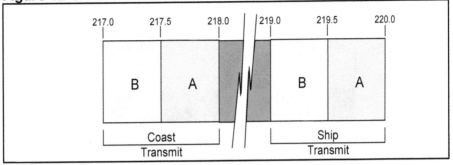

Channel Block	Frequency Bands	Bandwidth	Pairing	Channels	Licenses
A	217.5-218.0, 219.5-220.0	1 MHz	2 x 0.5 MHz	20	9
B	217.0-217.5, 219.0, 219.5	1 MHz	2 x 0.5 MHz	20	1

Source: FCC and Summit Ridge Group, LLC analysis

F. Former Interactive Video and Data Service: 218-219 MHz

The FCC is evaluating the future use of the spectrum located at 218 to 219 MHz. Current rules can be found at 47 C.F.R. Part 95. The FCC has proposed moving the service rules to Part 27 in 2010, and the proposal is still pending. This would move it from the "Personal Radio Services" category to "Miscellaneous Radio Service" category proving additional flexibility for users. However, this proposal is still pending. The spectrum is licensed in two channel blocks (A and B) in each of the 734 Cellular Market Areas (CMAs) in the U.S. The FCC auctions this spectrum, but has only had one auction, FCC Auction No. 2, in 1994. This spectrum is also available on the secondary market. The band plan for this spectrum is illustrated in Figure 12-4 below.

Figure 12-4: 218-219 MHz Band Plan

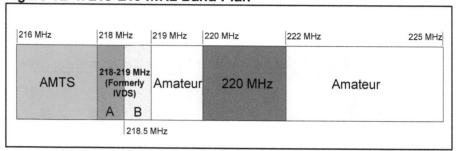

Application	Frequency	Bandwidth	License Type
AMTS	216-218 MHz	2 MHz	
IVDS A Block (former)	218.0-218.5	0.5MHz	CMA – 734 licenses nationwide
IVDS B Bock (former)	218.5-219.0	0.5MHz	CMA – 734 licenses nationwide
Amateur	219 MHz	1 MHz	

Source: FCC and Summit Ridge Group, LLC analysis

XIII. Ultra High Frequency (UHF) Services

Frequencies in the UHF band range from ten centimeters to one meter in length. UHF radio waves do not bounce off the ionosphere as they are generally blocked by hills and large buildings. Due to their relatively short wavelength, consumer equipment using this frequency band can utilize relatively small antennas. The lower end of the band has greater distance and building penetration capabilities than its higher end.

A. Personal Locator Beacons (PLBs): 406 MHz

Personal Locator Beacons (PLBs) operate in the 406 MHz spectrum band and transmit personalized distress signals primarily for search and rescue missions

Personal Locator Beacons (PLBs) operate in the 406 MHz spectrum band and transmit personalized distress signals. These signals are designed to aid in search and rescue missions. Backwoods skiers often use PLBs so they can be found in the event they are submerged in an avalanche.

B. FRS/ GMRS: 462-467 MHz

The spectrum band from 462 to 467 MHz is used for short-distance two-way communication, usually via small handheld devices. General Mobile Radio Service ("GMRS") is divided into 23 channels of 25 kHz each. GMRS devices are limited to 5 watts of effective radiated power (ERP) and generally have a range of five to twenty-five miles. Using Family Radio Services ("FRS"), the devices do not require a license, but they are limited to .5 watts of ERP and consequently have a much shorter range. Their use is regulated under 47 C.F.R. Part 95.

C. Specialized Mobile Radio: 800 MHz

Specialized Mobile Radio (SMR) is typically used for mobile business radio such as taxi dispatch, construction companies, and other business. The radios can be mounted in a vehicle or be used as hand-held devices. Typically, a business using SMR would pay a fee to a service provider who maintains a repeater to ensure coverage of a certain area for multiple customers. The spectrum band plan for specialized mobile radio is illustrated in Figure 13-1 below.

Figure 13-1: Specialized Mobile Radio Band Plan

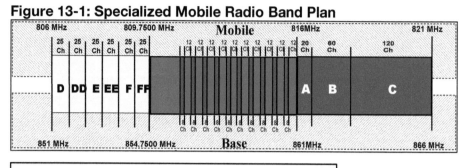

Band	Frequencies	Bandwidth	Pairing
General Category Pool	806-809.75, 851-854.75	7.5 MHz	2 x 3.75 MHz
SMR Category Pool/Public Safety (alternating)	809.75-816, 854.75-861	12.5 MHz	2 x 6.25 MHz
SMR Category Pool	816-821, 861-866	10 MHz	2 x 5 MHz

Source: FCC and Summit Ridge Group, LLC analysis

D. Air-Ground Radio Telephone Service: 800 MHz

Air-ground radio telephone (Air-ground) services are used to provide commercial telephone service to pilots and passengers aboard commercial aircraft. There are ten blocks of 6 kHz, and six control ranges of 3.2 kHz in the 849 to 851 MHz range (uplink from the ground) and in the 894 to 896 MHz (downlink from the plane). The band plan for air-ground services is illustrated in Figure 13-2 below. The primary operator in the band was Verizon Airfone who had limited commercial success due to high consumer costs and poor call quality. Verizon Airfone was sold to Jet Blue in 2008. General Aviation users (non-commercial planes) are allocated frequencies at 454 and 459 MHz for plane to ground phone calls.

Figure 13-2: Air-Ground Radio Telephone Service Plan (800 MHz)

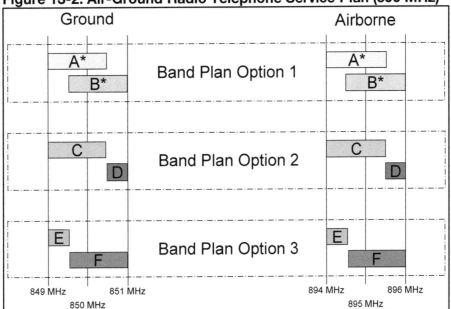

Location	Frequency	Bandwidth
Ground	849-851	2 MHz
Airborne	894-896	2 MHz

Source: FCC and Summit Ridge Group, LLC analysis

E. Narrowband Personal Communication Service (PCS)

Narrowband PCS is located in the ranges of spectrum at 901 to 902 MHz, 930 to 931 MHz, and 940 to 941 MHz. This spectrum is typically used for two-way paging and telemetry such as off-site utility monitoring. The FCC service rules for Narrowband PCS are located at 47 C.F.R Part 24. The band plan for the PCS band is illustrated in Figure 13-3 below.

Figure 13-3: Narrowband Personal Communications Service

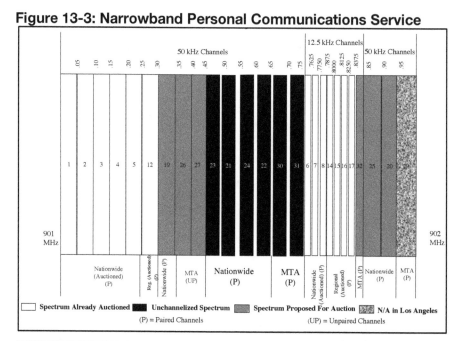

Status	Frequency	Bandwidth	Type
Nationwide (Auctioned)	901.0-901.25	250 kHz	5 channels, 50 kHz each. Paired
REG (auctioned)	901.25-901.30	50 kHz	1 channel, 50 kHz, paired
MTA (unauctioned)	901.30-901-35	50 kHz	1 channel, 50 kHz, paired
MTA	901.35-901.45	100 kHz	2 channels, 50 kHz each
Nationwide	901.45-901.65	200 kHz	4 channels, 50 kHz each, paired
MTA	901.65-901.75	100 kHz	2 channels, 50 kHz each, paired
Nationwide (unauctioned)	901.750-901.7875	37.5 kHz	3 channels, 12.5 kHz each
Regional (auctioned)	901.7875-901.8375	50 kHz	4 channels, 12.5 kHz each, paired
MTA	901.8375-901.85	12.5 kHz	1 channel, 12.5 KHz
Nationwide	901.85-901.95	100 kHz	2 channels, 50 kHz each
MTA	901.95	50 kHz	1 channel, 50 kHz each

Source: FCC and Summit Ridge Group, LLC analysis

F. LMS Location & Monitoring Service: 902-928 MHz

The propagation of [the LMS] frequency is highly dependent on a clear line of sight

Also known as the 33-centimeter band, the LMS, or Location and Monitoring Service, band ranges from 902 to 928 MHz. The propagation of this frequency is highly dependent on a clear line of sight. In ITU Region 2 (the Americas) it is used for ISM as well as low powered unlicensed devices such as wireless microphones as well as Wi-Fi. In Region 2, ISM also includes 2.400 to 2.4835 GHz and 5.725 to 5.875 GHz, which are also authorized for Wi-Fi.

This band was auctioned in FCC Auction 21 in 1999. The spectrum consists of three blocks: A, B, and C with 6.0, 2.25 and 5.75 MHz, respectively, in each of the 176 economic areas. The portion of this band not used by location and monitoring service is allocated to amateur radio service operators. The LMS band plan is shown below in Figure 13-4.

Figure 13-4: LMS/ISM Band Plan

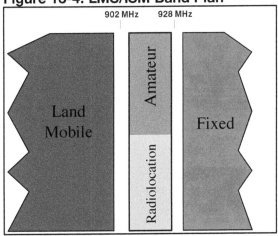

Application	Frequency	Bandwidth
Radiolocation	902-928	26 MHz
Amateur	902-928	26 MHz
ISM & formerly Wi-Fi	902-928	26 MHz
ISM & Wi-Fi	2.400 – 2.4825 GHz	82.5 MHz
ISM & Wi-Fi	5.725 – 5.875 GHz	150 MHz

Source: FCC and Summit Ridge Group, LLC analysis

G. Multiple Address Systems: 928/959 MHz and 932/941 MHz

Multiple Address Systems spectrum is available for terrestrial point-to-multipoint and point-to-point services, along with mobile transmission of a licensee's products or services (not including distribution of video entertainment). Users are primarily companies that need remote networks, such as energy companies using it for dedicated communications networks. Licenses were sold in FCC Auction 42 in 2001. Over 5,100 licenses were offered (twenty-nine licenses in each of the 176 economic areas) for a period of 10 years. In each market, 28 licenses were for a 25 kHz allocation while one was for 100 kHz. However, only 878 were assigned. In 2005, the FCC re-auctioned the remaining licenses in FCC Auction 59 and 2,223 of the remaining 4,226 licenses were assigned. The band plan for Multiple Address Systems is indicated below in Figure 13-5.

Figure 13-5: Multiple Address Systems Band Plan

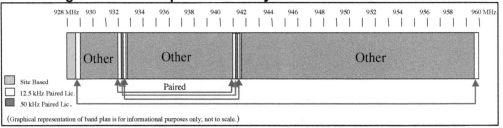

Application	Frequency	Paring	Licenses
Multiple Address Systems	928/959 and 932/941	2 x 12.5 kHz	176 (EA) 28 in each market
Multiple Address Systems	932/941	2 x 50 kHz	176 (EA) 1 in each market

Source: FCC and Summit Ridge Group, LLC analysis

H. Upper Paging Band: 929 and 931 MHz

The upper paging band frequencies are located on either side of the narrowband PDC spectrum at 929 to 930 MHz and 931 to 932 MHz as shown in Figure 13-6 below. The spectrum consists of 49 licenses of 20 kHz each. Twelve licenses were issued in the 929 MHz band and 37 licenses in the 931 MHz band. The FCC issues all of these paging licenses by Major Economic Area.

Figure 13-6: Upper Paging Band Plan

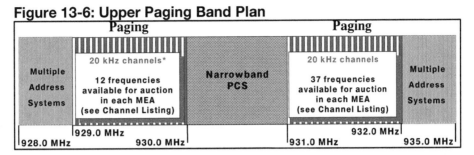

Application	Frequency (MHz)	Bandwidth	Licenses
Upper Paging	929.0-930.0	20 kHz	12 in each of 52 MEA
Upper Paging	931.0-935.0	20 kHz	37 in each of 52 MEAs

Source: FCC and Summit Ridge Group, LLC analysis

I. Mobile Wireless Services

Commercial mobile wireless services operate in various portions of the UHF band and are discussed in detail in Chapter VIII above.

XIV. Super High Frequency and Extremely High Frequency

A. Super High Frequency (SHF): 3-30 GHz

The SHF frequency range has superior capacity to carry data on a "bits per MHz" basis

As mentioned in Chapter VI.G of this *Handbook*, spectrum in this range has superior capacity to carry data on a "bits per MHz" basis. But propagation is largely limited to line of sight reception. Super High Frequency is used heavily by satellite communication systems (described in detail in Chapter X). Exceptions include the General Wireless Communication Service (GWCS), the 24 GHz band and LMDS. In addition to its original primary band at 2.4 GHz, Wi-Fi operates in the 5 GHz band. The FCC recently announced plans to expand Wi-Fi spectrum to include parts of the 5.9 GHz band.

1. General Wireless Communication Service

This band occupies 25 MHz-sized channels from 4660-4685 MHz, divided into five 5 MHz blocks. This space is in the gap between the satellite C-band uplink and downlink spectrum (the "duplex gap"). The FCC scheduled it for auction in Auction 30 in May 1998 but postponed it indefinitely in April 1998. The band plan for the GWCS band is illustrated in Figure 14-1 below

.

Figure 14-1: GWCS Band Plan

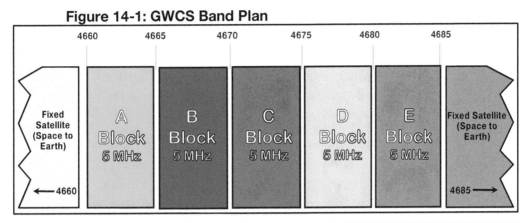

Block	Frequency	Amount	Type
A Bock	4660-4665	5 MHz	Unpaired
B Block	4665-4670	5 MHz	Unpaired
C Bock	4670-4675	5 MHz	Unpaired
D Block	4675-4680	5 MHz	Unpaired
E Bock	4680-4685	5 MHz	Unpaired

Source: FCC and Summit Ridge Group, LLC analysis

2. Connected Cars: DSRC and C-V2X

Every year approximately 40,000 people die in car accidents. The U.S. DOT started in 1998 working with the FCC and the auto industry to allow cars to be connected to each other directly with data exchanges to prevent accidents, and to radio units on the roads to help with slowing cars down where danger is ahead or a stop light. The U.S. Department of Transportation (DoT) proposed a solution many years ago that would allow cars to detect other cars approaching and avert collisions, but it failed to move forward at the pace projected. The DOT coined the technology, Dedicated Short Range Communications or DSRC. Now, a new technology dubbed C-V2X, (Cellular-Vehicle-to-X) proposed by equipment vendors and some of the major car manufacturers may overtake DSRC in the race to own the car. The FCC worked with the U.S. DoT since 1997 to allocate unlicensed spectrum at 5.9 MHz for the technology and, starting in 2016, the FCC is looking at modifying the spectrum allocation to include both DSRC and C-V2X.

The FCC designated unlicensed spectrum in the 5.9 GHz band as "Unlicensed National Information Infrastructure, or U-NII, devices. The

PART TWO: U.S. SPECTRUM

FCC set aside 5.850-5.925 GHz, or 75 MHz, called U-NII-4, for connected cars. The 5.9 GHz band is used by many unlicensed applications including Wi-Fi and this spectrum is also targeted for LTE-U which will use LTE-TDD optimized for Part 15 rules, and fixed outdoor broadband radios used by WISPs, cordless telephones, and airport wind shear doppler radar.

DSRC public-private initiative that failed to move forward in 20 years; however, state departments of transportation have recently worked with industry leaders to create test beds for existing DSRC and new C-V2X technology on the roads. Summit Ridge proposes that the significance for state and U.S. DoT is that one of the two technologies, or both, will be rolled out and working in just a few years. For example, Colorado DOT is spending $70 million installing 245 roadside units for DSRC and will have 500 miles of roads with smart safety monitoring. The Colorado DOT will also be installing 2000 vehicles now and 10,000 by 2020 with V2X units. The Utah DOT is also installing DSRC several test units at intersections and on state DOT vehicles. Michigan DoT is installing 400 roadside DSRC units and 5000 vehicle DSRC units by 2018.

The U.S. DoT is concerned that other unlicensed uses will interfere with DSRC units, causing a safety issue. Since 1997, the FCC has tweaked and conducted a rulemaking for unlicensed uses of 5.9 GHz. In 1997, the FCC issued rules for 5.15-5.25 GHz (U-NII-1 with 10 MHz), 5.25-5.35 GHz (U-NII-2A with 10 MHz), and 5.725-5.825 GHz (U-NII-3 with 10 MHz).[160] In 2003, the FCC amended the U-NII rules for 5.47-5.725 GHz creating U-NII-2C (with 275 MHz).[161] In 2013, the FCC issued amended the U-NII rules further to prevent interference opening up 5.350-5.470 GHz (U-NII-2B with 120 MHz), 5.725-5.850 GHz (more of the U-NII-3 block 125 MHz), and 5.850-5.925 GHz (U-NII-4 with 75 MHz).[162] In 2014, the FCC further amended the U-NII rules and added to U-NII 25 MHz of more spectrum at the upper edge

---

[160] *Amendment of the Commission's Rules to Provide for Operation of Unlicensed NII Devices in the 5 GHz Frequency Range*, ET Docket No. 96-102, Report and Order, 12 FCC Rcd 1576 (1997).

[161] *Revision of Parts 2 and 15 of the Commission's Rules to Permit Unlicensed National Information Infrastructure (U-NII) devices in the 5 GHz Band*, ET Docket No. 03-122, Report and Order, 18 FCC Rcd 24484 (2003).

[162] *Revision of Part 15 of the Commission's Rules to Permit Unlicensed National Information Infrastructure (U-NII) Devices in the 5 GHz Band*, ET Docket No. 13-49, Notice of Proposed Rulemaking, 28 FCC Rcd 1769 (2013).

of the U-NII-3 band from 5.825-5.850 GHz.[163] Figure 14-2 below shows where DSRC is located at the top end of 5.9 GHz.

Figure 14-2: DCRS Allocated Spectrum

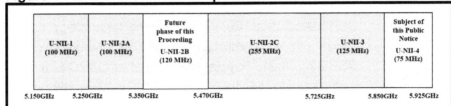

Source: FCC orders and Summit Ridge Group, LLC analysis

U-NII-4, the 5.850-5.925 GHz band is allocated for DSRC, commercial FSS, government radiolocation service, and Amateur Service. Four 10 MHz channels are dedicated for DSRC and two 10 MHz channels for public safety as shown in Figure 14-3 below.

Figure 14-3: DCRS 5.9 GHz Channels 170-184

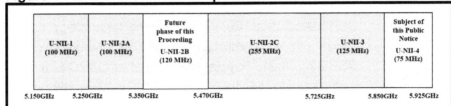

Source: FCC orders and Summit Ridge Group, LLC analysis

In 2016, the FCC opened the DSRC proceeding again to consider incorporating DSRC and C-V2V together into the 5.9 GHz band. One proposal is to have C-V2V turn off - or move to other spectrum - if the radio senses DSRC transmissions nearby.[164] Commissioner O'Reilly has been critical of the slow pace that DSRC has come to market, in light of the mandate for the FCC to deliver new spectrum and uses it as an example of being careful about dedicating spectrum for an unproven use or technology.

The technical argument is that DSRC works for the quick communication needed between vehicles approaching on a collision course and that base-station dependent C-V2X technology - LTE - is

---

[163] Revision of Part 15 of the Commission's Rules to Permit Unlicensed National Information Infrastructure (U-NII) Devices in the 5 GHz Band, ET Docket No. 13-49, First Report and Order, 29 FCC Rcd 4127 (2014).

[164] Office of Engineering and Technology Announces Schedule for Testing Prototype U-NII-4 Devices, Public Notice, 31 FCC Rcd 10518 (2016); The Commission Seeks to Update and Refresh the Record in the "Unlicensed National Information Infrastructure (U-NII) Devices in the 5 GHz Band" Proceeding, Public Notice, 31 FCC Rcd 6130 (2016).

PART TWO: U.S. SPECTRUM

not proven, is costlier, and is too slow for V2V collision reaction. It may be the force of will by mobile operators, equipment vendors, or the auto industry that will enable one connected car technology to "win" over the other. For example, Toyota is firmly committed to DSRC and has 100,000 cars with technology operating in 2018 in Japan with a commitment to have all Toyotas sold in the U.S. to have DSRC by 2021. Toyota contends that DSRC is a working technology that transmits car-to-car and that C-V2X is still not proven and could take years more for the auto industry to adopt.[165] On the other hand, Qualcomm and various global manufacturers are supporting C-V2X as a proven vehicle-to-vehicle technology.[166] It seems likely that both DSRC and C-V2X will be deployed globally and that the regulators will implement spectrum sharing guidelines that will allow both technologies to exist together – such as reallocating the 10 channels within the 75 MHz to prevent interference. Auto safety is imperative and both technologies, in particular with the self-driving car coming right around the corner, will require a V2V technology.

3. Former Digital Electronic Message Service (DEMS): 24 GHz

This band was auctioned in the FCC Auction No. 56 in July 2004 for use with digital fixed service. Each license consists of a pair of 40 MHz channels (total 80 MHz). One license was issued in each of the 176 Economic Areas in the U.S. as defined by the Department of Commerce and four were issued for ten-year terms each for the FCC defined Economic Areas. In 2016, the Spectrum Frontiers initiative created new rules to make this spectrum available for next-generation wireless services. FCC Auction 102 is scheduled to take place directly after the conclusion of FCC Auction 101, which is scheduled to begin November 14, 2018. A band plan for the 24 GHz spectrum is illustrated in Figure 14-4 below.

---

[165] FierceWireless, *Toyota emphasizes maturity, safety of DSRC* (July 3, 2018) https://www.fiercewireless.com/wireless/toyota-emphasizes-maturity-safety-dsrc.

[166] Qualcomm, *Panasonic, Qualcomm and Ford Join Forces on First U.S. Deployment for C-V2X Vehicle Communications in Colorado* (June 1, 2018) https://www.qualcomm.com/news/releases/2018/06/01/panasonic-qualcomm-and-ford-join-forces-first-us-deployment-c-v2x-vehicle.

Figure 14-4: 24 GHz Band Plan

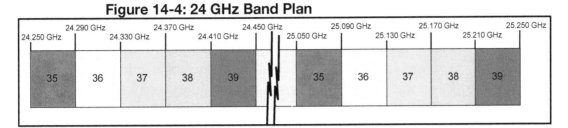

Channel	Downlink Frequency (GHz)	Uplink Frequency (GHz)	License Area	Licenses
35	24.250-24.290	25.050-25.090	Economic Area	176
36	24.290-24.330	25.090-25.130	Economic Area	176
37	24.330-24.370	25.130-25.170	Economic Area	176
38	24.370-24.410	25.170-25.210	Economic Area	176
39	24.410-24.450	25.210-25.250	Economic Area	176
Note: 80 MHz (paired 40 MHz segments) in each of five channels (Channel Numbers 35-39)				

Source: FCC and Summit Ridge Group, LLC analysis

4. MVDDS 12 GHz Spectrum Sharing Multichannel Video and Data Distribution Service v. Non-Geostationary Satellite

MVDDS was first proposed in 1998 by an FCC rulemaking proceeding as a method of providing shared, high bandwidth terrestrial service within the 12 GHz Ku band as long as there was interference protection for Direct Broadcast Satellite (DBS) and for a new proposed fixed satellite services (FSS) delivered from proposed non-geostationary satellite orbits (NGSO) using 500 MHz of 12 GHz, from 12.2-12.7 GHz.[167] In 2002, the FCC created spectrum sharing for

---

[167] Amendment of Parts 2 and 25 of the Commission's Rules to Permit Operation of NGSO FSS Systems Co-Frequency with GSO and Terrestrial Systems in the Ku-Band Frequency Range; Amendment of the Commission's Rules to authorize subsidiary

12.2-12.7 GHz determining it could be used for terrestrial use as long as it did not interfere with satellite use by limiting power levels. The terrestrial use was for one-way fixed, downlink video. MVDDS mobile use was excluded because of concerns of interference with DBS. There was a great deal of controversy, and litigation, regarding early MVDSS technology and patents, and in 2002 the FCC decided to auction the spectrum, affirming that it could be shared with the NGSO satellites and FSS.[168] In 2004, the FCC conducted Auction 53 selling 192 MVDDS licenses to 10 bidders for $119 million followed by Auction 63 in 2005 selling 22 more licenses, for a total of 214 licenses[169] Dish is the largest owner of MVDSS spectrum.

In 2016, the MVDDS Coalition requested that the FCC relax the rules for 12 GHz MVDDS to allow for mobile use and allow for new spectrum sharing to protect the DBS transmissions.[170] In 2017, the FCC opened a notice of inquiry to examine possible mid-band spectrum, 3.7-24 GHz, which included 12 GHz for possible use for mobile broadband.[171] The MVDDS Coalition urged the FCC to open up MVDSS 12 GHz for mobile use contending that since the FCC had approved NGSO in 2002, no NGSO had operated in the band for 15 years, that new spectrum sharing could help lessen the risk of interference, and that other bands were available for NGSO use including 11.7-12.2 GHz, 14-14.5 GHz, 18.8-19.3 GHz, and 28.6-29.1 GHz. Also, the MVDSS Coalition pointed out that the complexity of satellite and terrestrial spectrum sharing in other bands, for example,

---

Terrestrial Use of the12.2-12.7 GHz Band by Direct Broadcast Satellite Licensees and Their Affiliates, Notice of Proposed Rule Making ET Docket No. 98-206, 14 FCC Rcd 1131 (1998).

[168] *Amendment of Parts 2 and 25 of the Commission's Rules to Permit Operation of NGSO FSS Systems Co-Frequency with GSO and Terrestrial Systems in the Ku-Band Frequency Range; Amendment of the Commission's Rules to authorize subsidiary Terrestrial Use of the12.2-12.7 GHz Band by Direct Broadcast Satellite Licensees and Their Affiliates*, Memorandum Opinion and Order and Second Report and Order, ET Docket No. 98-206, Notice of Proposed Rule Making, ET Docket No. 98-206, 17 FCC Rcd 9614 (2002).

[169] FCC Auction 53: Multichannel Video Distribution & Data Service (MVDDS) https://www.fcc.gov/auction/53

[170] Petition of MVDDS 5G Coalition for Rulemaking, RM-11768 (filed April 26, 2016) https://ecfsapi.fcc.gov/file/60001692292.pdf

[171] *Expanding Flexible Use in Mid-Band Spectrum Between 3.7 and 24 GHz*, GN Docket No. 17-183, Notice of Inquiry, FCC 17-104 (Aug. 3, 2017). https://www.fcc.gov/document/fcc-opens-inquiry-new-opportunities-mid-band-spectrum-0

with 48 satellites are serving 4800 registered earth stations in the 3.7-4.2 GHz band and 1,535 earth stations in 5.925-6.425 GHz and that the 12 GHz band was essentially free of NGSO use and a simple to solve. The problem was timing because at least two firms, SpaceX and OneWeb, were aiming to launch a low earth orbit satellite system that would use 12 GHz to deliver 5G speeds -- a minimum of 100 Mbps -- to every point on the Earth. This mission of using reaching rural homes with broadband is the goal of every regulator around the world. It clashed with another mission to free up inefficiently used spectrum for mobile 5G with spectrum sharing techniques like CBRS.

In 2017, the FCC granted OneWeb's petition to use the spectrum for a projected 720 satellites and explained that future spectrum sharing could be worked out under the 2002 rules.[172] In March 2018, the FCC approved SpaceX's used of the 12 GHz band for 4,425 satellites.[173] OneWeb plans to put 1,980 NGSO satellites in orbit following its first scheduled launch in late 2018.

Summit Ridge Group believes the conflict over the 12 GHz band will continue. Dish and others spent $120 million in the 2004 auction for the spectrum and mobile use with small cell spectrum sharing could be a reasonable, and likely, method of protecting DBS and the NGSO SpaceX and OneWeb use of the spectrum. On the other hand, the FCC and governments globally are seeking to solve the problem of bringing broadband to hard to reach rural areas needed broadband, and SpaceX, OneWeb, and other NGSO satellite firms seem poised to actually deliver, in particular with the tremendous successes of SpaceX in the launch arena. The 12 GHz spectrum has 500 MHz available for mobile terrestrial and for satellite broadband delivery. There is potential interference for both in the 12 GHz band.

5. LMDS: 27.5 to 30 GHz and 31.075 to 31.225 GHz

Local Multipoint Distribution Service (LMDS) spectrum was originally

Local Multipoint Distribution Service (LMDS) spectrum was originally conceived to transmit digital television signals

---

[172] *Petition for a Declaratory Ruling Granting Access to the U.S. Market for the OneWeb NGSO FSS System*, Order and Declaratory Ruling, 32 FCC Rcd 5366 (2017) https://www.fcc.gov/document/oneweb-market-access-grant.

[173] *Application for Approval for Orbital Deployment and Operating Authority for the SpaceX NGSO Satellite System*, Memorandum Opinion and Order, SAT-LOA-20170726-00110 (Mar. 28, 2018) https://www.fcc.gov/document/fcc-authorizes-spacex-provide-broadband-satellite-services

conceived to transmit digital television signals and for fixed wireless last mile delivery. Its range is typically limited to 1.5 miles (2.4 km) due to rain fade issues, i.e. strong rain dampens the signal's strength. However, with a larger antenna and unobstructed line of sight, the range can reach 5 miles (8 km). Although it showed great hope of providing effective "wireless cable" in the 1990s, this was never a commercial success. Most providers abandoned efforts to build wireless cable using this spectrum. Given the amount of available spectrum available in the LMDS bad, there is some industry discussion about using LMDS to deliver residential broadband.

LMDS spectrum was auctioned in FCC Auction No. 17 in 1998. The licenses were auctioned for each of the 491 Basic Trading Areas (BTA) into which the FCC has partitioned the country. The band plan for LMDS spectrum is illustrated in Figure 14-3 below. The A block licenses are 1,150 MHz while B block license are 150 MHz each. After some winning bidders withdrew their bids, part of the spectrum was re-auctioned in Auction 23 in 1999.

Figure 14-5: LMDS Spectrum Band Plan

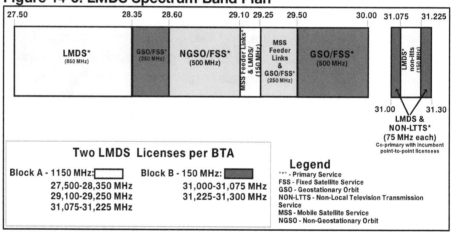

Block	Frequency	Bandwidth	Licenses
A Block	27.5-28.35, 29.1-29.250, 31.075-31.225	1,150 MHz	491 (BTA)
B Block	31.0-31.075 31.225-31.300	150 MHz	491 (BTA)

Source: FCC and Summit Ridge Group, LLC analysis

B. Extremely High Frequencies (EHF): 30-300 GHz

As mentioned in Chapter VI.H of this *Handbook*, spectrum at this level and above is sparsely utilized. It is subject to severe rain fade and has a poor ability to penetrate buildings and foliage. Nevertheless, portions of the lower end of the range including the Q-band (33 to 50 GHz) and the V-band (50 to 75 GHz), which are allocated for satellite and short distance terrestrial broadband, may be increasingly used in the future. An exception is the 39 GHz band described below.

1. 39 GHz band

The 39 GHz band is authorized for fixed point-to-point use for wireless back-haul and backbone communication

The 39 GHz band, comprising frequencies from 38.6-40 GHz was auctioned in FCC Auction 30 in 2000. The band is authorized for fixed point-to-point use for wireless back-haul and backbone communication. Licenses were issued in 172 Economic Areas with fourteen 100 MHz (50 MHz paired) blocks in each area. The Spectrum Frontiers initiative also identified this band for mobile and fixed wireless broadband use but the FCC has not yet announced any information regarding an auction. Figure 18-5 illustrates all the bands identified in the Spectrum Frontiers initiative for possible mobile use. The band plan for the 39 GHz band is illustrated in Figure 14-6 below.

Figure 14-6: 39 GHz Band Plan

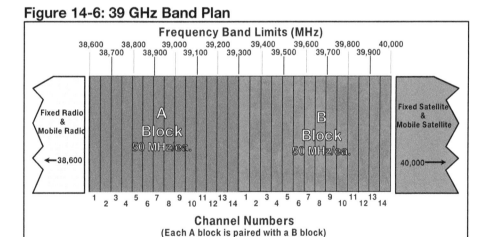

Block	Frequency	Bandwidth	Licenses
A Block	38.6-39.3 GHz	700 MHz	172 (EA)
B Block	39.3-40.0 GHz	700 MHz	172 (EA)

Source: FCC and Summit Ridge Group, LLC analysis

PART THREE: REGULATORY DYNAMICS

XV. Major Commercial and Policy Spectrum Issues

A. Spectrum Reallocation: A New Regulatory Regime

1. Spectrum Reallocation: "Spectrum Crunch" No More

In 2012, wireless experts, the mobile industry, and regulators were all talking about "the looming spectrum crunch."[174] Because spectrum was seen as a finite resource and because of the dramatic growth in smartphone adoption, thanks to Steve Jobs and the iPhone, the mobile industry was concerned that the allocated spectrum would not be sufficient. Mobile industry leaders, experiencing skyrocketing data use, believed that the only way out was through a massive reallocation of spectrum (see Figure 15-2 below for projected wireless traffic growth). The United States government and other countries across the globe agreed and began the reallocation of broadcast TV spectrum and inefficiently used military and satellite spectrum. Also, new spectrum sharing systems with an online database acting as a traffic cop for the spectrum selection for base stations opened the doors for much more efficient use of shared spectrum.

The spectrum crunch refers to a scarcity of spectrum available to commercial entities

New mobile technologies, such as small cells, antenna advances like MIMO, the capability for aggregation of different frequencies in the handset, and new chipsets allowing handsets to use super high frequencies such as 24 GHz and 28 GHz, would dramatically change the mantra away from spectrum crunch in 2018. In reality, there was not a spectrum crunch. There was merely a lack of efficient build-out of the licensed spectrum and a failure to embrace the latest solutions fast enough. Instead with changes like spectrum sharing, reallocation, and small cell, the only spectrum crunch problem left for the mobile industry will be fully rolling out the new technologies and infrastructure. With the feasibility that the mobile industry can, with the new solutions, capture revenue and increase ARPU from in-home Wi-Fi data use now being delivered by cable providers, the mobile industry is highly incentivized. The decision to spend available cash for network build-out or for new spectrum should be simple: the network build-out is the way forward.

---

[174] David Talbot, *The Spectrum Crunch That Wasn't* (Nov. 26, 2018) www.technologyreview.com/s/507486/the-spectrum-crunch-that-wasnt/.

Keeping infrastructure build-out cost down will be a key component to the build-out. There are 154,000 cell towers today in the U.S., but it is projected 800,000 small cells will be deployed in the next eight years. Analysts are predicting that the carriers will start sharing small cell infrastructure costs through third-party service providers. For instance, equipment vendors are creating possibilities for the carriers to share small cell infrastructure called C-RAN, or Cloud Radio Access Networks, where carriers share the small cell antenna, the back-haul, and parts of the small cell located on the street but control their portions of the system – like software-controlled antennas - using carrier software located in the "cloud." However, it is unlikely that carriers will share infrastructure they cannot completely control or that is used by a competitor. Carrier engineers would rather install the perfect small cell than have one installed that costs less but delivered some service. Summit Ridge Group believes that traditional mobile carrier engineers are going to be forced into using C-RAN or similar shared infrastructure technologies as they may watch newer, more nimble and previously unknown mobile carrier entrants take advantage of C-RAN, which could give new carriers a lower CAPEX and faster speeds.

2. The State of Spectrum: Explosive Demand for Data & Speed

Global mobile data traffic was reported to have grown by 63 percent in 2016 and by a similar amount in 2017.[175] One industry association reported that "wireless data" grew 400% from 2014 to 2017, or from 4.1 TB to 15.7 TB.[176] A trend in mobile awareness, caused by dramatic increases in cable DOCSIS speeds through home Wi-Fi, is increased bit rate. From 2014 to 2017, average mobile download speeds were reported to have increased from 14 Mbps to 24 Mbps, a 61% increase. When deciding where to move, consumers are prioritizing mobile connectivity over the school district quality.

---

[175] *The Cisco Visual Networking Index (VNI) Global Mobile Data Traffic Forecast Update, 2016-2021* is part of the comprehensive *Cisco VNI Forecast*, an ongoing initiative to track and forecast the impact of visual networking applications on global networks. This report presents some of the major global mobile data traffic projections and growth trends https://www.cisco.com/c/en/us/solutions/collateral/service-provider/visual-networking-index-vni/mobile-white-paper-c11-520862.pdf (*Cisco VNI Global Mobile Data Traffic Forecast Update, 2016-2021*).

[176] CTIA, *The Wireless Industry, Industry Data* https://www.ctia.org/the-wireless-industry/infographics-library.

PART THREE: REGULATORY

Figure 15-1: Mobile Download Speed

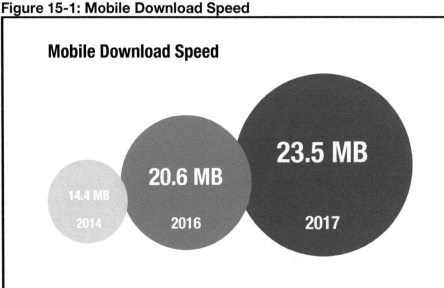

Source: CTIA and Summit Ridge Group, LLC analysis

Mobile data traffic has grown 18-fold over the past 5 years

Mobile phone penetration is at 5 billion users or 65% of the world's 7.6 billion people. Mobile Internet is at 3.3 billion users or 43% of the total global population.[177] By 2025, this number will grow to 5 billion mobile Internet users. In addition to user growth, global mobile data traffic had reached 11.2 exabytes per month by the end of 2017, up from 4.4 exabytes (EB) per month at the end of 2015.[178] Mobile data traffic has grown 18-fold over the past 5 years, and there is no end in sight. Mobile is projected to reach the following milestones:

- Monthly global mobile data traffic will be 49 EB by 2021, and annual traffic will exceed half a zettabyte.[179]

- Mobile will represent 20% of total IP traffic by 2021.

- The number of mobile-connected devices per capita will reach 1.5 by 2021.

- The average global mobile speed will surpass 20 Mbps by 2021.

- 53% of mobile connections will be 4G by 2021.

---

[177] GSMA, *The Mobile Economy 2018* https://www.gsma.com/mobileeconomy/wp-content/uploads/2018/02/The-Mobile-Economy-Global-2018.pdf

[178] One exabyte (EB) is equivalent to one billion GB, and 1000 petabytes. *Cisco Visual Networking Index (VNI) Global Mobile Data Traffic Forecast Update* 2016-2021, *supra* at note 175.

[179] One zettabite (1 ZB) is approximately equal to 1000 EB.

- 4G traffic will be more than three-quarters of the total mobile traffic by 2021. By 2025, 49% of mobile users will be on 5G in the U.S.

- Wireless (Wi-Fi combined with mobile networks) handled 55% of the total IP traffic in 2017, exceeding IP traffic to wired devices

- Video downloading represented 69% of consumer Internet traffic in 2017. Over 78% of the world's mobile data traffic will be video by 2021.[180]

Mobile data traffic continues to grow, and the graph below shows predicted growth of mobile data traffic between 2017 and 2022.[181] It depicts a continued strong increase in data and voice traffic growth in the mid-single digits per year.

Figure 15-2: Projected Mobile Data Traffic Growth

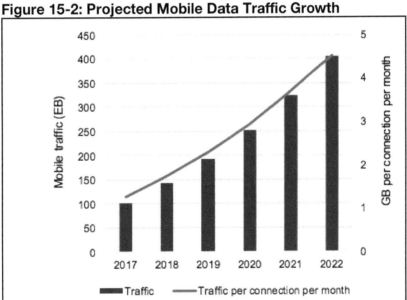

Source: *Analysys Mason: Global Race to 5G*[182]

The growth in data traffic is driven by a continued increase in average data volume per subscription. As noted above, data traffic is principally

---

[180] *Cisco Visual Networking Index (VNI) Global Mobile Data Traffic Forecast Update 2016-2021, supra* at note 175.

[181] Ericsson, *Mobility Report* (June 2018) https://www.ericsson.com/assets/local/mobility-report/documents/2018/ericsson-mobility-report-june-2018.pdf.

[182] Analysys Mason on behalf of CTIA: *Global Race to 5G* (Apr. 2018) https://api.ctia.org/wp-content/uploads/2018/04/Analysys-Mason-Global-Race-To-5G_2018.pdf.

PART THREE: REGULATORY

being fueled (69% of total mobile data is video) by Internet video such as Netflix, YouTube, Amazon, and over-the-top (OTT) cable video like HBO. It should be noted that there are large differences in traffic levels between markets, regions, and operators. Total mobile global data traffic is expected to rise at a compound annual growth rate (CAGR) of around 45 percent.

The growth in mobile data traffic is also due to the rising number of smartphone devices. In the U.S., 77% of U.S. adults owned a smartphone and 95% of adults owned a mobile phone, meaning that mobile phone penetration in the U.S. has matured. U.S. mobile carrier revenue can only grow by increasing ARPU (average revenue per user, also referred to as ARPA, or average revenue per account), which has been falling, or by taking customers from competing carriers. Winning over new customers requires lower ARPU or providing significantly better service. Intense competition by offering lower cost packages has generally driven ARPU down in the U.S., but ARPU varies from carrier to carrier.

Today, the wireless industry supports over 4.7 million jobs and contributes around $475 billion annually to the American economy

Purchasing new phones has been shown to increase data use. Demand for data quantity and download speeds increases every time a customer purchases a new phone or switches carriers. Switching to a new version of the same device can typically increase data consumption by 25–40 percent.[183]

Mobile is a big industry. Today, it supports over 4.7 million jobs and contributes around $475 billion annually to the U.S. economy. One study suggests that mobile carriers in the U.S. will spend $275 billion building 5G networks, creating 3 million new jobs and adding $500 billion to the economy.[184] Thus, the mobile industry by adding the new 3 million jobs that are projected to be created, will approach 5% of the total U.S. job market.

3. Spectrum Reallocation: Global Reaction to Deliver Spectrum for Mobile Use

Governments around the world have been moving to allocate more spectrum for mobile carriers. The regulators are not simply trying to

---

[183] Pew Research Center, *Mobile Fact Sheet* (Feb. 5, 2018) http://www.pewInternet.org/fact-sheet/mobile/.

[184] Accenture, *U.S. Wireless Industry Contributes $475 Billion Annually to America's Economy and Supports 4.7 Million Jobs*, (Apr. 5, 2018) https://newsroom.accenture.com/news/us-wireless-industry-contributes-475-billion-annually-to-americas-economy-and-supports-4-7-million-jobs-according-to-new-report.htm; CTIA, *The Wireless Industry: Industry Data* https://www.ctia.org/the-wireless-industry/infographics-library.

The U.S. has been the leader for spectrum innovation and regulation

help the mobile carriers succeed financially. Instead, they view the ubiquitous mobile service with high-speeds and no data caps as a requirement for encouraging the economy, schools, and even individuals and families succeed. Traditionally, regulators have been slow to act on spectrum policies and auctions, but since 2012 regulators across the globe have seized the opportunity and are working to reallocate inefficiently used spectrum for licensed mobile and for unlicensed use to meet rapid demand for wireless data. Many consider the U.S. to be the leader of the pack for spectrum innovation and regulation. Most countries view the FCC as the regulator to model.[185] They have been following the U.S. as it steps up and uses advanced spectrum sharing to reallocate TV station spectrum for mobile carriers. Also, countries are working to create a 650 MHz band from 3.5-4.2 MHz for mobile carriers and for unlicensed use, as well as delivering many more MHz of High Band mmW spectrum by using 24 GHz and 28 GHz. China, however, is following its own course and has already far surpassed the U.S. in terms of users and network growth with 700 million users. In China, 95% of mobile users accessed the Internet, exceeding U.S. mobile use. Both countries understand the importance of creating a healthy mobile regulatory environment.

While the total supply of spectrum can operate is finite, new technology and innovative network systems have increased spectral

While the total supply of spectrum that mobile can operate in is finite, new technology and innovative network systems have increased spectral efficiency, enabling service providers to offer more data throughput with reallocated federal government and satellite spectrum. The President, the NTIA (National Telecommunication and Information Administration), which is the agency responsible for federally used spectrum, and the FCC listened a range of participants, including credible innovators from Silicon Valley like Google delivering database systems to guide broadband radios to different spectrum, wireless equipment vendors innovating like Qualcomm, providers seeking to bring wireless broadband to rural homes, and, of course, mobile carriers seeking to gain more spectrum not efficiently used by the federal government.

The first major U.S. government move was in 2012 by the Obama administration's preparation and release of the PCAST (President Council of Advisors on Science and Technology) Report directing government agencies to identify poorly used spectrum and, working with the NTIA and FCC, to make the spectrum available for

---

[185] This is not universally accepted. An international regulator told on the authors, "We look to see how the FCC handles something, then we figure out how to do it correctly."

commercial carriers. The PCAST Report was led by a group that includes Google, Microsoft, a major Silicon Valley VC, and many other Internet executives. The report pointed out that the federal government owns approximately 60 percent of the prime U.S. spectrum supply. The report noted that much of this spectrum use was highly inefficient. For the needs of mobile wireless demand to be met, the federal agencies were directed to reallocate or share some of its valuable spectrum with commercial entities.[186]

4. Spectrum Sharing Regulation

Beginning in 2010, the FCC initiated spectrum sharing using a database connected to "flexible" base stations that could move from one spectrum to another instantly with authorization from the base station. Spectrum sharing was first used with unlicensed broadband base stations operating in the newly vacated UHF channels from 54-698 MHz. Spectrum sharing rules were approved in 2015 for 150 MHz of mid-band spectrum, called Citizens Broadband Radio Service, or CBRS. Spectrum sharing is a way for carriers and unlicensed providers to have a right to use spectrum that may change frequencies from time to time as incumbent owners of the spectrum occupy the slot. In the future, a spectrum license will be a right to occupy a range of spectrum frequencies, as long as the spectrum is available during the time the licensee seeks to use it.

a. Shared Spectrum: A Revision of Property Law?

Spectrum licenses are granted on a fundamental element of property law: one needs exclusive rights to property (i.e. licenses to spectrum) to economically justify putting capital into the property to develop it. If you cannot exclude others, then the "free rider" effect will prevent a return on investment to the builder. This is a fundamental justification for private property law – investors must be able to exclude others or no one will invest in projects on that property. However, there is a growing movement for advocating government allocation of large amounts of licensed and unlicensed spectrum for shared use.

In the beginning, advocates of spectrum sharing were primarily major Internet brands and proponents of unlicensed spectrum. Unlicensed mobile off-load – which is a mobile handset connected to the Internet using Wi-Fi and not the cellular network – represents much of the unlicensed use. One economist, whose study was embraced by two

Spectrum licenses are granted on a fundamental element of property theory... If you cannot exclude others, then the "free rider" effect will prevent a return on investment to the builder

---

[186] *PCAST Report, supra* note 76; Commissioner Ajit Pai (Diary), *Too Much Government, Too Little Spectrum* (Jan. 3, 2013) http://www.redstate.com/ajitpai/2013/01/03/too-much-government-too-little-spectrum.

FCC commissioners, concluded that unlicensed spectrum added $525 billion to the U.S. economy in 2017, with $29 billion in unlicensed devices and service, plus $469 billion from increased efficiencies for businesses and lower costs for consumers. Of the $469 billion, the economist attributed $25 billion to cellular off-load and $259 billion to residential Wi-Fi.[187]

While these numbers could be disputed, there was no dispute that unlicensed spectrum is important to the U.S. economy. The significance of unlicensed spectrum, from the view point of Summit Ridge Group and others, is that frequencies such as 2.4 GHz and 5 GHz, were designated as the "trash" spectrum and allocated for uses like microwave ovens. But because anyone could buy FCC approved devices and use the spectrum without a license, its use skyrocketed. The unlicensed spectrum allocated by the FCC was fully and efficiently utilized. There is no fallow unlicensed spectrum. In fact, regulation and licensing slowed the use of the spectrum and made its use inefficient.

However, the issue with unlicensed spectrum is that to prevent interference issues the power levels of the devices were regulated by FCC rule Part 15. This limited them serving very small areas, approximately 100 square meters outdoors. Mobile service required more power and, in order to maximize quality for end users, exclusivity of use. The other reason mobile carriers avoided embracing unlicensed spectrum is that exclusive licenses of spectrum have value.

The reason licensed spectrum created value for mobile carriers was that: a) being the only user of the spectrum ensured quality of service as exclusive licensing eliminated the issue of interference in the spectrum by other users; and b) no other carrier could use spectrum licensed exclusively to a carrier, which in turn limited competition from those carriers excluded from the spectrum.

Giving away unlicensed spectrum previously licensed to TV stations, as proposed in 2008 by Google and other supporters of unlicensed spectrum, collided with the incentives for mobile carriers owning exclusive licenses. The FCC designated the newly available TV channels as "white space" (the white spaces on spectrum charts

A reason carries avoided embracing unlicensed spectrum is that exclusive licenses of spectrum have value

PART THREE: REGULATORY

---

[187] Dr. Raul Katz, Study for WifiForward, *A 2017 Assessment of the Current & Future Economic Value of Unlicensed Spectrum in the United States* (April 2018) http://glenechogroup.isebox.net/Wi-Fiforward/economic-value-of-unlicensed-spectrum-to-reach-more-than-834-billion-by-2020.

without licensee), and the new spectrum sharing system created consequentially was called "TV White Space." Spectrum sharing was the solution to a spectrum assignment problem not encountered previously. Vacating the TV channels created a conundrum for approving an unlicensed use that was not encountered in other frequencies such as the Wi-Fi 2.4 GHz band. The 2.4 GHz band was available nationwide and Wi-Fi equipment could be used in any geography without interfering with a licensed provider. The TV channels were not available for unlicensed use nationwide but varied by location. In some geographies, a particular UHF channel was occupied by a TV station, but in another geography the same UHF channel was available for unlicensed use. In order to create a system where unlicensed users could know if a channel was available for unlicensed use in a particular geography, the FCC created a system of spectrum sharing requiring base stations to be always connected on the Internet to a database. The smart database knew the location of the base station and the boundaries of the TV channel and authorized the base stations to operate only in unoccupied TV channels. In addition, the FCC imposed strict power and spectrum "mask" requirements that would ensure that the base stations would not interfere with TV stations operating in adjacent channels.

Spectrum sharing technology in any band of spectrum requires an FCC approved database to help connect base stations to available spectrum

When the FCC, with input from the major Internet providers like Google and Microsoft, created the Part 15 unlicensed spectrum sharing rules to deliver more unlicensed spectrum in the UHF band, the mobile carriers objected to both spectrum sharing and creating more unlicensed spectrum. However, when the opportunity for using the 3.5 GHz mid-band arose because of an offer by the Navy and Department of Defense to make Navy radar 3.5 GHz spectrum available for shared commercial use, the mobile carriers started supporting the shared spectrum technology. By 2018, spectrum sharing was being suggested by mobile carriers for almost every band in which federal and non-federal incumbents were operating. The mobile carriers are recommending that, at a minimum, unused, or irregularly used spectrum, such as the 80/90 GHz mmW bands, be open for other shared use if the federal owner or the commercial owner -- such as a satellite user or fixed point-to-point provider -- is not using the spectrum efficiently. Just as in the TV White Space proceeding, spectrum sharing technology in any band of spectrum requires an FCC approved database to help direct connected base stations to available spectrum. When spectrum opens up in a particular geography, even for a limited time, the database can notify the base station that the spectrum is available. If the particular spectrum is occupied by the incumbent or a higher tiered owner, then the database can direct the base station to different nearby available spectra for that particular geography. Spectrum allocated to a user could be exclusive – meaning allowing only one carrier or it could be shared, similar to unlicensed Wi-Fi. Unlike 2.4 GHz unlicensed Wi-Fi, all service providers would be licensed but the service providers may not be required to pay for using the spectrum if sharing it with others.

Spectrum sharing, once opposed by mobile providers, is now curtailing the industry's "spectrum crunch" complaints

The FCC's new spectrum sharing system is now opening up large swaths of spectrum for mobile use. Spectrum sharing, once opposed by mobile providers, is now curtailing the industry's "spectrum crunch" complaints.[188] Spectrum sharing allows the sparsely used or fallow spectrum to be put to full use. Spectral efficiency can be maximized, or at least increased, and fears of a spectrum crunch are greatly diminishing. Large bands of both licensed and unlicensed spectrum are currently being made available, or seriously being considered, by the FCC using spectrum sharing.

Spectrum sharing is significantly altering the property right model of exclusive spectrum licensing. First, the end of exclusive licensing is approaching. Even the recent 2017 Broadcast Incentive Auction, while granting what may appear to be exclusive licenses in the lower band 600 MHz, is allowing unlicensed TV White Space use of licensed bands that the database shows as fallow, or not built out. Such a requirement means that valuations of the spectrum depend on current build-out and not on future potential. For example, if warehoused spectrum can be used by a competitor, then the warehoused spectrum does not have the same value as exclusive use spectrum. Competitors deploying small cells in geographies temporarily using spectrum auctioned to another carrier could simply move to other available unlicensed spectra in the same geography once the licensee begins to build-out the geography. Spectrum sharing, thus, allows a competitor to begin adding and serving customers using spectrum owned by another, and to later move to new spectrum without the risk of stranded network equipment. Spectrum sharing provides multiple incentives for use and discourages warehousing.

The FCC has allowed some "white spaces" found in commercial licensed spectrum bands to be used by unlicensed users under certain terms.

One specific spectrum sharing strategy suggested by the PCAST Report urges for the clearing of broad frequency bands from 2700 to 3700 MHz. The FCC has gone much further by considering several

---

[188] Summit Ridge Group contends that "spectrum crunch", as explained in Chapter XV.A, is not the result of available spectrum but primarily the result of carriers not fully building out the spectrum they already control - with more macro cells and/or with small cell densification.

bands for shared use from 3.5-80 GHz.

b. Opening Up Under Used Federal Spectrum: The New Smart Shared Homesteading of Spectrum

In addition to commercial spectrum, the spectrum sharing movement also targets portions of under-utilized U.S. government held spectrum. One challenge is that some government spectrum is for emergency purposes. Although seldom used, the government requires access to it. Many government agencies are fearful that if they share their spectrum with unlicensed users, they may not be able to effectively use it during an emergency. Spectrum sharing with the government has occurred prior to the PCAST report and TV White Spaces. For example, Verizon is required to share its D Block in the Upper 700 MHz band with the adjacent future public safety network, FirstNet, now being built out. Effectively Verizon is a secondary user of this spectrum and the public safety network has priority in case of an emergency (see Chapter VIII.H.1 of this *Handbook* for a discussion of this band plan).

Another issue with applying spectrum sharing to government held spectrum is the lack of incentive for the government to improve its spectral efficiency

Another issue with applying spectrum sharing to government-held spectrum is the lack of incentives for government agencies to improve spectral efficiency by sharing. While the commercial sector must report and justify its use of spectrum, as well as satisfy investors' expectations of optimal asset utilization, the federal government has had little required accountability, until this past decade, to keep its spectrum. This makes it unclear which pieces of the federal spectrum are used inefficiently and to what extent. As long as there is no common standard for determining commercial and government spectrum efficiency, it is unlikely the government will optimize its use of spectrum.

Various methods have been implemented to encourage federal agencies to share spectrum. The PCAST Report suggested that a "currency-like" accounting allocation[189] and incentive system be put into place to create a long-term motivation to manage and share government spectrum better. The 2013 Presidential Memo on spectrum sharing has put additional executive pressure on federal agencies to share spectrum. The Department of Defense holds a great deal of spectrum. Since the military is an organization that follows orders and reports to the President, when the President ordered spectrum sharing, the Department of Defense complied first and opened up the possibility for 150 MHz of spectrum use in the 3.5 GHz Band. There may be

---

[189] *PCAST Report, supra* note 76, at 55.

accounting-based incentives for the Department of Defense to encourage finding spectrum that could be shared. However, this would have minimal impact considering the large size of the DoD's budget. Spectrum allocated to the other federal agencies continues to be examined and explored for spectrum sharing by the NTIA.

Regardless of the incentives required, the federal agencies are starting to share spectrum that is able to be shared – by time and/or geography. The new sharing is creating a land grab of sorts, not unlike the homesteading so prevalent in the 1800's in the western United States. Spectrum that did not seem available is now available. The FCC is "cleaning house" using spectrum sharing technology that protects the first incumbent users who have deployed capital to build-out the spectrum. The FCC is also making sure that the large mobile carriers will share the new spectrum with unlicensed users. It also matters if the regulatory requirements on the unlicensed are low because that leads to easy to obtain, no-cost FCC licenses.

5. Narrowbanding

In addition to the Digital Television transition (DTV) which first freed up the upper and lower 700 MHz band and then freed up the Broadcast Incentive Auction 600 MHz band, the FCC has sought to free additional spectrum by taking advantage of new Narrowband technology. Narrowband radios use smaller channels of spectrum than cellular technologies. The new narrowband radios allow for greater spectral efficiency. The FCC also reallocated the narrowband public safety spectrum from the lower VHF and UHF spectrum. This spectrum will be auctioned and reallocated for commercial use up to the Upper 700 MHz band dedicated to public safety. The FCC required users of Narrowband equipment to start using new radios and base stations that use less spectrum. In 2013, public safety and industrial and business land mobile radio systems using the 150-174 MHz (VHF High band), consisting of 3.6 MHz of non-contiguous spectrum, and 421-470 MHz bands (UHF band), consisting of 3.7 MHz of non-contiguous spectrum, were required to switch from 25 kHz to 12.5 kHz radios, creating 24 kHz of new available spectrum.

A similar narrow-banding plan was put in place for the 470-512 MHz band (the T-Band) consisting of 6 to 12 MHz contiguous blocks used by public safety for two-way radios. The Middle Class Tax Relief and Job Creation Act of 2012, which provided funding for FirstNet's new 700 MHz public safety network, required that the FCC reallocate the T-band in two years for commercial use. The FCC is required to hold an auction of the T-band spectrum and the proceeds will be used to

New wireless technologies [that] have the ability to get more information through a given amount of bandwidth ...have played a significant role in delaying the spectrum crunch

PART THREE: REGULATORY

pay for the relocation of the Narrowband radios to the Upper 700 MHz spectrum reserved for public safety. The FCC, in 2014, set aside twenty-four 12.5 kHz channel pairs in 700 MHz (769-775 MHz and 799-805 MHz totaling 12 MHz) for this purpose. The Figure 15-3 below shows the narrowband public safety band plan.

Figure 15-3: Narrowbanding Public Safety Band Plan

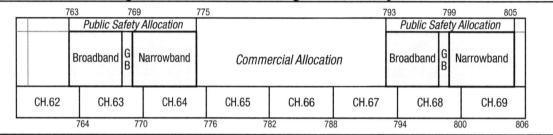

Source: FCC

The Narrowband radio, which is delivering voice and small text data, can use very small slices of spectrum. The FCC used the 12 MHz of Narrowband spectrum to assign 1920 channels or 960 pairs of up and down links at 6.25 kHz each. The pairs were divided into seven groups: 1) 64 pairs of Narrowband Interoperability channels administered by each state; 2) 616 pairs of General Use channels controlled by regional committees; 3) 48 pairs of General use allocated for relocated T-band public safety radios; 4) 192 pairs allocated to each state; 5) 16 pairs for airplane use; 6) 18 pairs for Low Power Channels used by terrestrial mobile administered regionally; and 7) 6 pairs of Low Power Channels dedicated to incident use on the ground not controlled regionally. Consolidating public safety use all into the same band of spectrum should insure that i) the spectrum assigned will be effectively used; ii) interference will be less likely than with public safety Narrowband use spread over various bands of spectrum; and iii) reallocating public safety from other bands effectively clears the band for commercial use, with the T-band being the best example of solid reallocation regulation.

Smaller than ideal blocks of spectrum and more users in a cell site degrade the performance as do interference factors such as physical obstructions (buildings)

6. Advanced Technologies are More Efficient

New wireless technologies have the ability to get more information through a fixed amount of bandwidth. Every time mobile providers believe that "everything that can be invented has been invented"[190] and that the only answer is allocating more exclusive spectrum to make sure the mobile industry will stay competitive, new concepts are created that deliver more from the same amount of spectrum. New

---

[190] The famous quote is misattributed to Charles Holland Duell, the commissioner of the United States Patent and Trademark Office from 1898 to 1901. The quote first appeared in Punch Almanac, 1899.

concepts keep reaching toward the data throughput ceiling per Hz of spectrum as determined by the Shannon-Hartley Theorem. The theorem set the maximum rate at which information can be transmitted over a frequency channel of a specified bandwidth in the presence of noise. For the mobile phone industry there are spectrum delivery techniques that took the industry from 1G to 5G without requiring more spectrum. These included AMPS, EDGE, WCDMA, HSPA, LTE, and LTE-TDD.

Figure 15-4 below graphically illustrates the improvements in spectrum utilization with various wireless technologies.

Figure 15-4: Downlink Bps/Hz by Spectrum Technologies[191]

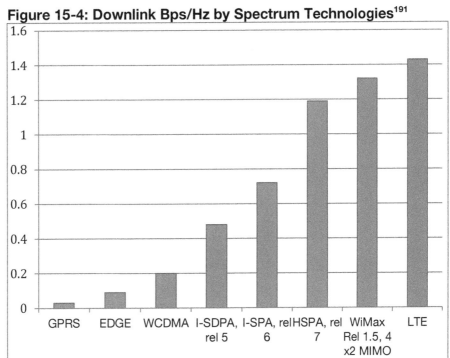

Source: FCC and Summit Ridge Group, LLC analysis

In addition to new radio technologies, other creative concepts have been implemented to better use existing available spectrum to increase throughput. These include beamforming antennas, MIMO antennas, spectrum aggregation within the handset, DAS, femtocells, and small cell densification. Also, at the more basic infrastructure

---

[191] 1 byte = 8 bits. The chart only displays the GSM/3GPP family of technologies. Performance of EV-DO standards is comparable with HSPA. *See* Letter from Dean R. Brenner, Vice Pres., Gov't Aff., Qualcomm Inc., to Marlene H. Dortch, Secretary, FCC, GN Docket No. 09-51 (Dec. 9, 2009). Figure shows downlink capacities calculated for 2x10MHz spectrum availability. Estimates of spectral efficiency calculated for each technology with the following antenna configuration: WCDMA, 1x1 and 1x2; HSPDA, Rel.5, 1x1; HSPA Rel. 6, 1x2; HSPA, Rel. 7, 1x1 and 1x2; LTE, 1x1 and 1x2. Information in this footnote is from the FCC – *National Broadband Plan*.

level, poor mobile service is more often attributable to (i) a carrier's limited build-outs in various pockets of urban areas that could be covered by distributed antenna systems (DAS), (ii) not building DAS or micro-cells inside buildings, (iii) or not deploying sufficient macro-cells on towers along on roadways.

The ability for the technologies to achieve the throughput performance indicated in Figure 15-4 is predicated on a number of factors. A lack of spectrum assignments, or a looming spectrum crunch, is more often not the cause of poor mobile service or slow speeds.

7. Broadband and LTE Technologies May Change Spectrum Needs

Broadband, LTE-TDD, and LTE-U technologies may significantly change the nature of spectrum needs.

a. More Downlink Spectrum Needed

In recent years the uplink-downlink asymmetric usage of the mobile service has increased significantly towards far more downlink than uplink. The introduction of mobile broadband has made it possible for users to apply the same behavior as they do with their fixed at home broadband. This has resulted in many asymmetric applications finding their way into mobile networks.

The FCC is considering fixing asymmetry as well as creating flexible band plans that allow for downlink expansion

Traditionally, wireless services had symmetrical demand for spectrum in both direction of use because each person in a voice conversation communicates about the same amount, both in transmitting and receiving voice calls. All early mobile standards, like AMPS and WCDMA, used uplink and downlink bands of equal amounts, with a guard band in the middle. As a result, all FCC and other countries' band plans allocated spectrum in equal sized pairs for uplink (from the handset to the base station) and downlink (from the base station to the handset). However, as Internet data traffic and video viewing has grown by mobile users, demand for capacity using spectrum down to the handset has greatly outpaced upward demand from the handset. Experts estimated that downlink traffic exceeded uplink traffic by a 4:1 ratio in 2005, but by 2011 had increased to as much as 30:1.[192]

---

[192] Stephan A. Wilkus, *TDD and Asymmetrical FDD*, presented at the FCC Band Plan Technical Forum (July 12, 2012) http://transition.fcc.gov/bureaus/oet/tac/tacdocs/meeting71612/PANEL2.2-Wilkus-Alcatel-Lucent.pdf. Al Jette estimates the ratio of downlink to uplink traffic at between 6 and 13 to 1. *See* Al Jette, *FCC Forum on the Future of Wireless Bands*, at 2-3 (July 16, 2012) http://transition.fcc.gov/bureaus/oet/tac/tacdocs/meeting71612/PANEL2.1-Jette-NokiaSiemensNetworks.pdf.

Downlink traffic is about twice as spectrally efficient as uplink traffic because the base station has a larger broadcasting antenna with more power delivering the data down than a smaller, lower powered handset delivering the data up. This offsets some, but not all of the difference. As a result of the higher demand for downlink spectrum, the future need for spectrum allocation in equal sized pairs is in doubt. An illustration of asymmetrical band plans is shown in Figure 15-5 below.

Figure 15-5: Asymmetrical Band Plans

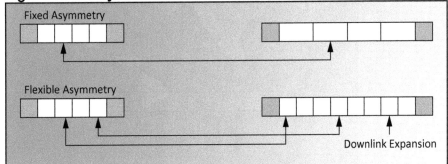

Source: FCC: Thoughts on Future Band Plans, July 2012.

To address asymmetrical usage, the FCC is considering non-paired spectrum allocations as well as creating flexible band plans that allow for downlink expansion on paired spectrum.

> ### b. Addressing Downlink Demand with LTE-TDD

LTE-FDD (Frequency Division Duplex) has traditionally been used by U.S. mobile providers. It requires symmetrically paired channels. For example, LTE-FDD was desired by carriers when the FCC conducted the Broadcast Incentive Auction, creating equal uplink and downlink pairs with a duplex gap in the middle. Until the recent 3.5 GHz proceeding, service providers have been reluctant to use LTE-TDD (Time Division Duplex). TDD uses one frequency block for both uplink and downlink but segments them by time to avoid interference. This often makes TDD better suited for asymmetrical traffic. However, large international operators such as China Mobile have been using LTE-TDD. As a result, a large number of handsets have chipsets capable of handling both LTE-FDD and LTE-TDD. These handsets are expected to become widely used in the coming years. Because of the 1.3 billion mobile handset market in China today, with 772 million of the users accessing the Internet on mobile phones, there is an assumption that LTE-TDD base stations and handsets chipsets have been driven down in price and are ready for use in the U.S. China Mobile, which has 60% of the China market with 670 million subscribers, uses LTE-TDD, as do the two other providers, China Telecom and China Unicom. An illustration of FDD and TTD band is shown in Figure 15-6 below.

Figure 15-6: FDD and TDD Frequency Usage

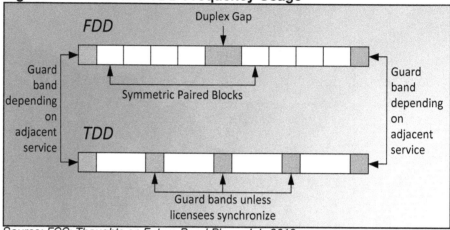

Source: FCC: Thoughts on Future Band Plans, July 2012

The new FCC 3.5 GHz CBRS band, which will allocate 150 MHz for mobile use, is being designed principally for LTE-TDD. The CBRS spectrum will include 10 MHz channels that can be combined up to 40 MHz for licensed and up a potential 150 MHz of licensed and unlicensed spectrum. The spectrum, using LTE-TDD, will not be paired, and there will be no duplex gaps. Not requiring paired spectrum channels is ideal for spectrum sharing where the amount and location of the spectrum can change from minute to minute. The mobile carriers have embraced LTE-TDD for this spectrum. When the C-band is approved, there will be a possiblity of using 450 MHz of spectrum for LTE-TDD when combined with CBRS. Thus, Summit Ridge Group believes that moving forward, most new spectrum plans may be in single non-paired blocks.

The FCC is focused on making additional low-, mid-, and high-band spectrum available for 5G services

c. Planning for a 5G Future

The U.S. is working to lead the world in 5G. The new networks and technologies made available by 5G will enable faster speeds and low latency wireless broadband services. 5G requires capital spending on new or upgraded base stations and moving to new spectrum. Also, 5G may require users to purchase new handsets, as current handsets may not operate in the spectrum used by 5G or its protocols like LTE-TDD. To help deliver 5G, the FCC has been working with several bands to implement a strategy that will ensure that the U.S. is the first to introduce the innovative technologies needed for 5G. FCC

Chairman Pai emphasized the importance of the 5G effort, saying, "Forward-thinking spectrum policy, modern infrastructure policy, and market-based network regulation form the heart of our strategy for realizing the promise of the 5G future." To assist in accelerating this process, FCC Chairman Pai formed a Broadband Deployment Advisory Committee (BDAC) in 2017. The purpose of the BDAC is principally aimed at creating a smooth roadway for installing small cells on poles and buildings with five committees such as the Removing State and Local Regulatory Barriers committee and the Streamlining Federal Siting committee.

To modernize infrastructure policy, controlled by the FCC's tower and pole rules and state and municipal laws, the FCC is working to eliminate unnecessary barriers to a cost and time effective implementation of the small cell and back-haul fiber needed to support 5G. This communications technology will depend on robust infrastructure, operating over both traditional cell towers and smaller deployments, such as small cells, to augment the data driven uses of 5G that will expand exponentially in the coming years. To promote market-based network regulation, the FCC states it seeks to actively reduce regulatory barriers to entry to further investment in 5G networks and that it endeavors to bring digital opportunity to every American.

To modernize infrastructure... the FCC is working to eliminate unnecessary barriers to a cost and time effective implementation of the small cell and back-haul fiber needed to support 5G

In addition, to pave the way for 5G, the FCC opened active spectrum reallocation proceedings for creating new low-band, mid-band, and high-band spectrum available for 5G services. The FCC, as required by Congress, acted first by auctioning in 2016 the 600 MHz bands in the Broadcast Incentive Auction in the low-band, promulgating new Part 96 rules creating a shared spectrum framework in the 3.5 GHz mid-band, and opening a proceeding to explore and define the next steps for terrestrial use of the 3.7 GHz mid-band occupied primarily by satellite, and reallocating high-band spectrum millimeter wave, or mmW, from 28-90 GHz.

B. Mobile Wireless Industry Spectrum Dynamics

The mobile wireless industry is one of the nation's most significant. In the U.S., $315 billion has been invested in the wireless industry since 2005. The mobile carriers spend around $10 billion in capital expense every year on network infrastructure. Globally, the mobile industry is growing rapidly in almost every country, with a total of 5.1 billion

PART THREE: REGULATORY

mobile users.[193] Consequently, finding sufficient spectrum for mobile broadband uses large portions of the resources of spectrum regulators worldwide.

1. Bands Used

The mobile industry uses a patchwork of frequencies in the following bands between 600 MHz and 2.7 GHz:

Mobile wireless services use a patchwork of frequencies between 700MHz and 2.7 GHz.

- **600 MHz:** 84 MHz of paired spectrum and a duplex guard band for LTE-FDD.

- **700 MHz:** 84 MHz using primarily LTE-FDD

- **800 MHz AMPS:** FCC permitted LTE use in 2017, formerly operating with CDMA and other protocols

- **1 GHz PCS:** 1850-1910 MHz and 1930-1990 MHz

- **L-band:** 1.6 GHz band. Satellite broadcasters are allocated 1482.352-1490.624 MHz, and 1525-1646.5 MHz is used for satellite radio and satellite telephony. The L-band is also for radio astronomy, military and GPS

- **S-band:** 2.0 GHz band

- **AWS-1:** 1710-1755 MHz and 2110-2155 MHz

- **WCS:** 2305-2310 MHz used for fixed, mobile, radiolocation or broadcast-satellite services

- **EBS/BRS:** 2.5-2.7 GHz Sprint holds most of its spectrum and uses it for its 4G network.

A Detailed analysis of mobile wireless spectrum bands can be found in Chapter XIII of this *Handbook*. Spectrum holding of major US wireless carriers is shown in the Allnet Insight and Analytics charts in Appendix A of this *Handbook*.

2. Managing Growth in Demand is Difficult

Mobile wireless services are relatively new, compared to services such as AM radio and television, but clearly grown rapidly while AM radio and TV have diminished in equal significance. Only 20% of U.S. homes watch over-the-air TV, which is an increase as cable customers have cut their cable TV service en masse. AM radio is a mere shadow of what it was in the 1960's. Starting in 1983, analog mobile wireless services was offered in the 800 MHz band. As

---

[193] CTIA, Infographics Library, *The Wireless Industry: Industry Data* https://www.ctia.org/the-wireless-industry/infographics-library.

demand grew and wireless services began to offer digital services, the FCC allocated additional spectrum to mobile wireless services, starting with the PCS spectrum at 1850-1990 MHz. Since 2006, the AWS (2 GHz band) and EBS/BRS (2.5 GHz) spectrum have also been allocated. Since 2006, spectrum available for cellular services has grown from 170-2,943 MHz (see Figures 15-7 and 15-8 below).

By one estimate, mobile data traffic will grow at a compound annual growth rate of 47% between 2016 and 2021.[194] Managing this growth has been a challenge for the FCC. Industry observers expect growth in additional services such as the Internet of Things (IoT) communications.[195]

Figure 15-7: Significant Growth in Mobile Spectrum

Band	Frequency	MHz	Year Added
Cellular	850 MHz	50 MHz	1981
PCS	1900 MHz	120 MHz	1994
SMR	900 MHz	14 MHz	2007
600 MHz	600 MHz	70 MHz	2017
700 MHz	700 MHz	70 MHz	2008
Add'l PCS	1900 MHz	10 MHz	2009
AWS-1	1710 MHz	90 MHz	2006
AWS-3	1700 MHz	65 MHz	2015
AWS-4	2000 MHz	40 MHz	2012
WCS	2400 MHz	20 MHz	2010
EBS/BRS	2500 MHz	194 MHz	2013
Total MHz: 743 MHz			

Source: FCC and Summit Ridge Group, LLC analysis

---

[194] *Cisco Visual Networking Index (VNI) Global Mobile Data Traffic Forecast Update 2016-2021, supra* at note 175.

[195] Jose Del Rosario, The Bottom Line, *The Cellular Threat to SCADA/M2M* (Jan. 8, 2013) http://www.nsr.com/news-resources/the-bottom-line/the-cellular-threat-to-satellite-scadam2m/.

PART THREE: REGULATORY

Figure 15-8: Future Growth in Mobile Spectrum

Band	Frequency	MHz	Year Added
CBRS	3.5 GHz	150 MHz	2018
C-Band	3.7 GHz	500 MHz	2018 NPRM
24 GHz	24 GHz	700 MHz	2018 Auction 102
28 GHz	28 GHz	850 MHz	2019 Auction 101
Total MHz: 2200 MHz			

Source: FCC and Summit Ridge Group, LLC analysis

An analysis by Oppenheimer & Co. estimates that approximately 250 MHz of the 414 MHz of mobile spectrum below 2.5 GHz has been built out.[196] To further increase mobile spectrum, the FCC has begun to move towards allowing Mobile Satellite Service (MSS) spectrum holders to use their spectrum terrestrially without handsets that also operate through the satellite. This essentially allows MSS spectrum license holders to use their spectrum like traditional mobile spectrum.

If an entity only makes use of its leased frequency range at certain times, the spectrum should be able to be subleased to another party at other times to increase efficiency

Innovations in technology have been a significant driver of efficiency in spectrum use. Technological developments, such as multi-antenna signal processing (MAS), MIMO antenna, small cell densification, advanced protocols like LTE-U, and spectrum sharing database regulation have allowed certain services to be provided in the same way while using less spectrum. Spectrum requirements are being reduced due to technical improvements that reduce interference and small cell rollouts. When the FCC changed its policy in 2008 to allow wireless services providers to switch their analog services to digital services, previously used spectrum became available for new purposes since the transmission of digital signals requires less spectrum than that of analog signals many countries still use. In 2017, the FCC in its Cellular Service Reform order again gave mobile carriers the authority to use 4G LTE in spectrum previous authorized for 3G WCDMA.[197] The transition of television broadcasting to digital

---

[196] Tim Horan, Oppenheimer & Co., *Spectrum White Paper* (Mar. 7, 2013).

[197] *Amendment of Parts 1 and 22 of the Commission's Rules with Regard to the Cellular Service, Including Changes in Licensing of Unserved Area; Amendment of the Commission's Rules with Regard to Relocation of Part 24 to Part 27; Interim Restrictions and Procedures for Cellular Service Applications; Amendment of Parts 0, 1, and 22 of the Commission's Rules with Regard to Frequency Coordination for the Cellular Service; Amendment of the Commission's Rules Governing Radiated Power Limits for the Cellular Service*, Second Report and Order and Second Further Notice of Proposed Rulemaking WT Docket No. 12-40, RM 11510 and 11660, 32 FCC Rcd 2518 (2017)

(discussed in depth in Chapter IX.C of this *Handbook*) has also facilitated repacking television stations and provided significant additional spectrum for mobile wireless service providers. This additional spectrum created by the vacating UHF TV stations was referred to by the FCC as the "Digital Dividend."

3. Cell-Splitting Has Limits

Splitting mobile wireless cells into smaller areas greatly increases frequency reuse, which, in turn, increases capacity for wireless operators. However, cell splitting has limits. As cells get smaller, placement options for antennas become more limited. As cell sites are reduced to below a few hundred meters, the number of possible locations for antennas for a particular cell declines. Moreover, these locations may not be available in certain urban environments leaving "holes" in coverage that frustrate consumers. As mentioned above, the FCC put together a task force to help change FCC, state, and local regulations allowing faster approval for small cells. The FCC pole attachment rules allow mobile carriers to use poles for small cell placement. Poles are where both fiber back-haul and electricity are within easy access. Currently, the limits of cell splitting are not a major issue in the U.S., which has cell site density approximately one-fifth of the level found in Japan. However, in 2018, small cell placement began a rapid upturn in urban areas across the country.

4. Spectrum Sharing May Increase Usage Efficiency

Spectrum sharing using a database connected over the Internet to flexible base stations is the second method of creating spectrum efficiencies. Spectrum sharing opens up under-utilized spectrum to entities that do not need to purchase the spectrum and allows carriers seeking better interference protection to purchase licenses of county size areas that provide more protection than the no-cost licenses. In spectrum from 54-698 MHz, TV White Space providers can use unlicensed spectrum, as long as it is available and not built-out by the license holder. The idea is that if a service provider only makes use of its leased frequency range at certain times, the spectrum should be able to be subleased to another party, or used at no cost, at other times to increase efficiency. Spectrum sharing is complex and requires policy changes to determine the technical conditions under which no-cost licensed users can access spectrum without interfering with the higher-tiered licensed users.

Spectrum sharing is one of the simplest methods to incentivize carriers to build-out purchased licenses because no-cost licensees can use a competitor's fallow spectrum until it becomes operational. As discussed by the 2012 PCAST report, the government believes that sharing spectrum will make spectrum abundant by multiplying the capacity of this commercial spectrum by a factor of 1,000.[198]

As the demand for spectrum increases in urban areas, wireless companies will seek to add higher frequency spectrum in urban areas where it is more readily available

5. Offloading is a Significant Strategy

Wi-Fi is the most common form of spectrum sharing, even though mobile carriers and end users do not always consider Wi-Fi offload as sharing. Smartphones are designed to move users off the mobile network and on to Wi-Fi when entering an approved area like home or work. The benefit to operators is enormous because Wi-Fi lowers cost to deliver a more densified infrastructure of microcells or small cells. When the user moves over to Wi-Fi, the mobile carrier is no longer providing service to the user. Wi-Fi at home is provided by the user's fixed Internet provider, typically the cable company. When watching the same amount of video while traveling outside of Wi-Fi, users can quickly reach the data caps implemented by their respective carriers. Even femtocells, referred to sometimes as extenders, allow the mobile operator to take advantage of the user's home Internet provider by offloading the user's voice and data through the femtocell and not through the operator's wireless infrastructure. Cisco reported that in 2016, 60% of global wireless traffic was offloaded via Wi-Fi and femtocells, thus more traffic was offloaded from cellular networks onto Wi-Fi than remained on cellular networks. That offloading is expected to increase to 63% in 2021.[199]

While it saves carriers money by eliminating unneeded infrastructure capital, offloading can be accomplished almost transparently without knowledge of the end user. Cable companies providing the actual service do not receive customer credit for delivering a superb wireless experience to the end-user through the home Wi-Fi. Cable companies have been working in the last few years to build the Wi-Fi experience out of the home. Cable companies' Wi-Fi access points are located on the fiber on the poles, and in shared Wi-Fi access points in buildings. Cable providers are giving free access to their customers and selling Wi-Fi access to non-cable customers. They are also creating service plans that use Wi-Fi in the geographies served by the cable companies, supplemented by MVNO agreements with carriers

---

[198] *PCAST Report, supra* note 76, at vi.
[199] *Cisco VNI,* 11-12.

when the user travels. Summit Ridge Group expects the trend toward greater Wi-Fi offloading to increase dramatically, with the strong possibility that several cable companies could become mobile operators primarily using unlicensed spectrum for Wi-Fi.[200] If one or more of the large cable providers enters the mobile business, the traditional mobile carriers could see strong downward pricing pressure, lower ARPU, and higher customer expectations with respect to data speeds and data caps. Moreover, if the cable companies succeed in using outdoor unlicensed service and 3.5 GHz no-cost "license by rule," called General Authorized Access, or GAA (3.5 GHz CBRS GAA is discussed in detail in Part II), to deliver ultra-fast, no data cap limit service, and begin poaching end users from mobile carriers, then there will be downward valuation pressure of licensed spectrum.

a. Wi-Fi Handoffs: Emulating the Mobile Experience

One of the more significant issues with using Wi-Fi as a substitute for mobile service is the seamless voice handoff between Wi-Fi access points, without the loss of the voice call between the access points. Mobile carriers solved this problem long ago but Wi-Fi was not designed for mobile service. This problem is being addressed in two ways. The Wi-Fi Alliance has created a standard called Passpoint to allow for a mobile user to travel between access points without losing a call. Passpoint is built into the Wi-Fi access point and allows for the automatic discovery of new networks through seamless and secure authentication and encrypted data transfer.

Another method that Summit Ridge Group believes will be implemented by the cable companies taking advantage of offloading by using LTE-TDD and the new 3.5 GHz CBRS, is spectrum sharing with no-cost GAA licenses. The 3.5 GHz CBRS will give mobile users with LTE-TDD smartphones the ability to move from GAA small cell to small cell with delivering all the benefits of a mobile operator. Cable companies already have Wi-Fi access points on aerial fiber and can simply add 3.5 GHz CBRS small cells to the fiber. Cable companies already have back-haul and power, through HFC cables in place. Cable companies also have brand names and customers using their Wi-Fi. Cable company customers may be enticed away from mobile

---

[200] Republic Wireless, for example, is a small mobile operator that offers service primarily on Wi-Fi and supplements this with MVNO roaming agreements with major carriers when a user is out of Wi-Fi range.

PART THREE: REGULATORY

carriers, as they will potentially receive much greater throughput speeds with Wi-Fi and CBRS and unlimited data without caps. Summit Ridge views mobile users transitioning to cable companies as a great opportunity for cable companies and a great threat for mobile operators. The new 3.5 GHz CBRS regulations that the mobile operators have been pressing for in order to add more spectrum to solve their perceived spectrum crunch could open a Pandora's box of competition, not expected. CBRS 3.5 GHz GAA will start operating in late 2018.

b. Access Network Discovery and Selection Function (ANDSF)

Access network discovery and selection function (ANDSF) is a set of standards currently being developed by 3GPP that provides a dynamic rules-based approach to selecting the best network to use based upon conditions the operator chooses. ANDSF gives devices the ability to access networks such as Wi-Fi and WIMAX that can be used for data communication in addition to LTE networks to achieve improved interoperability between cellular and Wi-Fi networks.

6. Spectrum Portfolio Diversity Becoming Increasingly Important

Given the proliferation of spectrum bands and the increasing cost of making advanced handsets..., [hardware] interoperability ...is becoming a significant issue

Wireless companies are petitioning for higher frequency spectrum to take advantage of new technologies like spectrum sharing and micro antenna advances for mmW spectrum. As mentioned previously, the spectrum is 3.5 GHZ for spectrum sharing and 28 GHz for mmW. This spectrum is needed in urban areas where it is readily available. In some respect, this higher frequency spectrum is better suited for small cell sites in urban areas, but it suffers from weaker building penetration. For example, an analysis by Nokia suggests that indoor penetration using 900 MHz can be 60-130% greater than using 2100 MHz. [201] Despite the limitation caused by brick walls, higher frequencies are critical to providing sufficient capacity in densely populated high-use areas. Radio access network (known as RAN) engineers can place small cells indoors to solve the indoor problem. The indoor 3.5 GHz CBRS small cells can cost as little as $1000 and can be located indoors just like Wi-Fi access points. Wireless operators will also need to cover rural areas where large cell sites provide the most economical way to cover vast areas. In rural areas, spectrum below 1 GHz is most desirable. Also, to spectrum required

---

[201] Nokia Siemens Networks, *WCDMA Frequency Refarming* (2014)
https://onestore.nokia.com/asset/200310

in rural areas, towers needed for wide coverage are limited and costly. The towers are almost always objected to by the area residents as unsightly blights on the landscape. Mobile providers are exploring methods of building towers that are more pleasing to the eye such as making them look like trees, using tethered aerostat balloons, and concealing macrocells inside church steeples. To accomplish the goals of delivering better quality and making it more ubiquitous, service wireless operators will need a diverse portfolio of spectrum and technologies to handle the environments that they serve.

7. Interoperability Becoming a Significant Issue

Given the proliferation of spectrum bands and the increasing cost of making advanced handsets capable of working on multiple bands, interoperability (handsets that can operate on all service providers' spectrum) is becoming a significant issue. In 2012, the FCC opened a rule making proceeding for the Lower 700 MHz band indicating its desire that all handsets made for the Lower 700 MHz band work on all channels within the Lower 700 MHz band. This was particularly important to licensees of the 6 MHz in the band's A Block of spectrum. Licensees of this block cannot use the full 6 MHz due to a requirement not to interfere with the then existing adjacent TV Channel 51. As a result, smaller wireless operators typically bid for the more affordable A Block at auction. Licensees of the more attractive spectrum blocks had little incentive to ask equipment manufacturers to make handsets to work on the A Block. Moreover, equipment manufacturers did not have the economies of scale to make handsets at attractive prices for smaller operators on this block. As a result, valuable spectrum was underutilized. Hence, the FCC stepped in with the RM-11592 to require interoperability so that handsets would be able to work on the full 700 MHz band, thus maximizing its use. As more spectrum becomes available, similar interoperability issues will arise. One advantage of the FCC's 3.5 GHz CBRS spectrum sharing regulations, is that LTE-TDD smartphones will be able to operate on all the available 150 MHz of spectrum licensed to all the providers of CBRS base stations. Smartphones have carrier specific chipsets and software to deliver the full array of carrier bells-and-whistles service, but the LTE-TDD handsets will, regardless, be able to operate on any CBRS LTE radio. It should be noted that LTE-TDD is not required to be used in 3.5 GHz CBRS. Many fixed, and possibly some mobile providers, will use other protocols, both standards-based and proprietary.

8. Thoughts on Valuation

In the past, the lower frequency mobile wireless bands were the most valuable, due to their greater coverage, and propagation capability. In particular, it was thought that if a band was unencumbered, without needing to grandfather or work around former licensees and had equipment and chips sets available for the band, that the valuations would be higher. However the 2015 AWS-3 auction, covering various blocks from 1175-2180 MHz, resulted in a surprise $45 billion in spectrum purchases, which was far above the $10-20 billion expected. The 2017 Broadcast Incentive Auction resulted in only $19 billion in license sales far below the $86 billion hoped for by the TV station. This meant a reverse of the traditional concept that lower spectrum had more value to mobile carriers than higher spectrum.

There were many factors for the shift in focus from acquiring low-band spectrum to middle and high bands, but one of the possible factors was that some of the major mobile operators may have begun to view the 3.5 GHz CBRS spectrum with 150 MHz available and the higher mmW spectrum, as better spectrum to roll out small cells in urban areas. It is in urban areas where larger populations live, of course. Larger populations will typically deliver better revenue for less infrastructure cost than rural areas. Also, the higher 3.5 GHz CBRS is more adaptable to densification and lower interference (because of tighter spectrum masks) than 600 MHz. Summit Ridge Group thus expects the future values of higher frequency spectrum, such as the 3.5 GHz band and the mmW bands to increase. Industry-wide, however, there is little consensus on the rate of future growth on which bands will be more valued. It is becoming clear that mobile carriers are working to have alternatives and to be capable of using low, middle, and high bands to deliver quality mobile service inside and outside buildings, on the highways, and in rural areas.

...the emerging consensus in the industry is that [spectrum sharing related] interference issues are manageable with modern technology

C. Unlicensed Spectrum/Spectrum Sharing

The challenge of allocating sufficient licensed spectrum to mobile broadband has led to new ideas. The most prominent of these is shared spectrum. The FCC has allocated several bands for low-powered unlicensed services. These are particularly common for devices using small amounts of bandwidth on a short-term basis over short distances. Such devices include the Internet of Things (IoT), machine-to-machine (M2M) devices, remote cameras, heart monitors, RFID, Bluetooth, Zigbee, and remote-control devices for household appliances. Generally, these uses are uncontroversial since the limited transmission range and power avoids interference, and spectrum capacity limits are rarely an issue. However, governments around the world are examining the prospect of making additional unlicensed (shared) spectrum available for mobile broadband through Wi-Fi and other technologies. These new broadband applications raise more complex interference issues. While the debate is far from settled, emerging consensus in the industry is that interference issues are manageable with modern technology. Consequently, the debate is now turning to how to manage interference in shared spectrum and how conservative the rules should be put in place to protect the rights of priority users.

1. Bands for Unlicensed or Spectrum Sharing Broadband

The following bands are used for spectrum sharing or are unlicensed:

- 54-698 MHz TV White Spaces (on available channels)

- 902-928 MHz cordless phones, garage openers

- 1920-1930 MHz Unlicensed Personal Communications Service

- 2400-2483 MHz Wi-Fi Bluetooth, Zigbee, RFID, Microwave ovens

- 3550-3700 MHz CBRS-Citizens Broadband Radio Service licensed

- 5150-5350 & 5470-5825 MHz Wi-Fi

- 76-77 GHz unlicensed Long-range vehicular radars (LRRs)

Unlicensed spectrum, or ISM (industrial, scientific and medical), radio bands may be the most efficiently used spectrum.[202] The ISM band was created in 1947 by the ITU for use by microwave ovens. In 1985, the FCC approved the use of spread spectrum for the unlicensed 2.4 GHz, a concept opposed by the equipment makers. One engineer on the FCC staff, Michael Marcus, conceived and promoted the use of unlicensed use for spread spectrum. Wi-Fi was created in the 1990s and branded by the Wi-Fi Alliance in 1999.

Steve Jobs first promoted unlicensed wireless networking after seeing

---

[202] Note: Unlicensed spectrum is generally associated with ISM bands which are allocated to spread-spectrum unlicensed use. However, U-NII (used by IEEE-802.11a devices) also falls into this category. Moreover, unlicensed use at very low power levels is allowed in most bands. As a result of the foregoing, the definition of unlicensed frequency bands is complex.

a demonstration of the product by Lucent Technologies for Wireless LAN in 1999 which led him to include the Lucent card in the Apple iBook using the Apple Airport base station – the first Wi-Fi router and access point.[203] Wi-Fi, which uses contention-based radios for limiting interference and 2.4 GHz spread spectrum, has been an enormous success. The shared spectrum success of Wi-Fi, as well as the U.S. government's under-use of potentially valuable spectrum is driving the government towards a sharing model for maximizing its use of the spectrum. As discussed above, much of the spectrum that might be allocated to mobile broadband is currently in the hands of federal government agencies whose use is often inefficient. Since moving these agencies is difficult and costly, spectrum sharing is an appealing policy.

Wi-Fi equipment operators have embedded low-cost radar detection chips in their devices – a primitive form of cognitive radio

2. Precedent for sharing government spectrum

Wi-Fi and airport weather radar systems share the same 5 GHz band which set a precedent for government users being able to share spectrum with private users. Airports use Terminal Doppler Weather Radar, or TDWR, for wind-sheer detection, in the 5600-5650 MHz band. In 2014, the FCC issued an order allowing for unlicensed equipment, including 802.11ac, to use low-cost radar detection chipsets, or receiving sensors, in their outdoor unlicensed devices. When the unlicensed access point receives a signal that TDWR is operating nearby, the unlicensed access point stops operating in the TDWR spectrum. As a result of the 2014 order authorizing spectrum sharing using the sensors, new available unlicensed spectrum use was expanded in the 5 GHz band from 160-480 MHz.[204] The 480 MHz of spectrum increased throughput from a theoretical maximum of 1.8 Gbps to 5.5 Gbps.

Most industry observers believe that sharing is now technically viable in most frequency bands used by the federal government

Most industry observers cited the 5 GHz spectrum sharing order as a great success. But exporting this simple model to other frequencies like 3.5 GHz was more complex. Unlike 5 GHz that requires a simple sensor to detect nearby TDWR radar causing the base station to turn off, with 3.5 GHz spectrum sharing a cloud database and external sensors are required because i) the Navy radar is moving up and down the coast requiring special DoD approved external sensors and

---

[203] Cees Links, *The Secret Success of Steve Jobs: Wireless Internet,* EE Times (Oct. 12, 2011) https://www.eetimes.com/author.asp?section_id=36&doc_id=1266019.

[204] *Revision of Part 15 of the Commission's Rules to Permit Unlicensed National Information Infrastructure (UNII) Devices in the 5 GHz Band,* First Report and Order, ET Docket No. 13-49, 29 FCC Rcd 4127 (2014); 47 C.F.R. Part 15 Subpart E— Unlicensed National Information Infrastructure Devices.

delivering on-off only information to the database which in turn sends direction to hundreds of base stations to move channels off of the Navy radar and ii) the fixed satellite service (FSS) earth stations are receive-only requiring a database to calculate the FSS interference boundary needed to protect the FSS from CBRS base stations that could, depending on power levels, antenna height, antenna direction, and terrain, interfere with the FSS earth station. This asymmetry is not present in most other government uses so more complex systems are required to ensure compliance by lower priority users. Still, dynamic spectrum allocation technology is rapidly being developed across several bands (for more detail, see Chapter XV.C of this *Handbook*). Most industry observers believe that sharing is now technically viable in most frequency bands used by the federal government.

D. Broadcasters (Television and Radio)

Television broadcasters occupy 210 MHz of prime spectrum that many observers suggest is underutilized. Consequently, regulators and industry participants have focused significant attention on how to reallocate this spectrum efficiently.

1. Bands Used

The broadcast industry uses the following bands:

- **AM Radio:** 540 kHz to 1.7 MHz

- **FM Radio:** 92.1-107.9 MHz

- **VHF Television:** 54-88 MHz and 174-216 MHz

- **UHF Television:** 470-698 MHz

2. Major Business and Regulatory Issues

The FCC issues television broadcasting licenses in 210 Television Market Areas (TMAs) for seven-year terms. Television broadcasting licenses are 6 MHz each with 6 MHz guard bands on each side. From a macroeconomic perspective, U.S. broadcast television is in a secular decline. At the time of the 2009 transition, it was estimated that only 10% of homes watched over the air TV and it was expected that local over the air TV was facing its demise. However, by 2012, it had grown to an estimated 17%. In 2018, a study determined that cable TV "cord-cutters" were using digital antennas in 20% of U.S.

Television broadcasting licenses are 6 MHz each

PART THREE: REGULATORY

broadband homes to watch local TV.[205] In 2018, 74% of households now subscribe to pay TV, either satellite (DBS) or cable television, rather than broadcast television and the number, though large, is falling.[206]

The FCC has thrice reduced the allocation for television broadcasting services over the past 30 years. In 1983, UHF channels 70-83 (806 MHz-890 MHz) were re-allocated to the initial analog wireless services. In 2009 when the U.S. started the digital conversion of television broadcasters, channels 52-69 (698 MHz-806 MHz) were "repacked" into lower channels. This opened the way for auctions of the 700 MHz band for mobile wireless. The FCC began the third reduction of 84 MHz of the industry's 294 MHz in an incentive auction to eliminate another 20 additional channels in 2016.[207] When the digital TV transition was completed in 2009 many economists believed that the over the air TV spectrum would be better used if it were allocated for broadband and mobile service providers. This pressure along with the TV stations' belief that local broadcasts were declining, gave impetus for creating the TV Incentive Auction proceeding. Mobile carriers had become a better choice for spectrum use than local TV, many mobile industry leaders contended. The FCC created a win-win proceeding with the Incentive Auction.

TV stations also believed their market value was dropping as advertisers moved to the Internet, and in 2016 many UHF stations bid to close or relocate and successfully sold rights to their assigned spectrum in the Broadcast Incentive Auction. The other reason for

The FCC did not conduct auctions when it initially allocated television broadcasting spectrum

---

[205] 14 million homes (or 18% of the total cable homes and 11% of all homes in the U.S.) are using broadband only. Adweek, Jason Lynch, *The Number of OTT-Only U.S. Homes Has Tripled* (Mar. 2018) https://www.adweek.com/tv-video/the-number-of-ott-only-u-s-homes-has-tripled-over-the-last-5-years/ and 20% of broadband only homes use digital TV antennas for local over the air TV, MulitChannel News, Jeff Baumgartner, *Study: 20% of U.S. Broadband Homes Use Antenna for TV* (Mar. 15, 2018) https://www.multichannel.com/news/study-20-us-broadband-homes-use-antenna-tv-418705; 18% of all U.S. homes watch over the air TV. *See*, NAB, *Over-the-air TV Viewership Soars to 54 Million Americans* (June 18, 2012) https://www.nab.org/documents/newsroom/pressRelease.asp?id=2761.

[206] Although pay TV is suffering from downward pressure caused by cord cutting, a study showed that homes are staying with pay TV primarily because it is bundled with Internet. *See*, BGR, Chris Mills, *The number of cord-cutters has tripled in the last 5 years* (Mar. 28, 2018) https://bgr.com/2018/03/28/cord-cutting-best-streaming-services-2018-vs-cable/ Pay TV homes dropped from 84% in 2014, to 79% in 2017, to 74% in 2018, MulitChannel News, Jeff Baumgartner, *Pay TV Universe Shrinks to 79% of U.S. Households* (Sept. 26, 2017) https://www.broadcastingcable.com/news/pay-tv-universe-shrinks-79-us-households-168927.

[207] The number of channels may be reduced by less than 20 (120 MHz reclaimed at 6 MHz per channel) if some existing stations agree to share 6 MHz license allocations. The FCC may also elect to reclaim less than 120 MHz.

FCC's relocating and repacking the TV channels was that TV digital service created large amounts of available spectrum giving the FCC the opportunity to move the remaining stations close together, creating a large swath of spectrum that could be used for mobile service. As a result, there has been a global movement to reallocate spectrum from television broadcasting to mobile services.

In an interesting twist, there is a small movement to allow low power television operators the authority to provide broadband service.[208] If the technical spectrum and hardware issues could be resolved, this might ease the conflict between television broadcasters and wireless broadband operators.

E. Satellite Communications Spectrum Dynamics

The satellite industry is focused on higher spectrum bands, but regulators and terrestrial mobile operators have targeted several of its lower bands for reallocation.

1. Bands Used

- **L-band**: Satellite broadcasters are allocated the 1482.352-1490.624 MHz and 1525-1646.5 MHz bands. The former is used primarily for satellite radio and related services while the latter is for satellite telephony (MSS) services. The middle of the band is reserved for radio astronomy, military and satellite positioning systems such as the U.S. GPS, the European Galileo, and the Russian GLONASS systems.

- **S-band:** 2.0-2.7 GHZ. This is used primarily for satellite radio services as well as mobile satellite services.

- **C-band:** 3.4-4.3 GHz (receive) and 4.25-6.425 GHz (transmit). Used primarily for satellite transmission and desirable in tropical areas due to its resistance to rain fade. Many countries are considering reallocating the lower portion of the receive band for terrestrial broadband, which is mainly used by Fixed Satellite Service (FSS) operators. A disadvantage of C-band is that it requires larger antennas on the ground.

- **Ku-band:** 12-18 GHz. Used primarily in satellite communications. Most commercial satellite television signals

The satellite industry is seeing a trend of regulatory action to reallocate or share satellite spectrum to support terrestrial applications

PART THREE: REGULATORY

---

[208] *See,* Broadcast Engineering, *Group Propose to Allow LPTV Stations to Deliver Wireless Broadband Service* (June 2, 2011) http://www.tvtechnology.com/news/group-pushes-proposal-to-allow-lptv-stations-to-deliver-wireless-broadband-service.

over the U.S. and Europe are transmitted in Ku-band. Although not as resistant to rain fade as C-band, its higher frequency allows consumers to use much smaller reception antennas. This band is used for DBS services (12.2-12.7 GHz) and FSS (12-14 GHz). It is also used for terrestrial mobile.

- **Ka-band:** 26.5-40 GHz. This satellite band was the newest addition to the commercial FSS bands. It has historically suffered from significant weather-related interference, making it less valuable than C-band and Ku-band. However, higher-powered satellites developed over the past 10-15 years have largely overcome this problem. This band is heavily used in state-of-the-art satellite broadband systems. Local Multipoint Distribution Service (LMDS) is a terrestrial technology that operates in the Ka-band at 28-31 GHz to transmit signals from a single point to multiple points or a single point.

2. Major Business and Regulatory Issues

The satellite industry is seeing a trend of regulatory action to reallocate or share satellite spectrum to support terrestrial applications. Three major instances of this trend include:

The satellite industry is seeing a trend of regulatory action to reallocate or share satellite spectrum to support terrestrial applications

1) C-band spectrum has been underutilized by satellite operators in many regions. This is particularly in areas not subject to heavy rainfall, a condition that favors robust C-band transmissions. It is also increasingly feasible to use this band terrestrially due to the need for small cell sites in urban areas. Many countries are seeking to reallocate the lower portion of this band for terrestrial or dual satellite/terrestrial use to ease the spectrum crunch. Until recently, satellite operators have resisted this reallocation pressure. Starting in 2017, however, some satellite providers began to suggest a process where they could sell 500 MHz of C-band spectrum to mobile carriers. Tests performed by the Broadband Access Coalition demonstrated that the 3.7-4.2 GHz C-band downlink spectrum could be safely shared, although some of the satellite operators disputed the test results. If the FCC adopts the plan in its 2017 proposed rulemaking proceeding, 100 MHz of the 500 MHz would be cleared and made available for mobile use, while the other 400 MHz would be shared.[209] There has been a mixed reception of this initiative, however. Virtually every United States TV and

---

[209] *Expanding Flexible Use in Mid-Band Spectrum between 3.7 and 24 GHz*, Public Notice GN Docket No. 17-183, 32 FCC Rcd 5575 (Jul 13, 2017) https://www.fcc.gov/document/public-notice-establishing-gn-docket-number-17-183.

radio relies on C-band satellite operations for content distribution, and they are understandably concerned over the potential for harmful interference.[210]

2) The FCC recently began a Notice of Proposed Rulemaking ("NPRM") process to potentially allocate 500 MHz of Ku-band satellite spectrum in the 14 GHz band for two-way broadband service to airplanes via a terrestrial-based system.[211] While the FCC apparently believes this can be done in a manner that will not interfere with satellites, the satellite industry is highly concerned about the issue as the Ku-band is the most valuable satellite spectrum.

Mobile Satellite Services (MSS or "satellite telephony") operators seek increased rights to use their spectrum terrestrially

3) Mobile Satellite Services (MSS or "satellite telephony") operators seek increased rights to use their spectrum terrestrially. As the satellite telephony ventures of the 1990s largely failed, several of the license holders were able to lobby to have their spectrum rights expanded for terrestrial wireless service in conjunction with their satellite service. This was known as Alternative Terrestrial Component ("ATC"). In 2013 DISH Network obtained relief from the ATC obligation and is now allowed to provide terrestrial service using phones without a satellite component. This obviates the expense of building a satellite network for dual satellite/terrestrial phones. The satellite industry is not opposing this action, presumably because it provides significant added value to the license holders.

3. Thoughts on Valuation

Orbital Slots over oceans or less developed countries have much lower values, often for little more than the legal fees involved in securing the licenses

The FCC does not auction most satellite spectrum because it falls under the ITU definition of international spectrum. Domestic spectrum is generally auctioned and licenses obtained through this process are often sold in an informal secondary market where prices vary considerably.

Satellite spectrum that targets large numbers of consumers, such as

---

[210] Howard Buskirk, *Early C-Band Comments Offer Preview of Fight to Come, Communications Daily* (June 1, 2018).

[211] *Expanding Access to Broadband and Encouraging Innovation through Establishment of an Air-Ground Mobile Broadband Secondary Service for Passengers Aboard Aircraft in the 14.0-14.5 GHz Band*, Notice of Proposed Rulemaking, GN Docket No. 13-114 RM-11640, 28 FCC Rcd 6765 (May 9, 2013) http://transition.fcc.gov/Daily_Releases/Daily_Business/2013/db0509/FCC-13-66A1.pdf

satellite television, is considered the most satellite valuable. In 1996, MCI bid a record $682 million in an FCC auction for the 110-degree West Longitude orbital slot for DBS that covered the entire continental U.S.. This record orbital slot valuation has not been surpassed. Satellite television appeared set for significant growth with only three slots covering the whole country. For comparison, the two satellite radio licenses sold in 1997 went for $83.4 million and $89.9 million, although they included far less spectrum.

For FSS applications, spectrum value is much lower as most end users are businesses that can use multiple satellites with their reception equipment and can change to other satellites easily. However, locations over continents with large populations have the highest values—up to $70 million per orbital slot.[212] Orbital slots over oceans or less developed countries have much lower values, often for little more than the legal fees involved in securing the licenses. Higher spectrum, such a Ka-band, sells for multiples less than C-band or Ku-band. However, orbital slot values are volatile and each situation must be carefully evaluated. Further analysis of spectrum valuation can be found in Part Five.

F. Government/Military Spectrum Dynamics

The U.S. government and military bands occupy approximately 60% of the spectrum below 3650 MHz. This federally controlled spectrum is highly desired by mobile users.[213] As described in Chapter VII.F of this *Handbook*, the NTIA controls spectrum used by the federal government.

1. But Government Efficiency is Questionable

Federal government agencies do not have to compete for spectrum or justify their demand for it

The largest government spectrum users are the Department of Defense and the Federal Aviation Agency. As determined by the Government Accountability Office, federal government agencies do not have to compete for spectrum or justify their demand for the use of it. For this reason, federal spectrum users are under little pressure to increase efficiency or to sell fallow or lightly used spectrum.[214]

Although government use of spectrum has increased during the last few years, its inefficient use remains a serious issue in light of the shortage of frequencies available for commercial use. The rapid

---

[212] There are certain exceptions, most notably Eutelsat's and SES's "Hotbird" slots over Europe which would likely command far higher prices.

[213] *PCAST Report, supra* note 76, at 8.

[214] *PCAST Report, supra* note 76, at 55.

increase in the development and use of smartphones and tablets is higher greater demand for data-intensive services and spectrum.

2. It is Hard to Move Government Users

The FCC has allowed unused spectrum to be reallocated and used by unlicensed users under certain terms. However, this reallocated spectrum came primarily from commercial entities rather than government users.

Transferring under-utilized government-owned frequency bands to commercial entities would reduce or even eliminate the spectrum crunch as previous transfers have shown. When 90 MHz of spectrum owned by the government was reallocated to public entities, mobile 4G broadband services took its place. Studies of government spectrum determined that the Navy was using around 20 MHz of 3.5 GHz CBRS from 3550-3650 MHz, but that 3500-3550 was not used.

While it would be ideal for inefficient government users to vacate underutilized spectrum, this approach faces serious difficulties

While it would be ideal for inefficient government users to vacate underutilized spectrum, this approach faces serious difficulties. Much government spectrum, while rarely used, is reserved for emergencies. Moving or consolidating them would entail innumerable administrative hearings over the course of years. Additionally, many government agencies have custom equipment, which makes the cost of replacing user terminals, antennas and repeaters, and conducting the radio frequency engineering needed to move to a new frequency prohibitive. In the 1755 MHz band, the National Telecommunications and Information Administration (NTIA) concluded that clearing the 1755-1880 MHz band would cost $18 billion alone.[215] This would absorb most or all of the revenue that an auction might raise. It is estimated that the Federal government investment in frequency bands below 3650 MHz totals approximately $281 billion. A breakdown of this investment is illustrated in Figure 15-9 below.

PART THREE: REGULATORY

---

[215] NTIA, *An Assessment of the Viability of Accommodating Wireless Broadband in the 1755-1780 MHz Band* (2012) https://www.ntia.doc.gov/report/2012/assessment-viability-accommodating-wireless-broadband-1755-1850-mhz-band.

Figure 15-9: Government Investment in Various Frequency Bands

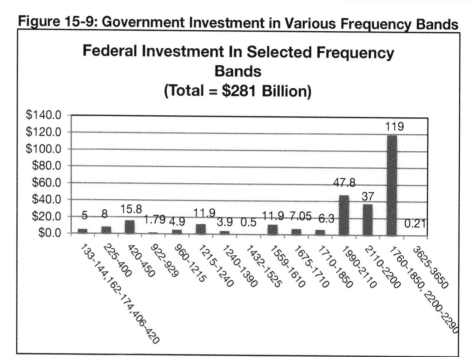

Source: *NTIA and Summit Ridge Group, LLC analysis*

The PCAST report concludes that sharing spectrum between existing government users and private users is a more efficient method than clearing government users

Because of the challenges in relocating inefficient government users, the PCAST report concludes that it does not believe that the FCC should clear and reallocate more government spectrum in the same way.[216] Instead, it concludes that encouraging sharing of spectrum between existing government users and private users is a more efficient method to increase utilization. Specifically, the PCAST report recommends that the government share 1,000 MHz of spectrum below 3.7 GHz with private users.[217] The Department of Defense has stepped up to the plate on cooperating in the 3.5 GHz CBRS protocol process, which should deliver GAA service, including protection for Navy radar, by late 2018. Summit Ridge believes the federal government will be cooperating on sharing and releasing more spectrum in the future.

3. Cognitive Radios Enable Sharing

Cognitive radios can sense signals and utilize spectrum simultaneously on wide swaths of contiguous spectrum. However, there is some debate over the current state of technology for cognitive radios. With the database approach, radios check with a central database such as the ones approved for TV White Spaces or the SAS databases approved in the 3.5 GHz proceeding. The databases know the availability of the frequencies in different areas of the country.

---

[216] *PCAST Report, supra* note 76, at 50.

[217] *PCAST Report, supra* note 76, at 8.

Spectrum flexible radios have designed to be authorized by the database before transmitting. The database can assign them an unused frequency based on their location.

XVI. Sources and Timing of New Mobile Spectrum

The FCC has significantly increased the amount of mobile spectrum over the past several years. However, many observers do not believe enough spectrum has been allocated to meet projected demand growth, and forecasts suggest that the trend of growing demand for mobile spectrum will continue. To address this challenge, the FCC unveiled two strategies that involve the reallocation of existing commercial spectrum from underutilized applications to mobile services and opening spectrum formerly reserved for government use for commercial users.

A. National Broadband Plan and Television Incentive Auction

The 2010 National Broadband Plan is the centerpiece of the FCC's plan to expand spectrum for mobile broadband

In 2010, the FCC released the National Broadband Plan. The National Broadband Plan contained many of the concepts delivered by the FCC from 2010 to 2018. The broadband proposals in the Plan included spectrum sharing, finding more efficient spectrum use, reallocation, delivering faster broadband speeds, providing more ubiquitous service to rural areas with both fiber and fixed wireless, finding new wireless technologies to deliver more throughput, implementing cell tower and pole attachment reforms, and expanding spectrum for mobile broadband. The Plan outlined a strategy to reallocate commercial spectrum from underutilized applications to mobile broadband. After considerable success with implementing many of the proposals articulated in the National Broadband Plan, FCC Commissioners in 2018 are laser-focused on delivering more spectrum in every band, creating a forward-looking calendar for planning into the next 10 years the auctioning and reallocation of spectrum, and on spectrum sharing with commercial, federal, and unlicensed spectrum.

1. FCC Surpassed the Plan's Goal of Adding 300 MHz of Additional Mobile Wireless Spectrum by 2015

The FCC met the Plan's spectrum goal by adding more than 300 MHz of frequency for mobile wireless services by 2015. Moreover, the FCC surpassed the Plan's 2020 spectrum goal in 2018 by adding more than 200 MHz through the TV Incentive Auction (84 MHz) and the 3.5 GHz CBRS proceeding with 150 MHz, for a total of 234 MHz.

2. FCC Seeks an Additional Mobile Wireless Spectrum by 2020

The C-band is above the 3 GHz range limit traditionally considered viable for mobile wireless service. But as technology improves and cell sites become closer, this spectrum becomes increasingly viable

The satellite C-band spectrum move to wireless is being pursued in the U.S. as of 2018. On August 3, 2017, the FCC opened a Notice of Inquiry to examining using the Mid-Band spectrum from 3.7-4.2 GHz, the C-band to make it available for wireless broadband use.[218] On May 31, 2018, mobile providers Verizon, AT&T, and T-Mobile have submitted comments to the FCC in support of permitting mobile operations in the C-band. In particular, Verizon said, "The U.S. is facing a mid-band spectrum deficit that could ultimately stop 5G deployment, particularly beyond dense urban areas… the promise of the 3.7-4.2 GHz band for 5G far outweighs the challenges of adding new terrestrial mobile allocation to the band. The U.S. can no longer afford the luxury of inefficient licensing of this band in this spectrum-constrained world and in the context of the global race to 5G."[219] In July 2018, the FCC unanimously passed a Notice of Rulemaking Proposal addressing several options to transition the C-band to terrestrial use.

3. Intelsat and SES's C-Band Spectrum Solution Proposal

Satellite operators Intelsat and SES Global, who together control over 90% of the C-band spectrum licensed in the U.S., submitted a joint proposal to the FCC in February 2018 presenting a solution to open approximately 100 MHz of C-band downlink spectrum to mobile networks for terrestrial mobile use while ensuring the protection of previously established satellite services. If the proposal is accepted, the spectrum could be cleared and available for terrestrial mobile use within 18-36 months. The proposal is intended to provide mobile wireless providers with the spectrum needed to support the deployment of next-generation 5G services.[220]

In July 2018, the FCC passed a Notice of Rulemaking Proposal

---

[218] *Expanding Flexible Use in Mid-Band Spectrum Between 3.7 and 24 GHz*, Notice of Inquiry, RM 17-183 (Aug. 3, 2017) https://docs.fcc.gov/public/attachments/FCC-17-104A1.pdf.

[219] Verizon Comments to *Expanding Flexible Use in Mid-Band Spectrum Between 3.7 and 24 GHz*, Notice of Inquiry (May 31, 2018) https://ecfsapi.fcc.gov/file/1053167720256/2018%2005%2031%20Verizon%20midband%203.7-4.2%20GHz%20comments.pdf.

[220] Intelsat, Intel, and SES, *C-band Joint-Use Proposal Fact Sheet* http://www.intelsat.com/wp-content/uploads/2018/02/SES-Joins-Fact-Sheet_FINAL.pdf.

(NPRM), asking for comment on a number of proposals for making C-band available for mobile broadband.[221] Proposals roughly in-line with Intelsat and SES's private market proposals were prominently featured.

The ongoing C-band proceeding is notable in that the FCC is seriously considering delegating the spectrum reallocation process to private entities. The justification is that the current satellite spectrum holders can do this faster than the FCC could if the FCC had to force the reallocation on the satellite industry. This ability to accelerate the process is given for the rational to potentially allow the satellite operators to reap billions of dollars in upside from the sale.

4. TV Broadcast Incentive Auction Reallocation of Spectrum

On April 13, 2017, the FCC released a public notice following the closing of the incentive auction to announce the results of the reverse auction and forward auction, along with final band plan assignments for the 600 MHz band. It consists of an uplink from 663-698 MHz, and a downlink from 617-652 MHz. Between the uplink and downlink there is a duplex gap from 652-663 MHz, and between the top of the downlink and Channel 37, which is allocated for the Radio Astronomy Service and Wireless Medical Telemetry Service, is the guard band from 614-617 MHz to prevent interference between the two. The 600 MHz band plan is illustrated in Figure 16-1 below.

Figure 16-1: Post-Incentive Auction Band Plan

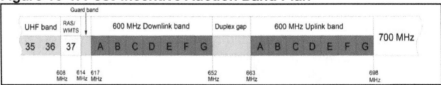

Source: FCC[222]

Parts of the 700 MHz band previously allocated for television channels 62-64 and 67-69 have also been allocated for a nationwide public safety network named by the acroynm "FirstNet."[223] The U.S. Congress has authorized $7 billion for the FirstNet project, which was funded from the proceeds received from the mobile carriers in the 600 MHz

---

[221] *Expanding Flexible Use of the 3.7 to 4.2 GHz Band*, Order and Notice of Proposed Rulemaking, GN Docket No. 18-122, RM 11719 (July 13, 2018) https://docs.fcc.gov/public/attachments/DOC-351868A1.pdf.

[222] The lettered squares in the chart represent the paired wireless blocks that will be licensed, while the sequentially numbered squares (35 through 37) represent TV channels. The rectangles labeled 3 and 11 are the guard band and duplex gap, with the numbers representing their respective sizes in MHz.

[223] FirstNet, *see*, https://www.firstnet.gov.

auction.

5. ATC Authorization increases value

MSS licensees may apply for an additional authorization to their licenses pursuant to the Ancillary Terrestrial Component (ATC) rules. These rules enable them to use a frequency for both terrestrial and satellite uses simultaneously. More specifically, ATC authority waivers allow licensees to use satellite telephony spectrum to provide service terrestrially at the same time as using it to provide service via satellite. To date, Globalstar, Inmarsat, Skyterra (which became LightSquared and subsequently Ligado) and Terrestar have received ATC waivers.

...ATC authority allow licensees to use satellite telephony spectrum to provide service terrestrially at the same time as using it to provide service via satellite

Inmarsat PLC and LightSquared Co. (formerly Skyterra), both have ATC waivers for L-band frequencies that are broken into interspersed pieces: Inmarsat/LightSquared/Inmarsat/LightSquared etc. To gain contiguous spectrum and maximize their capacity for 4G wireless services, LightSquared has agreed to a spectrum swap whereby it would pay Inmarsat in return for swapping its spectrum such that their respective spectrum becomes contiguous, as opposed to interspersed. However, in February 2012, the FCC withdrew its approval for a waiver of the ATC requirements as they apply to LightSquared. The FCC did this due to the potential for LightSquared signals to interfere with GPS receivers that frequently enter LightSquared's spectrum. Thus, LightSquared could not use its spectrum for ATC at the time. LightSquared subsequently entered Chapter 11 bankruptcy. LightSquared was only able to exit Chapter 11 after a long and litigious case in December 2015 after the FCC agreed to allow the transfer of LightSquared's valuable wireless spectrum into a newly formed company, Ligado Networks.[224]

The L- and S-bands are increasingly valuable frequency ranges due to the integration of satellite radio services and mobile satellite services.

The L- and S-bands are increasingly valuable frequency ranges due to the integration of satellite radio services and mobile satellite services. Along with other spectrum bands using ATCs, the L- and S-bands are capable of providing mobile services since the voice and data functions they provide are similar to those provided by terrestrial-based bands for cellular services. Another advantage of the L- and S-bands with ATC authorization is the increased coverage range compared to conventional terrestrial cellular networks. However, the ATC spectrum has significant disadvantages. The ATC rules for terrestrial spectrum

---

[224] Reuters, Tracy Rucinski, *Lightsquared strikes spectrum deal and exits bankruptcy* (Dec. 8, 2015) https://www.reuters.com/article/us-lightsquared-bankruptcy-idUSKBN0TR2QL20151209.

PART THREE: REGULATORY

use require service providers to integrate the network with a costly satellite platform thereby reducing its value. Also, the high cost of handsets needed for dual mode terrestrial/satellite-based services further increases the cost of the system.

6. DISH's AWS-4 Spectrum and Globalstar's 2.4G Petition

In 2012, the FCC eliminated ATC requirements for DISH's AWS-4 spectrum in the 2000-2020 MHz and 2180-2200 MHz band.[225] This included elimination of the expensive requirement that all terrestrial handsets be integrated with the satellite network. The spectrum is now available for stand-alone terrestrial use as well as Mobile Satellite Service, or MSS, use. Summit Ridge Group believes that the FCC will show similar flexibility to the other ATC providers to encourage greater use of the spectrum.

Other ideas for spectrum have been suggested… one challenge common to each is that, in most cases, there is insufficient hardware available to use the spectrum in the short-run

Globalstar petitioned the FCC for authorization to use its 2.4 GHz spectrum (2483.5-2495 MHz) and the adjacent guard band (2473-2483.5 MHz) for Wi-Fi service. At the time, the Wi-Fi spectrum just below Globalstar's, 2473-2483.5 MHz was largely unused because there was not enough spectrum to provide a full Wi-Fi channel without interfering with Globalstar's system. However, if Globalstar could use both groups of frequencies, it could have offered the market a full channel of additional Wi-Fi service that would otherwise be unavailable. Globalstar's petition sparked vehement objections, forcing Globalstar to revise and scale back their proposal. After considering potential interference issues with the adjacent Wi-Fi channel, the FCC approved Globalstar's revised request in December 2016. Globestar intends to use this new spectrum for LTE small cells.[226]

There is a total 90 MHz of broadband-capable MSS spectrum (split between the L-band and the S-Band) including DISH's AWS-4 spectrum as shown in Figure 16-2 below:

---

[225] *Service Rules for Advanced Wireless Services in the 2000-2020 MHz and 2180-2200 MHz Bands*, Report and Order of Proposed Modification WT Docket Nos. 12-70, 04-356, ET Docket No. 10-142, (2012) https://docs.fcc.gov/public/attachments/FCC-12-151A1.pdf; The FCC also modified Part 27 for flexible use of ATC terrestrial operations.

[226] Monica Alleven, "*Globestar positions its 2.4 GHz as prime for LTE small cells*," January 6, 2017. https://www.fiercewireless.com/tech/globalstar-positions-its-2-4-ghz-as-prime-for-lte-small-cells.

Figure 16-2: Broadband and Broadband Capable MSS Bands

MSS Band	Allocated Bandwidth	Bandwidth Usable for Terrestrial Broadband	Licensees	Subscribers
L-band	Two 34-megahertz blocks at 1525–1559 MHz, 1626.5–1660.5 MHz	40 megahertz	SkyTerra	18,235
			Inmarsat	254,000
S-band[227]	Two 20-megahertz blocks at 2000–2020 MHz, 2180–2200 MHz	40 megahertz	DISH	-
			DISH	-
Big LEO	Two 16.5-megahertz blocks at 1610–1626.5 MHz, 2483.5–2500 MHz	10 megahertz	Globalstar	382,313
			Iridium	359,000

Source: FCC National Broadband Plan and Summit Ridge Group, LLC analysis.

As a result, ATC could be a significant addition to spectrum capacity should the FCC continue its precedent with the aforementioned DISH waiver and allow a seamless addition to the supply of terrestrial mobile wireless spectrum without the expense of building a satellite network.

7. AWS-1, AWS-2 and AWS-3 Potential

AWS is primarily used for cellular 3G and, to a lesser extent, 4G services. One advantage of this spectrum is its suitability for a range of uses due to its robust propagation capacity (although it has a smaller coverage range than lower frequencies such as the 700 MHz band). For the spectrum to be utilized efficiently, two issues must be resolved. First, existing government users in the 1710-1755 MHz range (Uplink for AWS-1) must relocate (see Figure 9-7 for AWS-1 band plan). Second, more equipment must be developed to support AWS. However, equipment manufacturers are reluctant to invest in new technologies given the uncertainty of the timeframe for the band clearing.

---

[227] This spectrum, controlled by DISH, was authorized to for terrestrial mobile use and is referred to as AWS-4 spectrum discussed in Chapter VII.H above.

PART THREE: REGULATORY

a. AWS-1

In 2002, the FCC released an Order that allocated 90 MHz of spectrum for AWS in the 1710-1755 MHz and 2110-2155 MHz spectrum range and designated it as AWS-1. In 2003, the FCC released an Order that established rules to license AWS in the 1710-1755 and 2110-2155 MHz spectrum range. Auctions for AWS-1 spectrum took place in 2006 during FCC Auction 66 and in 2008 during FCC Auction 78.

b. AWS-2

AWS-2 spectrum contains two blocks: the H Block including frequency ranges of 1915-1920 KHz and 1995-2000 MHz, and the J Bock including frequency ranges of 2020-2025 MH, and 2175-2180 MHz. Dish Network acquired the H Block for $1.564 billion in FCC Auction 96 in 2014. Sprint owns the adjacent G Block.

c. AWS-3

The AWS-3 spectrum runs from 2155-2175 MHz and is paired with the 1755-1780 MHz band. The U.S. government used the AWS-3 band before it was reallocated and auctioned. FCC Auction 97 closed on January 29, 2015. The FCC auctioned a total of 65 MHz in what became the highest grossing spectrum auction in history, with total proceeds of $41 billion.

B. Citizens Broadband Radio Service (3.5 GHz)

The CBRS is based on a three-tier access model that was originally presented in the 2012 PCAST Report

On April 17, 2015, the FCC established the Citizens Broadband Radio Service (CBRS) for shared wireless broadband use in the 3550-3700 MHz band (3.5 GHz band).[228] The CBRS spectrum sharing was created, in part, as a response to the 2010 National Broadband Plan, which had a goal of making an additional 500 MHz of spectrum available for new mobile users – this is the first time this has ever happened. Before 2015, the United States Navy and satellite service providers were using 20 MHz of the 150 MHz of spectrum. As explained in detail in Part III Chapter VIII.K, Naval radar use will be protected using a system of CBRS sensors placed along the coast sending data to CBRS approved commercial databases. The CBRS database will send information to CBRS base stations, directing them to stop transmitting with the Navy's radar frequency when it's detected as operational. So when the Navy broadcasts, all other

---

[228] *Amendment of the Commission's Rules with Regard to Commercial Operations in the 3550-3650 MHz Band*, Second Further Notice of Proposed Rulemaking, GN Docket No. 12-354, 30 FCC Rcd 3959 (2015) https://www.fcc.gov/document/fcc-releases-rules-innovative-spectrum-sharing-35-ghz-band.

activity takes a backseat.

The Spectrum Access System and Environmental Sensing Capability services will be implemented to avoid any possible interference between users. The CBRS is based on a three-tier access model that was originally presented in the 2012 PCAST Report. Incumbent Access users are the first tier, and it includes the U.S. Navy and grandfathered fixed satellite service users who were originally operating in the 3.5 GHz band, and they are protected from harmful interference by the other two tiers. The second tier is the Priority Access tier. Access to this band will be through a spectrum auction where users can bid for a Priority Access License, which will give authorization to use a 10 MHz channel within the 3550-3650 MHz portion of the band. The final tier is the General Authorized Access tier, which is licensed-by-rule to promote open, flexible access for the widest possible group of potential users. These users will have access to any portion of the 3500-3700 MHz band not assigned to a higher tier, along with the ability to operate opportunistically on unused Priority Access channels.[229]

The tiered access approach is a potential model for future spectrum allocation as it allows for new users without needing incumbent users to completely vacate the spectrum. This model is particularly attractive in a situation where relocating a small number of incumbents is very expensive, such as government or military users with special equipment and slow bureaucratic processes.

C. 65 MHz in Required Auctions per Spectrum Act

Section 6401 of the "Middle Class Tax Relief and Job Creation Act of 2012," known as the Spectrum Act, directed the FCC to auction several spectrum blocks, 65 MHz in total, by early 2015. These blocks are shown in Figure 16-3 below.

---

[229] FCC, *3.5 GHz Band / Citizens Broadband Radio Service*, https://www.fcc.gov/wireless/bureau-divisions/broadband-division/35-ghz-band/35-ghz-band-citizens-broadband-radio.

Figure 16-3: 65 MHz of Spectrum Auctioned per Spectrum Act

Band	Amount	Comments
1675 - 1710 MHz	15 MHz	FCC to identify 15 MHz within the 35 MHz block to auction
1915 – 1920 MHz	5 MHz	Lower AWS H Block – likely to be paired with below
1995 – 2000 MHz	5 MHz	Upper AWS H Block – Likely to be paired with above
2155 - 2180 MHz	25 MHz	AWS-3 Band with upper AWS J Bock
1755-1780 MHz	15 MHz	FCC to auction 15 MHz in spectrum it determines
Total	**65 MHz**	

Source: Summit Ridge Group, LLC Analysis

The addition of 65 MHz of mobile broadband spectrum is significant. However, it only increases the prior allocation of 608 MHz by just over 10%. Meanwhile, mobile broadband usage, by any measure, is growing much more rapidly.

FCC Auction 96 for 10 MHz from the Lower AWS H Block's 1915-1920 MHz and 1995-2000 bands began on January 22, 2014, and closed on February 27, 2014. One bidder won all 176 licenses.[230]

The Spectrum Pipeline Act calls on the NTIA to identify 30 MHz of federally owned spectrum below 3 GHz

The FCC held an auction for 65 MHz from the AWS-3 bands, comprised of 1695-1710 MHz, 1755-1780 MHz, and 2155-2180 MHz. FCC Auction 97 began on November 13, 2014, and closed on January 29, 2015, resulting in thirty-one bidders winning 1611 licenses for a total of $41 billion, making this the largest grossing spectrum auction in history.[231]

D. Spectrum Pipeline Act of 2015

The Spectrum Pipeline Act[232] calls on the NTIA to identify 30 MHz of federally owned wireless communications spectrum below 3 GHz (excluding 1675-1695 MHz) by 2022 and reallocate the spectrum to have the FCC auction it off for commercial or shared use by 2024. The

---

[230] FCC *Auction 96: H Block, Fact Sheet* https://www.fcc.gov/auction/96/factsheet.

[231] FCC *Auction 97: Advanced Wireless Services (AWS-3), Fact Sheet* https://www.fcc.gov/auction/97/factsheet.

[232] Spectrum Pipeline Act of 2015, Bipartisan Budget Act of 2015, Public Law 114-74 Title X, Spectrum Pipeline, https://www.gpo.gov/fdsys/pkg/PLAW-114publ74/html/PLAW-114publ74.htm.

Act directs the Secretary of Commerce to submit a report to the President and the FCC identifying the 30 MHz, which must consist of at least 10 MHz of continuous frequencies for such reallocation. The President is then directed to withdraw or modify the licenses of federal spectrum holders after which the FCC will designate the spectrum for other uses. Federal agencies would be compensated for 110 percent of the costs incurred in relinquishing their spectrum and reallocating their activities through the auction proceeds.

The Act required the Commission to submit a report with an analysis of its new rules for the innovative 3.5 GHz CBRS band. The report must also analyze proposals to promote and identify additional bands that can be shared and identify at least 1 GHz of spectrum between 6 GHz and 57 GHz for such use by November 2018. Moreover, by January 1, 2022, the FCC must submit a report, in coordination with the Assistant Secretary of Commerce for Communications and Information, which identifies at least 50 MHz of spectrum below 6 GHz for potential auction. Finally, by January 2, 2024, the FCC must submit a report, in coordination with the Assistant Secretary of Commerce for Communications and Information, which identifies at least an additional 50 MHz of spectrum below 6 GHz for potential auction. Both of these latter reports must contain an assessment of the federal operations in such spectrum, an estimated timeline for the competitive bidding process, and a proposed plan for balance between unlicensed and licensed use.

1. Spectrum Efficient National Surveillance Radar (SENSR)

In response to the Spectrum Pipeline Act, the Federal Aviation Administration (FAA), the Department of Defense (DoD), the Department of Homeland Security (DHS), and the National Oceanic and Atmospheric Administration (NOAA) formed a cross-agency team to study the feasibility of an initiative called SENSR. After receiving approval and funding from the Office of Management and Budget (OMB), the SENSR team began assessing the feasibility of making a minimum of 30 MHz of the 1300-1350 MHz band available for reallocation for shared federal and non-federal use and evaluate the capability to auction this spectrum by 2024. The bandwidth would be vacated for auction by consolidating functions of certain existing surveillance radars, which would be replaced by a surveillance solution that would address the requirements of all four agencies.

PART THREE: REGULATORY

E. Spectrum Frontiers

The FCC adopted the Spectrum Frontiers initiative... for wireless broadband operations in frequencies above 24 GHz

In the endeavor to open high-band spectrum for the 5G future, the FCC adopted the Spectrum Frontiers initiative on July 14, 2016[233]. This proceeding created new rules for wireless broadband operations in frequencies above 24 GHz and made the U.S. the first country in the world to make this spectrum available for next-generation wireless services. High-frequency spectrum bands have historically been best suited for satellite or fixed microwave applications, but recent technological breakthroughs have newly enabled advanced wireless services to be feasible in these bands, particularly very high speed and low latency services. The Spectrum Frontier rule-making order has opened up nearly 11 GHz of high-frequency spectrum for mobile and fixed wireless broadband licensed use in the 24 GHz, 28 GHz, 37 GHz, 39 GHz, and 47 GHz bands, unlicensed use in the 64-71 GHz band, and shared use in the 37-37.6 GHz band.

In 2018, the FCC announced their plans for the 28 GHz band and 24 GHz band auctions.[234] Beginning on November 14, 2018, the 28 GHz band auction, FCC Auction 101, will be comprised of two 425 MHz blocks of spectrum to be auctioned on a county-by-county basis. The 24 GHz band auction will begin immediately after the 28 GHz auction ends, and it will consist of seven 100 MHz spectrum blocks to be auctioned on a partial economic areas (PEA) basis. Between the two auctions, about 6,000 licenses will be offered. Auctioning off spectrum in the 28 GHz band for mobile use has been controversial because satellite operators fear competition and interference in the Ka-band (26.5-40 GHz), which is heavily utilized by state-of-the-art satellite broadband systems.

Innovative uses for mmW spectrum are being developed to deliver high bandwidth service. For example, in May 2018, the Elefante Group filed a petition for rulemaking proposing a stratospheric-based communications service in the 22-23 GHz and 26 GHz bands with feeder links operating in the 70/80 GHz band. Elefante Group plans to deploy lighter-than-air airship platforms capable of station keeping at 65,000 ft to support 5G and IoT services.

---

[233] *Use of Spectrum Bands Above 24 GHz for Mobile Radio Services,* Report and Order and Further Notice of Proposed Rulemaking, GN Docket No. 14-177, RM-11664, 31 FCC Rcd 8014 (2016) https://www.fcc.gov/document/spectrum-frontiers-ro-and-fnprm.

[234] *Auctions of Upper Microwave Flexible Use Licenses for Next-Generation Wireless Services,* Public Notice, AU Docket No. 18-85 (Apr. 17, 2018) https://www.fcc.gov/document/spectrum-frontiers-auction-comment-pn.

Figure 16-4: 28 GHz License Summary

Block	Frequencies (GHz)	Total Bandwidth	Geographic Area Type	Number of Licenses
1	27.5-27.925	425 MHz	County	1,537
2	27.925-28.35	425 MHz	County	1,537

Source: FCC Fact Sheet March 27, 2018

Figure 16-5: 24 GHz License Summary

Block	Frequencies (GHz)	Total Bandwidth	Geographic Area Type	Number of Licenses
1	24.25-24.35	100 MHz	PEA	416
2	24.35-24.45	100 MHz	PEA	416
3	24.75-24.85	100 MHz	PEA	416
4	24.85-24.95	100 MHz	PEA	416
5	24.95-25.05	100 MHz	PEA	416
6	25.05-25.15	100 MHz	PEA	416
7	25.15-25.25	100 MHz	PEA	416

Source: FCC Fact Sheet March 27, 2018[235]

Additionally, in July 2018, the FCC published a Further NPRM[237] regarding auctioning the 47 GHz, 39 GHz, and upper 37 GHz bands. The FCC proposes an incentive auction mechanism that would offer continuous blocks of spectrum in the 47 GHz, 39 GHz, and upper 37 GHz bands to allow an efficient transition to a new flexible use band plan. The FCC hopes to move forward with a single auction for all three of these bands in 2019. The auction would offer continuous blocks of spectrum throughout the 39 MHz and upper 37 MHz bands while protecting spectrum usage rights under existing licenses. The existing 39 GHz spectrum holdings are licensed in small spectrum

[235] *Id.*

[237] *Use of Spectrum Bands Above 24 GHz for Mobile Radio Services*, Fourth Further Notice of Proposed Rulemaking, WT Docket No. 14177 (Aug. 3, 2018) https://www.fcc.gov/document/making-39-ghz-band-auction-ready.

PART THREE: REGULATORY

block sizes and mismatched geographic areas, so the FCC's goal is to reconfigure the band into more continuous 100 MHz blocks of spectrum, which are more conducive to wireless broadband deployment. The proposed incentive auction would have two phases: a clock phase, in which bidders bid on generic license blocks; and an assignment phase, in which clock phase winners can bid on specific frequencies. Both new entrants and participating incumbents could bid for new licenses, and incentive payments would be offered to incumbents who choose to relinquish their spectrum usage rights to make new licenses available.

Figure 16-6: Spectrum Frontiers Bands

Band	Size	Channel Block Size	Status
24.25-24.45/24.75-25.25	700 MHz	100 MHz	No incumbents, will likely be auctioned in 2019 directly after Auction 101
27.5-28.35 GHz	850 MHz	425 MHz	Verizon holds about 50% MHz/PoPs. FCC Auction 101 begins November 14, 2018
37-37.6 MHz	600 MHz	TBD, will be shared	Currently shared spectrum, no incumbents
37.6-38.6 GHz	1 GHz	200 MHz	Incumbents cover 14 military bases, no commercial use
38.6-40 GHz	1.4 GHz	200 MHz	Verizon and AT&T hold the majority of the channels
47.2-48.2 GHz	1 GHz	200 MHz	No incumbents
64-71 GHz	7 GHz	Unlicensed use	No incumbents

Source: WISPAmerica

(Detailed analysis of the mmWave spectrum bands can be found in Chapter XIII of this *Handbook*)

F. MOBILE NOW Act

The 2018 Making Opportunities for Broadband Investment and Limiting Excessive and Needless Obstacles to Wireless Act, or MOBILE NOW Act, directs that spectrum be made available for new technologies to maintain America's leadership in the future of communications technology.[238] To achieve this, it calls for the FCC and NTIA to identify at least 255 MHz of Federal and non-Federal spectrum below 8,000 MHz for mobile and fixed wireless broadband use by December 31, 2022. Of that total, 100 MHz below the frequency of 8,000 MHz must be identified for unlicensed use and 100 MHz below the frequency of 6,000 MHz must be identified for exclusive licensed use, along with another 55 MHz below 8,000 MHz for either licensed or unlicensed use or a combination of the two. The MOBILE NOW Act specifically requires the FCC and NTIA to evaluate the feasibility of opening the C band (3700-4200 MHz) for wireless broadband services and excludes the 1695-1710 MHz, 1755-1780 MHz, 2155-2180 MHz, and 3550-3700 MHz (Citizens Broadband Radio Services) frequencies from consideration. Additionally, the act orders that the FCC shall publish a rule that'll consider use of the 42-42.5 GHz band for mobile or fixed terrestrial wireless through licensed, unlicensed or shared usage.

Already, the NTIA has identified 100 MHz of spectrum from the 3450-3550 MHz band as having the potential to be repurposed for wireless use.[239] In July, the NTIA announced that they will be starting a feasibility study for the band for 5G use. Making the 3450-3550 MHz band available will amount to a massive amount of bandwidth for 5G, connecting the spectrum from 3450-3550 MHz to the 3550-3700 MHz CBRS band and the 3700-4200 MHz C-band. There is also discussion of making the 6 GHz band, which is the C-band uplink, available for unlicensed use. Advocates of rural broadband access, in particular, are optimistic about the implications of MOBILE NOW for their cause. Broadcasters are less enthusiastic about the act due to concerns regarding their satellites and content distribution, although their opposition is primarily focused on the C-band.

The various sources of new spectrum highlighted in Chapter XVI of the *Handbook*, will be heavily leveraged by mobile carriers, cable providers, and hyperscale companies for 5G deployment, as illustrated in Figure 16-7.

---

[238] MOBILE NOW Act, *Making Opportunities for Broadband Investment and Limiting Excessive and Needless Obstacles to Wireless Act* https://www.congress.gov/bill/115th-congress/senate-bill/19/text.

[239] NTIA, *Building Spectrum Policy to Meet Advanced Communications Capabilities* (June 21, 2018) https://www.ntia.doc.gov/speechtestimony/2018/building-spectrum-policy-meet-advanced-communications-capabilities.

Figure 16-7: Next Generation Networks: Carrier 5G Plans

Carrier	Spectrum Bands	5G Deployment
Verizon	28 GHz and 39 GHz	mmWave for 5G fixed wireless
AT&T	39 GHz	mmWave for mobile 5G
T-Mobile	600 MHz and 700 MHz	Low band for mobile 5G
Sprint	2.5 GHz	Mid band for mobile 5G

Other Potential Competitors

Cable	New Projects
Comcast	xFinity Mobile/Spectrum Mobile
Charter	Trialing 3.5 GHz spectrum for in home LTE
Hyperscale	
Facebook	60 GHz for connectivity
Google	Project Loon, Project Fi

Source: Oppenheimer & Co. report and Summit Ridge Group, LLC analysis

G. Other Sources of Additional Mobile Spectrum Capacity

Several other ideas for additional spectrum have been suggested. This sub-chapter addresses those that are discussed most. A challenge common to each of them is that, in most cases, there is insufficient hardware available to take advantage of the spectrum in the short-run. While the development of smart radio technology may ameliorate this challenge, we are years away from wide-scale availability at competitive prices.

1. Wi-Fi and WiMax

Broadband Radio Service (BRS), formerly allocated for wireless television as MMDS band, is a spectrum range between 2.5 and 2.7 GHz. It is primarily used for two-way integrated communication services such as voice, data and Internet services transmitted through cellular systems. The BRS spectrum currently offers an opportunity for significant expansion of services transmitted in the WiMax format.

This is because only a fraction of the 194 MHz of spectrum in the 2.5 GHz band has currently been built out. The WCS band also includes WiMax-based and the FCC recently announced a plan for opening additional spectrum in the 5 GHz band for future Wi-Fi services.

Closer cell spacing mitigates the disadvantage of the distance limitations of 2.5 GHz spectrum

Until recently BRS was much less valuable than lower frequencies since much of it remained unused despite the availability of commercial equipment. This was due to its inferior building penetration and limited distance range. However, as spectrum has become more crowded, wireless companies have placed cell sites closer together, particularly in metropolitan areas. Closer cell spacing mitigates the disadvantage of the distance limitations of 2.5 GHz spectrum. While closer cell spacing is more expensive, it also increases system capacity by increasing the number of times frequency is reused, which allows greater power levels needed for higher data transmission rates. At the same time, recent equipment developments have reduced building penetration obstacles. Consequently, this spectrum has become more desirable for mobile wireless applications, particularly in heavily used urban markets.

Other countries around the world share the FCC's plan to use the 2.5 GHz band to expand wireless spectrum capacity. The ITU has created three recommendations for dividing the band as described in Figure 16-8 below. Several countries in the Americas including Brazil, Canada, Chile, and Columbia have adopted Option 1. The U.S. is currently not in compliance with any of these options. One party, Sprint, controls most of the 2.5 GHz spectrum. Should equipment manufacturers and market forces affect harmonization with other countries in the Americas, it should be relatively easy for them to accomplish the FCC's goal of using the spectrum for additional wireless spectrum capacity.

PART THREE: REGULATORY

Figure 16-8: ITU Recommendations for the 2.5 GHz Band

Frequency arrangement	Mobile station transmitter (MHz)	Centre gap (MHz)	Base station transmitter (MHz)	Duplex separation (MHz)	Centre gap usage
C1	2 500-2 570	50	2 620-2 690	120	TDD
C2	2 500-2 570	50	2 620-2 690	120	FDD DL (external)
C3	Flexible FDD/TDD				

Source: ITU Recommendation M1036-3[239] and Summit Ridge Group, LLC analysis

2. More Aggressive FCC Rule Enforcement

The FCC has often been reluctant to enforce its rules related to build-out milestones

The FCC has often been reluctant to enforce its rules related to build-out milestones. It likely fears driving away smaller new entrants, who are often the most promising innovators. But these smaller entrants are often capital constrained and encounter delays in being able to finance the required build-outs. It has been Summit Ridge Group's general observation that the FCC is frequently flexible in granting waivers for various construction delays, particularly with new entrants.

Providing waivers for required build-out milestones may help new undercapitalized entrants. But it also leaves valuable spectrum underutilized. More aggressive enforcement of FCC license rules could provide additional spectrum. However, the FCC needs to balance those benefits against the possible long-term costs of fewer new entrants if stricter license rules deter investors.

3. Un-auctioned or Reclaimed Federal Spectrum

The FCC has resisted selling [spectrum that it failed to sell at auction] on the secondary market

In many previous auctions, the government failed to sell the entire spectrum available for sale. Summit Ridge Group's analysis of Scott Wallsten's FCC auction data[240] shows that as of 2013, of the 98 FCC Spectrum Auctions that have taken place since 1994, the FCC failed to sell all of the licenses in 37 of them. Additionally, many purchasers returned or forfeited their spectrum rights because they were unable to meet various build-out requirements. As a result, the FCC holds numerous slivers of spectrum that remain unallocated. The FCC has resisted selling this spectrum on the secondary market. Rather, they seek to hold the spectrum until there is enough to justify an additional auction. In certain bands, this is not likely to happen for several years.

---

[239] http://www.itu.int/rec/R-REC-M.1036-3-200707-S/en .

[240] Scott Wallsten, "Is there Really a Spectrum Crisis? Quantifying the Factors Affecting Spectrum License Value." Technology Policy Institute, 9.

4. Opening Unused Spectrum for Sharing

Another concept to increase spectrum availability is to open unused licensed spectrum on a temporary basis.[241] Smart radio technologies have arguably made this idea increasingly viable. Licensees of the unused spectrum may oppose this out of fear that once people start using the spectrum in large numbers, it may be difficult to remove them. There is also a risk of a "tragedy of the commons" whereby low-priority use dominates spectrum use because it is available at no cost, crowding out more valuable uses. One solution would be to have micro-payments in crowded markets.[242] One small mobile operator, Republic Wireless, offers a service for $20 a month that uses unlicensed Wi-Fi spectrum and only "roams" to licensed spectrum if unlicensed spectrum is unavailable.

H. Government Spectrum Sharing

1. Smart Radios and Spectrum Databases Enable Sharing

The invention of spectrum sensing radios and spectrum databases has made it possible to share spectrum dynamically

The invention of spectrum sensing radios and spectrum databases has made it possible to share spectrum dynamically. Spectrum sensing radios detect unused spectrum while spectrum databases monitor allocated and unallocated spectrum as well as the priority of each user. A spectrum sensing radio detects an unused channel, then verifies with the database to see if the spectrum is reserved for a higher priority use before allowing the radio to operate in that spectrum. If a higher priority user signaled that they wanted to use the spectrum, the database would shut down or move the lower priority user to available spectrum. This process is illustrated in Figure 16-9 below.

---

[241] For a detailed analysis of this proposal, *see* Michael Calabrese, *Use it or Share it: Unlocking the Vast Wasteland of Fallow Spectrum* (Sept. 25, 2011) TPRC 2011, SSRN: http://ssrn.com/abstract=1992421.

[242] For an analysis of this proposal, see Eli Noam, *The Next Stage in the Digital Economy: Nano-Transactions and Nano-Regulation*, Columbia Institute for Tele-Information (Dec. 2000) http://www.citi.columbia.edu/elinoam/articles/con_info_money.htm.

Figure 16-9: Sharing Mechanics

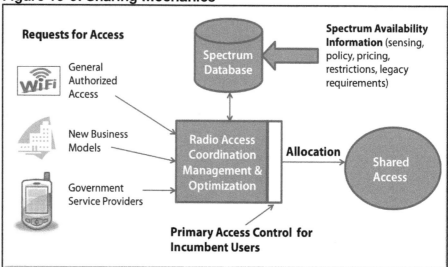

Source: PCAST Report

The PCAST Report recommends improving spectral efficiency by requiring federal agencies to "share" unused spectrum with commercial users

Current spectrum-sharing research proposals include the Authorized Shared Access (ASA)/Licensed Shared Access (LSA) system and the Wireless Access Policy for Electronic Communications Services (WAPECS). The LAS and WAPECS are European Union policy concepts. Other spectrum sharing proposals include those developed from the white space trials carried out in the United Kingdom.

2. Government Users Pushed to Share Spectrum

As mentioned in Chapter VIII and XV of this *Handbook*, the PCAST report recommends against moving government users. Instead, it proposes improving spectral efficiency by requiring federal agencies to "share" unused spectrum with commercial users. This would build on the success of Wi-Fi sharing radar spectrum in the 5 GHz band.

Due the availability of modern spectrum sensing radios, such sharing is potentially viable from a technical perspective. A chart showing federal spectrum under consideration for sharing is shown in Figure 16- below. The PCAST report also recommends the sharing of commercial spectrum when not used by the primary licensee.

Figure 16-10: Federal Spectrum Under Investigation for Shared Use

Frequency Band (MHz)	Amount (MHz)	Current allocations/usage (Federal, non-Federal, Shared)
406.1 - 420.0[1]	13.9	Federal
1300 – 1390[1]	90	Federal
1675 – 1710[2]	35	Federal/non-federal
1755 – 1780[2]	25	Federal
1780 – 1850	70	Federal
2200 – 2290	90	Federal
2700 – 2900[1]	200	Federal
2900 - 3100	200	Federal/non-Federal shared
3100 – 3500	400	Federal/non-Federal shared
3500 – 3650[2]	150	Federal
4200 - 4400[1] [4200-4220 & 4380-4400]	200	Federal/non-Federal shared Federal/non-Federal shared
Total	**1,473.9**	

[1] Band obligated by U.S.-Canada or U.S. Mexico bilateral agreement(s).

[2] Bands selected for Fast-Track Evaluation. For purposes of future analysis, 1755-1850 MHz – consisting of 1755-1780 MHz and 1780-1850 MHz – will be assessed as a single block.

Source: PCAST Report and Summit Ridge Group, LLC analysis

The PCAST Report suggests a three-tier system of rights for sharing government spectrum. Under this plan, government users would have first priority to their spectrum; second priority would be to commercial users who would pay a fee for using spectrum on a temporary basis. The lowest priority would go to users who could use any remaining unused spectrum at no charge. This tiered system was implemented in the Citizens Broadband Radio Service for shared wireless broadband use. An illustration of this hierarchy is shown in Figure 16-11 below.

PART THREE: REGULATORY

Figure 16-11: Suggested Sharing Hierarchy of Government Spectrum

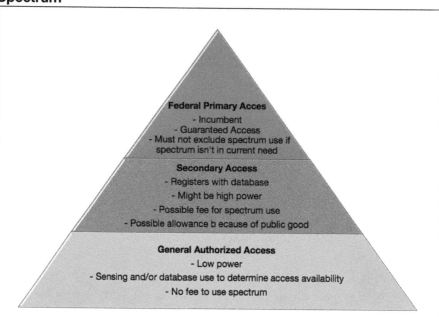

Federal Primary Acces
- Incumbent
- Guaranteed Access
- Must not exclude spectrum use if spectrum isn't in current need

Secondary Access
- Registers with database
- Might be high power
- Possible fee for spectrum use
- Possible allowance b ecause of public good

General Authorized Access
- Low power
- Sensing and/or database use to determine access availability
- No fee to use spectrum

Source: PCAST Report and Summit Ridge Group, LLC analysis

3. Greater Licensing Flexibility Possible

A significant implication resulting from the development of spectrum sharing is the possibility of creating intermediate- and short-term spectrum licenses. Under the current regulatory system, a long-term spectrum license is available via auction or in the secondary market. Unlicensed spectrum can also be used but with no guarantee of future availability or freedom from interference.

Under a spectrum sharing scenario, second-tier users could reserve spectrum for short or intermediate-terms by the hour, day, week or month. The primary users can grant access for such periods with assurances of availability through the database authorization system. This spectrum sharing scenario treats spectrum like other property that can be secured for various periods. This is shown in Figure 16-12 below.

A significant implication resulting from spectrum sharing is the possibility of creating intermediate- and short-term spectrum licenses

Figure 16-12: Potential for Increased License Flexibility

Source: PCAST Report.

4. Timing of Federal Sharing

The NTIA appears to be taking the push to share federal spectrum seriously. In 2012 they began working on the "Test Bed Pilot Program" to evaluate the possibility of dynamic spectrum access. Dynamic spectrum involves using technology such as smart radios and spectrum databases that allow spectrum users to change frequencies as needed on a continuous basis. Such technology would be critical for commercial users to be able to share sensitive federal spectrum on a non-interfering basis with rules potentially modeled after the TV white spaces in commercial spectrum.

Summit Ridge Group believes most shared government spectrum allocation will grow over time as the enabling technology hurdles and business models are settled

Spectrum sharing is being evaluated and/or implemented by several developed countries. The international nature of the movement gives it significant credibility and momentum. Summit Ridge Group believes shared government spectrum allocation will grow over time as technological hurdles and business models are settled. However, given the significant nature of the policy change, it will be years before government agencies fully embrace this option.

As shown in Figure 16-13, there is between 605 MHz and 1,005 MHz of shared spectrum that has been allocated or is in the FCC NPRM stage at levels of advanced consideration.

Figure 16-13: Shared Spectrum Status

Band	Amount	Status
1695-1710 MHz	15 MHz	Auction 97
1755-1850 MHz	95 MHz	Auction 97
3550-3700 MHz	150 MHz	Citizens Broadband Radio Service Auction
3700-4200 MHz	100 MHz-500 MHz	NPRM GN Docket No. 18-122
4940-4990 MHz	50 MHz	WP Docket No. 07-100
5.35-5.47 GHz, 5.85-5.925 GHz	195 MHz	ET Docket No. 13-49
Total	**605-1,005 MHz**	

Source: FCC and Summit Ridge Group, LLC analysis

XVII. Regulatory Conclusions

Summit Ridge Group believes that the risk of the "spectrum crunch" turning into a full-blown crisis is becoming remote despite various uncertainties

Making more spectrum available and sharing bands to increase efficiency would ease the spectrum supply challenge and improve the quality of wireless services – both in the U.S. and internationally. This would also have a positive macroeconomic effect. Increasing the amount of spectrum available to commercial entities will stimulate growth by creating jobs and making businesses more efficient, while also improving the quality of life and competitiveness of each country's economy.

In the U.S., the FCC has been working aggressively to reallocate spectrum for uses that are in the highest demand. With multiple processes in place, it has granted a number of license waivers and made other regulatory accommodations to facilitate the reallocation of spectrum to the areas of the most vital need. Wireless operators have also learned to do more with less spectrum. As a result, Summit Ridge Group believes that the risk of the "spectrum crunch" in the U.S. turning into a full-blown crisis is becoming remote. We acknowledge, however, that this is not the consensus opinion among industry experts given the uncertainties over the timing of the reallocation process and demand projections. Few countries are close to the U.S. in terms of allocating additional spectrum to mobile broadband, but most developed economies are making significant progress.

PART FOUR: GLOBAL PERSPECTIVES

XVIII. Global Perspectives

The U.S. is not alone in its need for additional spectrum for mobile data applications. As of the end of 2016, the global demand for mobile data was eighteen times greater than in 2011 and Cisco projects a seven-fold increase between 2016 and 2021.[243] This growth is ubiquitous around the globe regardless of geographic, political, and socio-economic factors. While almost every country has its own policies to address spectrum issues, most have adopted or are considering the approaches that the U.S. has taken to handle the challenge. To date, developed countries have been more successful at allocating additional spectrum for mobile data, the most important area (see Figure 18-1).

Figure 18-1: Mobile Broadband Spectrum Allocated by Country (MHz, 2018)

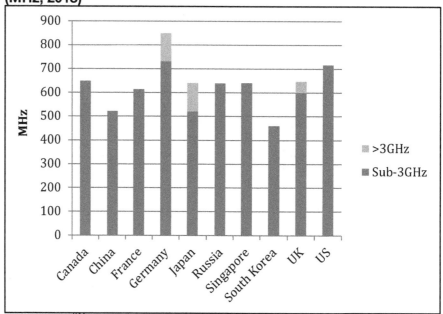

Source: CTIA[244] and Summit Ridge Group, LLC analysis

Governments and communications service providers around the world recognize that a global standard will lead to economies of scale of equipment that will reduce costs and increase spectral capability. In addition, operators would like to be able to allow their customers to move from one country to another and continue to use their carrier branded smartphone. Currently, unlicensed Wi-Fi facilitates smartphone usage from one country to another. By harmonizing

---

[243] *Cisco Visual Networking Index (VNI) Global Mobile Data Traffic Forecast Update 2016-2021, supra* at note 175.

[244] Analysys Mason on behalf of CTIA: *Global Race to 5G, supra* at note 182.

frequency uses, advanced wireless technology will be able to function in different markets without adaptions, providing significant economies of scale. If global networks use similar technology and standards, there will be more competition among equipment developers that will likely increase the quality of products and reduce prices. Unfortunately, harmonization has lagged spectrum allocation for mobile broadband, making the former even more challenging to achieve.

Although only a minority of countries have globally harmonized spectrum, in major markets the most valuable spectrum has already been or is currently being harmonized, primarily in the 700 MHz band in the 698-806 MHz range. For ITU Region 2 (the Americas) and for nine countries in ITU Region 3, including China, India, Japan and South Korea, the World Radio Congress (WRC-07) targeted the 700 MHz band for reallocation from television broadcasters after the industry shifted to digital.

A. General Trends

Governments globally have increased their effort to regulate spectrum with the recognition of the importance of mobile communications for economic development. Each country's ability to influence hardware providers has led to varied strategies. Anticipated spectrum license allocations for mobile broadband will narrow the gaps between countries as shown in Figure 18-2 below.

Figure 18-2: Licensed Spectrum Available for Mobile (MHz)

Country	Current	Pipeline	Current+ Pipeline
U.S.	673	5080	5753
Australia	478	230	708
Brazil	554	0	554
China	227	360	587
France	555	50	605
Italy	540	20	560
Japan	500	10	510
Spain	540	60	600
U.K.	353	265	618

Source: FCC[245] and Summit Ridge Group, LLL analysis.

---

[245] FCC White Paper: *The Mobile Broadband Spectrum Challenge: International Comparisons.* Wireless Telecommunication Bureau, Office of Engineering & Technology (Feb. 26, 2013)

Although only a minority of countries have harmonized spectrum, in major markets the most valuable spectrum has already been or is currently being harmonized

The United States and Germany are the global leaders in spectrum allocation to mobile broadband

PART FOUR: GLOBAL

B. Greater Influence of Standards on the Way

Historically, large developed countries such as the United States have been less compliant with international norms

Historically, large developed countries such as the U.S. have been less compliant with international norms. Regulators and service providers in these countries have felt less pressure to adapt to international standards, knowing that manufacturers must accommodate them. Countries like Canada more readily adopt standards set by larger neighbors to manage interference and benefit from economies of scale that these standards provide in equipment manufacturing. Some countries moved in two directions. For example, Mexico is under pressure to adopt the standards of the U.S., its major trading partner, against regional market forces to embrace those of fellow Spanish-speaking Latin American countries which also account for significant trade and political influence. Similar dynamics play out around the world.

The [global wireless telecom] market is maturing, new technology and equipment is becoming less expensive, and operators' traditional product and service offerings are generating less and less value

Recently, the influence of global standards has become stronger. Even large countries find it more difficult to act independently. In 2012, foreign operators increased their stakes in the U.S. market. Japan's Softbank completed a merger with Sprint in 2013,[247] while Deutsche Telecom's increased its exposure and stake in the U.S. market by T-Mobile U.S. subsidiary's October 2012 announced acquisition of MetroPCS. And now, in 2018, Sprint announced a merger with T-Mobile, further increasing Deutsche Telecom's U.S. market presence. Many of these deals were publicly justified, in part, to increase leverage and economies of scale with equipment manufacturers. They also tie the largest market in ITU Region 2 (the Americas) to ITU Regions 1 and 3. As a result, we expect greater international coordination across the board shortly.

C. ARPU is Falling Globally

In general, competitive pressure is increasing in the global wireless telecom industry. The market is maturing, new technology and equipment are becoming less expensive, and the operators' traditional product and service offerings are generating less and less value. Latin America ARPU has been decreasing across operators. A recent study published by Strategy& PricewaterhouseCoopers's global strategy consulting team indicates the average revenue per user (ARPU) in the telecom industry has fallen in virtually every region, including North America, Western Europe, Middle East, Latin America,

---

[247] Hiroko Tabuchji, *Confidence From Chief of Softbank in Sprint Bid,* New York Times (June 21, 2013) http://www.nytimes.com/2013/06/22/business/global/confidence-from-chief-of-softbank-in-sprint-bid.html?pagewanted=all

and Asia, between 2006 and 2016. [247] Although the ARPU compounded annual rate of change is negative in all five regions, the rates are decelerating at different speeds, as illustrated in Figure 18-3 below. Latin America has seen a dramatic drop in ARPU spreads (but not ARPU) between operators. ARPU spread is the difference between the highest and lowest ARPUs in each market. The ARPU spread decrease is often due to regulatory efforts to promote competition throughout a region which enables new competitors to grow market share and to begin to compete with the dominant incumbents.

Figure 18-3: APRU Compounded Annual Rate of Change

Region	ARPU compounded annual rate of change 2006-2016	ARPU compounded annual rate of change 2011-2016	2016 ARPU
North America	-1%	-2%	$36
Western Europe	-6%	-6%	$15
Middle East	-4%	-4%	$5
Latin America	-6%	-10%	$6
Asia	-4%	-1%	$3

Source: Strategy& and Summit Ridge Group, LLC analysis

A narrowing ARPU spread implies that prices are converging through commoditized markets. In Western Europe, there has been a decline in market share between the largest and smallest operators. This is in response to the consolidation of smaller operators, as operators become less differentiated and low-cost providers become acquisition targets. A low market share spread may indicate a commoditized market, where pricing wars lead to even greater interchangeability among providers, which, in turn, leads consumers to change providers rapidly.

Conversely, market share spread between the largest and smallest operators in the U.S. has increased. This increase has been driven by ongoing consolidation by the largest operators and resulting shifts in market share, while increased price competition has narrowed the

---

[247] Strategy&, *An Industry at Risk: Commoditization in the Wireless Telecom Industry* (2017) Pricewaterhouse Cooper's global strategy consulting team. https://www.strategyand.pwc.com/media/file/An-industry-at-risk.pdf

PART FOUR: GLOBAL

ARPU spread. In the US, the lack of differentiation in terms of market coverage and service quality has begun to force operators to compete based on price, putting downward pressure on the ARPU spread. [248]

Even with the downward price pressure, U.S. ARPU is significantly higher than in other regions. One of the reasons for higher ARPU in the U.S. is the packaging of data and texting into bundles, has been a practice for longer in the U.S. than in other countries. In other countries, where there can often be little packaging, using the same amount of data could result in a much larger monthly bill than in the U.S. This is especially true in developing countries such as India. Carriers in various countries are experimenting with unlimited data plans which are driving higher ARPU and customer growth, but at the same time lowering data speeds. The higher ARPU in the U.S. could be the result of U.S. customer getting a better overall price on data and text use than in other countries. Additionally, new technology, new smartphones, and network upgrades are typically introduced first in the U.S. before making their way to other regions.

---

[248] *Id.*

XIX. North America

A. United States

The U.S. wireless market has been described throughout this Handbook, and the information below highlights the current market developments in the U.S.

1. Number of Cell Sites

The number of cell sites in the U.S. has increased from 51,600 in 1997 to 325,00 in 2017. Cell sites include DAS, microcell, and small cells. It should be noted that the number of cell sites does not equal the number of cell towers. As of 2017, the U.S. had some 154,000 cell towers.[250] As indicated in the Figure 19-1 following, between 1997 and 2017, the year-over-year change in the number of cell sites fluctuated between an increase of 30,229 cell sites in 2003 and a decrease of 6,305 in 2014. Furthermore, the five-year average change in the number of cell sites decreased from 17,548 for the years 1997 through 2002 to 4,334 for the years 2012 through 2017.

Figure 19-1: Absolute Change in the Number of Cell Sites

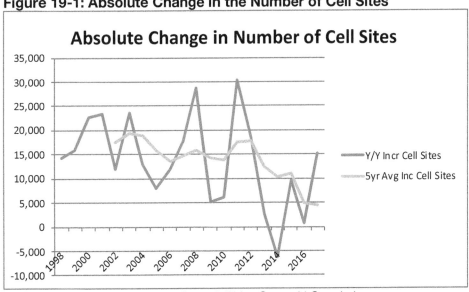

Source: CTIA industry survey and Summit Ridge Group, LLC analysis

Furthermore, the compound annual growth rate (CAGR) decreased from 22.0% for the years 1997 through 2002 to 1.4% for the years

---

[250] *Industry Data,* CTIA (2018) https://www.ctia.org/the-wireless-industry/infographics-library?topic=22

2012 through 2017. U.S. cell site growth rate is also on a downward trend as shown in Figure 19-2. It is hard to reconcile this trend with the move to higher frequencies and significant discussion of cell site densification.

Figure 19-2: Percentage Change in the Number of Cell Sites

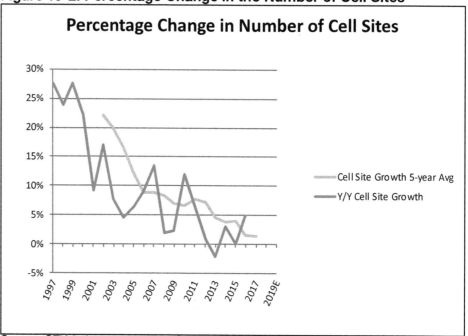

Source: CTIA industry survey and Summit Ridge Group, LLC analysis

The amount of spectrum used has been significantly less than what was forecasted in 2010

In recent years, the major U.S. wireless operators have invested more in spectrum and in advanced technology on existing cell sites, as opposed to adding more cell sites. As a result, the U.S. lags behind other countries in cell site infrastructure growth. According to a recent report by Deloitte Consulting, the U.S. has 4.7 sites per 10,000 population while China has 14.1 sites per 10,000. The U.S. has 0.4 sites per square mile, while China has 5.3 sites per square mile. Germany has 5.1 sites per square mile, and Japan has 15.2 sites per square mile. China Tower added 350,000 sites in 2015 alone, which surpassed the total number of sites in the U.S. China has 1.9 million sites compared to the 320,000 sites in the U.S.[250] The relatively small number of cell sites in the U.S. may impact its 5G deployment which will incorporate higher frequencies and likely require denser networks.

2. Spectrum Usage

The amount of spectrum used has been significantly less than what was forecasted in 2010. As presented in the Figure 19-3, actual

---

[250] *5G: The Changes to Lead for a Decade,* Deloitte Consulting (2018)
https://www2.deloitte.com/content/dam/Deloitte/us/Documents/technology-media-telecommunications/us-tmt-5g-deployment-imperative.pdf

spectrum used increased from 170 MHz in 2009 to 348 MHz in 2014, which is equal to a CAGR of 15.4%, compared to estimated CAGR as of 37.1%.

In 2014, spectrum usage was forecast to increase at a CAGR 24.7% between 2015 and 2019. While less than what was predicted in 2010, this updated growth rate is higher than actual growth during the prior four years.

Figure 19-3: Change in Spectrum Usage

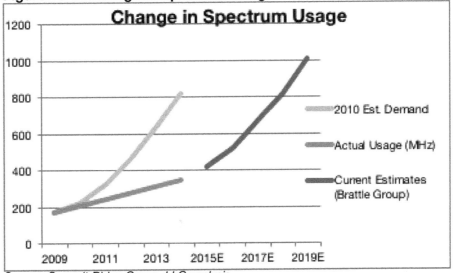

Source: Summit Ridge Group, LLC analysis

3. Wireless Capital Expenditures

Capital expenditures in the U.S. by the wireless industry increased from $13 billion in 1997 to $25.6 billion in 2017. The rate of capital expenditures has slowed from a CAGR of 20.5% between 1997 and 2002 to a CAGR of 7.09% between 2012 and 2017, as shown in Figure 19-4 below. At the same time, revenue growth has slowed to low single digits. This trend suggests a slowly tightening business model.

Figure 19-4: Annual Change in U.S. Wireless CAPEX

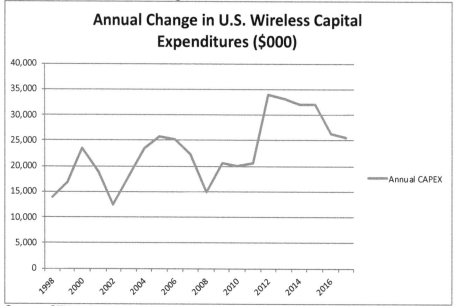

Source: CTIA industry survey and Summit Ridge Group, LLC analysis

4. Wireless Industry Revenue Growth

Revenue in the U.S. wireless industry increased from $27.85 billion in 1997 to $179.09 billion in 2017. This is equal to a CAGR of 9.75%. However, the annual rate of growth has decreased from 18.99% in 1998 to a negative 5.0% in 2017. Similarly, the five-year CAGR decreased from a rate of 22.4% between 1997 and 2002 to a negative 0.65% between 2012 and 2017, as illustrated in Figure 19-5 below.

Figure 19-5: Wireless Industry Revenue Growth Over Time

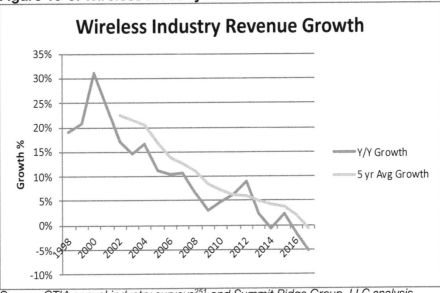

Source: CTIA annual industry surveys[251] and Summit Ridge Group, LLC analysis

5. Wireless Throughput (bps/Hz)

Wireless throughput, measured in terms of bits per second (bps)/Hz, has increased with each successive generation of wireless technology. As indicated in the Figure 19-6 below, bps/Hz increased from 0.03 using GPRS (General Packet Radio Services) to 1.92 bps/Hz using LTE+ technology.

Figure 19-6: Wireless Throughput for Different Technologies

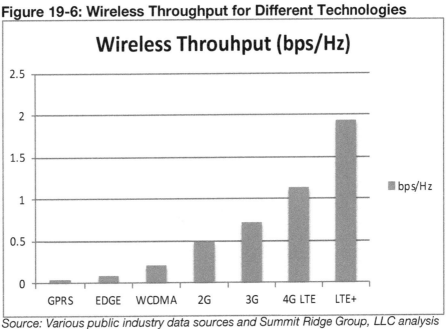

Source: Various public industry data sources and Summit Ridge Group, LLC analysis

---

[251] CTIA, *Wireless Industry Survey*, 2018 https://api.ctia.org/wp-content/uploads/2018/07/CTIA_ToplineWirelessIndustrySurvey.pdf

PART FOUR: GLOBAL

6. U.S. Mobile Data Growth is Slowing

Compared to other countries, mobile data growth in the U.S. is slowing

Compared to other countries, mobile data growth in the U.S. is slowing. The U.S. is in the middle of the pack for average GB per SIM card of mobile data. Finland, Taiwan, and even Italy lead the U.S. in terms of average GB per SIM in 2017. Finland leads all countries at 12.3 GB per SIM, Taiwan at 10.7 GB, the U.S. at 3.3 GB, and China at 1.5 GB. The U.S. average GB per SIM mobile data growth increased from 2 GB in 2015 to 3 GB in 2016 but then flattened in 2017.

In terms of percentage growth of mobile data from 2016 to 2017, India took the number position at 300% growth, with China following at 150% growth, and France at 110%. On the other hand, the U.S. experienced only 11% growth during the same period.[252] The decline in growth of average data per SIM in the U.S. could be caused by the fact that the U.S. is a maturing market, or that other markets like China and India are growing at a faster rate because they were much further behind and are now enjoying exponential technological gains. Another possible reason for slowing data growth in the U.S. is some carriers had "unlimited" plans in order to drive growth, and then converted those plans to unlimited but with data caps which caused the service to dramatically slow down after hitting the cap limit.[253]

7. Market Concentration

Mobile data growth in the U.S. appears to be significantly slowing

Each year the FCC is required to issue a report on the state of competition in the U.S. mobile industry. In its 2017 competition report, the FCC noted that U.S. growth from 2015 to 2016 grew at 5% from 378 million to 396 million users. Mobile data increased in 2017 to 15.7 billion GB from 13.7 billion GB in 2016, an increase of 14%. From 2015 to 2016 mobile data increased from 9.6 billion GB or 42%. From 2014 to 2015, it increased to 24.1 billion GB or 238%. Thus, mobile data growth in the U.S. appears to be significantly slowing. Coverage of the population has increased. In 2017, there were four service providers covering 92% of the U.S. population with 3G or better as compared to 82% in 2014. There are four major providers in the U.S. providing "nationwide coverage" including Verizon, AT&T, T-Mobile, and Sprint, the "Big-4." However, none cover all the U.S. land or provide service to all the U.S. population. Data use increased from

---

[252] *Unlimited moves the needle – but it's when mobile addresses slow fixed Internet that something happens*, tefficient AB (2018) https://tefficient.com/wp-content/uploads/2018/07/tefficient-industry-analysis-1-2018-mobile-data-usage-and-revenue-FY-2017-per-country-10-July-2018.pdf.

[253] *See*, for example, Chris Welch, *Verizon's good unlimited data plan is now three bad unlimited plans*, The Verge (Aug. 22, 2017) https://www.theverge.com/2017/8/22/16181362/verizon-new-unlimited-data-plan-video-throttling-net-neutrality.

2015 to 2016 by 39% to 3.9 GB per month on average, and in 2017 increased to 5 GB on average per device or 28% growth. Thus, from 2015 to 2017, mobile data acceleration decreased from 39% to 28% year over year.

Together, the Big-4 provide service to 411 million connections or 98% of the total connections. One other carrier covers 5 million, and a second 1 million. In addition, there are approximately 90 facilities-based rural mobile carriers. Several traditionally non-mobile companies are providing service using a combination of Wi-Fi and MVNO with the major carriers; these relatively new competitive entrants include Google, Comcast, and Charter.

The FCC measured the degree of market concentration of mobile carriers in the U.S., measured using the Herfindahl-Hirsch or HHI, an economic measure of market concentration, adopted by the FCC. The mobile competition HHI increased to 3101 in 2016, from 2151 in 2003.[254] The HHI is calculated by taking the sum of the squared market shares of the firms in an industry. Factors considered in the HHI calculation include prices, trends in prices, non-price rivalry, investment, innovation, and any barriers to entry. The FCC HHI uses an average weighted by population across the 172 EAs. At the end of 2016, the FCC reported in its *Twentieth Report* that Verizon had a market share by revenue of 36.8%, AT&T's market share was 32.8%, T-Mobile was 15.4%, Sprint was 13.4%, and U.S. Cellular was 1.7%.

The weakness of the HHI, is that it can be tweaked by changing the weightings. U.S. antitrust officials classify HHI markets into three categories based on the results: i) Unconcentrated competition is under 1500, ii) Moderately Concentrated is between 1500 and 2500, and iii) a Highly Concentrated, meaning less competition market, is 2500 and above. If there is just one provider, the number would be 10,000. The FCC determined that for 2016, the HHI for mobile carriers was 3,101, signifying a market that could be more competitive. The 2017 HHI was a slight decrease from the 2014 HHI of 3,138 and a larger increase from the 2007 HHI of 2674. Historic U.S. HHI Indexes are shown below in Figure 19-7.

---

[254] *Implementation of Section 6002(b) of the Omnibus Budget Reconciliation Act of 1993; Annual Report and Analysis of Competitive Market Conditions With Respect to Mobile Wireless, Including Commercial Mobile Services*, Twentieth Report, 32 FCC Rcd 8968 (WBT 2017) para. 5-7 (*Twentieth Report*); The Herfindahl-Hirschman index (HHI) is a commonly accepted measure of market concentration. It is calculated by squaring the market share of each firm competing in a market and then summing the resulting numbers. It can range from close to zero to 10,000.

Figure 19-7: HHI Market Concentration Index

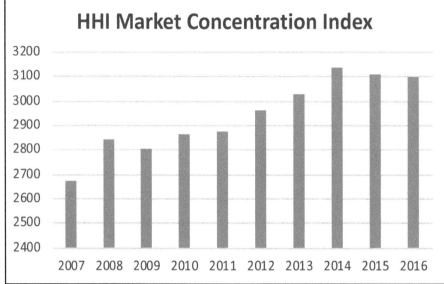

Source: FCC HHI Annual Reports from The Tenth to the Twentieth Report

Figure 19-7 above indicates growing market share, possibly due to consolidation, but possibly also due to organic growth of customers switching from the weaker carriers to the top two providers. The mobile industry's HHI, according to the FCC, has increased from more than 4000 points and is solidly in the Highly Concentrated category. The higher number is driven by the top two carriers increasing their market share, a number that is then squared. According to the FCC's HHI numbers, the competitive choice is decreasing in the U.S. over the last ten years, despite a small improvement in the past two years.

8. U.S. Spectrum Policy: Opening the Path for Mobile

The U.S., due to the responsiveness of the FCC, has led other countries in coping with the spectrum crunch

As noted before, around 2012, mobile industry leaders became concerned that there was a spectrum crunch; that there would not be enough spectrum to meet demand by consumers. It was thought that the FCC in its early days had given away, at no cost, the most valuable spectrum to the TV industry and even to early mobile providers. Other bands of spectrum were occupied but lightly used by satellite providers, fixed broadband, and the federal government. However, starting with the DTV transition clearing out the Lower and Upper 700 MHz band, followed by spectrum sharing methods developed by TV White Space in 2010, followed by the Broadcast Incentive Auction, the AWS-4 highly successful auction, the 3.5 GHz CBRS proceeding, and then the 24 GHz and 28 GHz planned auctions, the U.S. was able to reclaim and reallocate large bands of spectrum for mobile use.

The U.S. government, particularly the military, also controls large segments of usable spectrum. After the 2012 PCAST report and Presidential Executive Order directing agencies to share inefficiently used spectrum, the Department of Defense, working with the FCC and industry, worked cooperatively to make its Navy radar spectrum available in the 3.5 GHz CBRS proceeding helping to deliver 150 MHz of spectrum.

Despite the challenges it faces, the U.S., due to the responsiveness of the FCC, has led other countries finding ways to deliver more spectrum for mobile and unlicensed use. Thus U.S. spectrum policy now influences global spectrum policy such as the allocation for mobile use as shown in Figure 5-1 in Chapter V of this *Handbook*. The U.S. also has been leading the movement in shared spectrum. Of course, this lead rapidly shrank as other countries like China and India rolled-out their LTE systems.[255] However, recent reports suggest the U.S. still has one of largest LTE penetrations by percent of total users in the world.[256] South Korea, Japan, Norway, and Hong Kong lead the U.S. in LTE penetration in 2017, from 97.49% to 90.32% in the U.S.[257]

The FCC appears to be proactive in the dialogue with other governments and international organizations to encourage the harmonization of spectrum allocations to wireless broadband. The most recent World Radio Communication Conference (WRC), hosted by the United Nations in 2015, provided a forum for this. The U.S.'s relationship with international technology standards bodies is not always positive. Some FCC commissioners, including Michael O'Reilly, have hinted at withdrawing from the ITU.[258]

A recent Oppenheimer & Co. analysis reported that in the last decade, from 2010 to 2018, wireless companies have invested over $450 billion consisting of $350 billion in capital expenditures and $100 billion in spectrum, have generated more $100 billion per year in EBITDA to support $35 billion per year in capital expenditures, and

---

[255] The U.S. lead is not necessarily considered a good thing. One European regulator has said, "We [in Europe] watch the FCC race ahead [with a certain regulatory issue], then we examine their mistakes and do it right ourselves a few years later."

[256] 5G Americas, *LTE Achieves 39% Market Share Worldwide* (June 22, 2018) http://www.5gamericas.org/en/newsroom/press-releases/lte-achieves-39-market-share-worldwide/.

[257] *The State of LTE* (Feb. 2018), OpenSignal https://opensignal.com/reports/2018/02/state-of-lte.

[258] Commissioner O'Rielly's Remarks at New America (Jan. 12, 2016) https://www.fcc.gov/document/commissioner-oriellys-remarks-new-america.

have expended around $5 to $10 billion per year in spectrum on average. [259] Although the U.S. telecommunications industry had a disappointing 2017, Nasdaq reports point towards improved performance that is likely to continue throughout 2018.[260]

The U.S. is a leader in commercial 5G efforts globally

According to a recent study by Analysys Mason that was commissioned by the CTIA, the U.S. is currently ranked third, after China and South Korea, in the race to 5G. Due to extensive commercial trials and aggressive deployment timelines, Analysys Mason found that the U.S. is a leader in commercial 5G efforts globally, with many wireless providers committed to 5G launches by the end of 2018.

Making new low-, mid- and high-band spectrum for wireless use could push the U.S. to win the 5G race. In the high-band, the FCC took the first steps to unlock spectrum in the 28 GHz, 37 GHz, and 39 GHz for wireless use in 2016. Then, in late 2017, an additional 1700 MHz were made available in the 24 GHz and 47 GHz bands for 5G. Most recently, the FCC has announced that the first high-band spectrum auction will begin in November 2018.

In the mid-band, the FCC established an experimental spectrum sharing system in the 3.5 GHz CBRS band in 2015. The first use in the CBRS band is scheduled for 2019. In 2017, the FCC began to explore how three bands, including the 3.7-4.2 GHz band, could be used for commercial use. Additionally, earlier this year the 3.4 GHz band was identified as a government band that could be potentially allocated for mobile broadband use.

In the low-band, the 1.3 GHz and 1.7 GHz bands are being considered as candidates for reallocation by Congress. Timely government action is critically important if the U.S. hopes to lead the world in the deployment of 5G.[261] It is so essential to have adequate spectrum in all of the bands because each serves a different purpose. Low-band spectrum is needed for reliability and nationwide coverage, mid-band spectrum is needed for densification, consistent capacity, and speed, and high-band spectrum is needed for dense urban areas that require capabilities such as low latency or gigabit speeds to

---

[259] Timothy Horan, Oppenheimer & Co., *Wireless Set to Transform Communications/Cloud* (June 21, 2018).

[260] Zacks Equity Research, *U.S., Telecommunications Industry Outlook – March 2018* (Mar. 20, 2018) https://www.nasdaq.com/article/us-telecommunications-industry-outlook-march-2018-cm937417.

[261] Analysys Mason on behalf of CTIA: *Global Race to 5G, supra* at note 182.

deliver the equivalent of fixed broadband into the home wirelessly.[263]

The one area that the U.S. is not leading in is cell site infrastructure development, as noted above in this Chapter. Other countries, like China, India, Germany, and Japan are outpacing the U.S. Like a Marathon race, the pack has left the U.S. behind in cell site infrastructure. Most of the recent infrastructure is being built for 5G. Without infrastructure growth that matches spectrum allocation and licensing, the spectrum, no matter how much is allocated, cannot be put to work.

B. Canada

1. Regulatory Bodies

In Canada, there are multiple regulatory bodies responsible for the telecommunications industry. These include:

- The Canadian Radio-television and Telecommunications Commission (CRTC) is an independent public authority that regulates and supervises all Canadian broadcasting and telecommunication activities.
- The Department of Innovation, Science, and Economic Development (ISED), formerly known as Industry Canada, supports Canadian innovation efforts, trade and investment, enterprise growth, and customized economic development in Canadian communities. ISED regulates spectrum allocations and is tasked with planning spectrum auctions.

2. Spectrum

Spectrum tends to sell for lower prices in Canada compared to in the U.S.

Since 1999, the Canadian government has relied on auctions to allocate wireless spectrum licenses. The ISED allocates licenses in geographical service areas at four tier levels. Tier 1 consists of a single national area representing the entire country, Tiers 2 and 3 are province or territory-wide areas, with some subdivisions made in densely populated regions, and Tier 4 consists of 172 regional service areas. When a license for a specific band is awarded to a service provider, the license is exclusive. License terms vary but are typically set for terms of 10 or 20 years. License holders may trade, lease, or sell their allocations. However, these arrangements must comply with

---

[263] Statements made by Karri Kuoppamaki, T-Mobile's VP of Network Technology Development & Strategy, at recent *CTIA Race to 5G Summit.*

the original auction conditions and must be approved in writing by the ISED. Spectrum tends to sell for lower prices in Canada compared to the US. Canada has some of the world's highest telecom prices and the ISED aims to simulate competition through the timing and conditions of wireless spectrum auctions.

In March 2019 Canada will be following the US's lead by auctioning a total of 70 MHz of spectrum in the 600 MHz band. The ISED has indicated, however, that Canada will not be following the incentive auction model because two communications behemoths, BCE and Rogers Communications, own both broadcast providers and wireless carriers. Similar to the US, this repurposing of the spectrum will require a TV channel repack to clear the spectrum for wireless carriers. The Canadian government is also reserving 30 MHz of the band (43%) for smaller and regional wireless operators, with the intent to level the playing field for carriers with less than 10% of the market. Other mobile operators will be able to bid on the remaining 40 MHz.

The ISED announced on June 6, 2018, that Canada will be holding an auction of 3.5 GHz spectrum for 5G networks in 2020 and have announced they are expanding the consideration of frequencies in the 3.4-4.2 GHz range further to identify additional spectrum in the band to be reallocated for 5G. Additionally, the ISED plans to hold a millimeter wave spectrum auction in 2021.

XX. Latin America

Spectral efficiency has been a more pressing issue in Latin America than in the United States and Europe

Latin America has grown its LTE deployment to a 31.5% market share in 2018, compared to 46% in Western Europe and 76% in North America. By the end of 2018, there will be 258 million LTE connections, representing 37% of the total 2018 Latin American connections and 8% of the total 2018 global LTE connections projected. Delivering broadband to Latin America is important for the economy as every 10% growth of the broadband market increase is projected to raise GDP by 3.19% and increase productivity by 2.61%.[263]

Spectral efficiency has been a more pressing issue in Latin America, where relatively little spectrum has been allocated to mobile broadband service than compared to the U.S. and Europe. As of 2016, Brazil, Argentina, Chile, Costa Rica, and Nicaragua were the only Latin American countries with more than 400 MHz allocated to mobile services. Most Latin American countries have less than 300 MHz allocated, causing concerns about the lack of spectrum and spectral efficiency. Given the less developed state of fixed access networks in Latin America, the region's wireless networks are even more critical. Underutilized frequency bands exist in Latin America as they do in the United States. However, plans for most of these bands are not developed enough in the region so there will be significant delays before these frequencies can effectively support broadband services. Initial steps have been taken in Chile and Mexico for under-utilized spectrum bands to be used to provide broadband services, including the AWS 2.5 GHz, 700 MHz, 850 MHz and 1900 MHz bands. One specific issue is the width of the frequency blocks for mobile wireless services. Making broader blocks available for certain uses, such as LTE networks, will increase network efficiency.

As part of the global harmonization effort to coordinate frequency usage, the U.S. has over the years entered dozens of bilateral and regional agreements with Canada and Mexico that set the terms for sharing spectrum in the U.S. and near the border regions.

[263] 5G Americas, *Analysis of ITU Spectrum Recommend. in Latin America* (Apr. 2016) http://www.5gamericas.org/files/8414/6126/4784/ English_Spectrum_in_LatAm_White_Paper_April_FINAL_AB.pdf; 5G Americas, *LTE Achieves 39% Market Share Worldwide* (June 22, 2018) http://www.5gamericas.org/en/newsroom/press-releases/lte-achieves-39-market-share-worldwide/;5G Americas, *Spectrum Allocation in 700 MHz and 2.5 GHz in Latin America* (June 2017)http://www.5gamericas.org/files/1315/0843/7824/700_MHz_y_25_GHz_Oct_2017_Final-EN.pdf

A. Wireless Markets Regional Overview

1. Market Size

There are an estimated 690 million mobile subscribers in Latin America out of a total population of 652 million, a penetration rate of 106%. The four largest national markets are Brazil with 251 million subscribers, Mexico with 112 million, Argentina 61 million, and Colombia with 59 million. Four operators dominate the Latin mobile industry: Mexico's Américan Móvil at 37% of the total, Spain's Telefónica with 28%, Telecom Italia with 10%, and Altice with 8%.

In terms of size, Brazil has 39% of the subscribers, Mexico 17%, Argentina 10%, Colombia 9%, and Peru 6%.

Figure 20-1: 4G Subscribers in Latin America

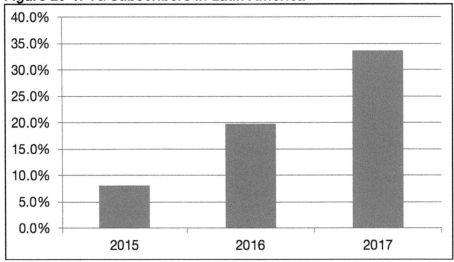

Source: Dataxis and Summit Ridge Group, LLC analysis

Operators in Latin America have been increasingly successful in monetizing data usage

The total installed base of mobile subscribers in Latin America in 2018 is 654 million out of a population of 639 million, which is a penetration rate of 107% which compares to a U.S. penetration rate of 130%. At the same time, several key indicators increased, including revenues of $87 billion in 2016. Post-paid subscribers increased from 2015 to 2017 to 27% and 4G users to 34%.[264]

Mobile operators in Latin America have solid penetration and room to grow revenues as users begin to depend on Internet connectivity from

---

[264]A postpaid mobile phone is a mobile phone for which service is provided by a prior arrangement with a mobile network operator. The user is billed after the fact according to their use of mobile services at the end of each month. Postpaid service typical requires two essential components; credit history/contractual commitment and service tenure.

their mobile phones only.[265] Latin American ARPU is lower than the U.S. ARPU, ranging from $6-$15 per subscriber compared to the U.S. ARPU range of $43-$50.[266] Thus, Latin American mobile operators have a future upside of delivering more ARPU per user. In 2017, Latin America operators saw positive ARPU growth for the first time since 2012. Key factors behind ARPU growth could be attributed to new data revenue growth from networks evolving from 3G to 4G, new low-cost smartphones, and low, fixed line broadband penetration.

Figure 20-2: Penetration Rate Latin American Subscribers 2018

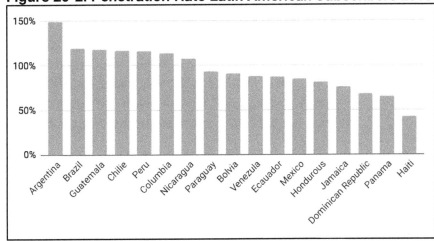

Source: Summit Ridge Group, LLC analysis

2. Smartphone Penetration

Smartphones accounted for 59% of Latin American connections in the first half of 2017 and are expected to grow to 71% of connections by 2020, compared to a global smartphone adoption rate in 2020 of 66%. There were 147 million smartphones sold in Latin American in 2017, increasing by 5% over 2016. Samsung led with 49 million smartphones many in the $100-$199 range. This rate of smartphone adoption will drive 171 million new smartphone users by the decade's end.[267] Of the 235 million Brazilian mobile connections, 73% are currently smartphones. Given these strong adoption rates, it is estimated that mobile broadband subscriptions will outnumber fixed

---

[265] GSMA, *The Mobile Economy Latin America and the Caribbean 2017* https://www.gsmaintelligence.com/research/?file=e14ff2512ee244415366a89471bcd3 e1&download.

[266] *Id.*

[267] GSMA, *The Mobile Economy Latin America and the Caribbean 2017, supra at note 268;* Tina Lu, *2017: A Year of Mixed Results in the Latin American Smartphone Market,* Counterpoint (Mar. 28, 2018) *https://www.counterpointresearch.com/2017-year-mixed-results-latin-american-smartphone-market/*

PART FOUR: GLOBAL

broadband subscriptions by five to one by early 2020.[268] Smartphone penetration goes drives 4G in Latin America. Users with smartphones expect 4G quality service because without 4G the smartphone services are close to useless. The largest mobile markets also have the highest penetration of smartphones including Brazil, Mexico, and Argentina.

3. Mobile Internet

The Latin American region is experiencing strong growth in mobile Internet users as measured by the number of smartphones. The number of mobile smartphone subscribers in Latin American is expected to increase from 420 million smartphone users in 2017, which is higher than the 310 million mobile smartphone users in the U.S., to 550 million smartphone users by 2023. In 2023, Western Europe will have 60 million fewer smartphone users and North America will have 150 million smartphone users than Latin America.[269]

4. Data Usage and Revenue

Mobile data usage is projected to grow 800% from 2017 to 2023, which is on par with other regions such as the U.S and Western Europe. Latin America mobile today uses an estimated 1 EB per month of data, by 2023 it will be 8 EB. Data growth per smartphone will grow from around 3 GB per month to 15 GB, compared to 25 GB in Western Europe and 48 GB in North America, the same year. Latin America smartphone data use will be similar to Asia and India.[270]

5. Regional Regulatory Organizations

a. OAS CITEL

The Inter-American Telecommunication Commission (CITEL)[271] is an entity of the Organization of American States (OAS). CITEL's objective is to contribute to the region's economic and social development. This role includes:

- Coordinating the rules between countries to facilitate infrastructure deployment and mobile service delivery;

---

[268] Frost & Sullivan White Paper, *5G in Latin America: A Region's Global Competitiveness at Stake* (Feb. 26, 2018) https://www.principalglobal.com/documentdownload/82341.

[269] GSMA, *The Mobile Economy Latin America and the Caribbean 2017, supra at note 268.*

[270] Ericsson Mobility Report, *Latin America and the Caribbean* (June 2018) https://www.ericsson.com/assets/local/mobility-report/documents/2018/ericsson-mobility-report-june-2018.pdf (*Ericsson Latin America Mobility Report*).

[271] OAS CITEL https://www.citel.oas.org/en/Pages/About-Citel.aspx05.

- Working to harmonize national spectrum regulation to drive efficiencies in mobile infrastructure;
- Telecom regulatory and technology training; and
- Helping countries devise mobile development strategies

b. COMTELCA

The Regional Telecommunications Technical Commission (COMTELCA) is an intergovernmental organization that coordinates and promotes the integration and development of telecommunications in Central America.

6. Spectrum Developments

To expand the deployment of mobile broadband technologies in the region, allocating more spectrum to mobile service providers is paramount. In particular, increasing the amount of spectrum available for mobile services will support technological advancements is needed to satisfy the region's growing demand and sustain the quality of service in the future. The U.S., Canada, and Mexico have auctioned the AWS-3 (1755-1780 MHz and 2155-2180 MHz) sub-band for mobile use in the past three years. The U.S. has already auctioned the 600 MHz band in the 2016 Broadcast Incentive Auction. Canada has plans to allocate this spectrum in March 2019. The Federal Telecommunications Institute of Mexico approved the relocation of 48 digital TV stations from 614-698 MHz in March 2018, freeing up 84 MHz of the 600 MHz band for an auction set for the first quarter of 2019. The spectrum will be for 5G mobile only, making it the first country in the world to auction spectrum solely for 5G service. Argentina plans to auction the 600 MHz band in 2018.

As a result of the WRC-15, several countries in the region made modifications to their national frequency plans. The spectrum modification has included in this reallocation consists of the 1417-1518 MHz band, the 2.3 GHz band, the 2.6 MHz band, and segments of the 3.3-3.7 GHz band. Argentina, with a healthy mobile operator environment, auctioned the 850 MHz band, 1900 MHz band, and the 1700 MHz band for 4G in 2014. Then in 2017, Argentina auctioned 2500-2690 MHz, or 190 MHz to the three major mobile operators. try of Information Technology and Communications, or MinTIC, raised cap for mobile operators in 800 MHz band from 30 MHz to 45 MHz per operator and the cap for 1710–2690 MHz band from 85 MHz to 90 MHz. Until 2017, the 850 MHz band was the only common spectrum band offered in all Latin American markets. But, thirteen Latin American nations have auctioned the 1.7-2.1 GHz band -- 1710-1755

The United States, Canada, and Mexico have auctioned the AWS-3 sub-band for mobile use in the past three years

PART FOUR: GLOBAL

MHz paired with 2110-2155 MHz -- and eight nations have opened up the use of the 2.5 GHz band, from 2500-2690 MHz, for mobile services. Ten countries have also awarded the 700 MHz band for mobile broadband, either through an auction process or by a direct award.[272] Figure 20-3 illustrates spectrum allocation in Latin America.

Figure 20-3: 4G Spectrum Allocations in Latin America

Source: Summit Ridge Group, LLC analysis

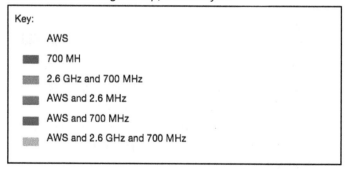

Key:

    AWS

    700 MH

    2.6 GHz and 700 MHz

    AWS and 2.6 MHz

    AWS and 700 MHz

    AWS and 2.6 GHz and 700 MHz

---

[272] 5G Americas, *Analysis of ITU Spectrum Recommendation In Latin America: Understanding Spectrum Allocations and Utilization in Latin America* (June 2017) http://www.5gamericas.org/files/6814/9797/9037/V2White_Paper_Espectro_English.pdf.

7. Technology Trends

Latin America, particularly Brazil, was considered to be lagging in terms of adopting new mobile technologies.[273] However, by 2018, a study found that with one major operator 4G was experienced 70% of the time and for all the operators over 50%.[274] Widespread rollout of 5G in the consumer market is unlikely to occur until Latin America's mobile network operators recover their 4G investment costs.[275]

Widespread rollout of 5G in the consumer market is unlikely to occur until Latin American mobile network operators recover their 4G investment costs

a. 4G Technology

The current focus of Latin American operators and consumers is 4G. 4G adoption rates are now accelerating. The rate across the region more than doubled in 2016. By 2020, the region will largely close the gap with the rest of the world by reaching 42% of connections compared to the global average of 44%.[276] Brazil was the first country in the region to exceed 4G on more than half of total connections. In Argentina, 4G was available 73% of the time in 2018 but delivered only 12 Mbps speed compared to the U.S. at 17 Mbps and Mexico at 23 Mbps.[277] In terms of LTE, by 2017 mobile operators in Latin America had launched 108 LTE networks in 45 different markets. The aggressive rollout of 4G has caused LTE coverage to rise sharply to 70% of Latin America's population. The evolution to 5G is around the corner with 5G trials taking place in Argentina and rollouts in 2019. LTE-Advanced trials with speeds up to 1 Gbps have taken place as well.[278]

b. 4G Investments

From 2010 to 2016, mobile operators in Latin America invested more than USD $11.2 billion to acquire additional spectrum, mainly due to the licensing of the AWS 4G spectrum bands including 1700-2100 MHz, 2.6GHz, 3.5GHz and 700MHz. Local operators are expected to invest nearly $70 billion in their networks by 2020 to expand 4G coverage across the region. These investments will expand mobile

---

[273] Gabriella Jeakins, *5G to Come to Latin America in 2012/2022* (Jan. 29, 2018) https://knect365.com/5g-virtualisation/article/02031a8c-9a5b-41d9-8b6a-1d8b8d2bbee5/5g-to-come-to-latin-america-in-20212022 (*5G to Come to Latin America in 2012/2022*).

[274] OpenSignal, *State of the Mobile Networks: Brazil (January 2018)* https://opensignal.com/reports/2018/01/brazil/state-of-the-mobile-network

[275] Kevin Pritchard, *The State of LTE in Latin America* OpenSignal (Nov.1, 2016) https://opensignal.com/blog/2017/11/01/the-state-of-lte-in-latin-america/.

[276] Frost & Sullivan White Paper, *5G in Latin America: A Region's Global Competitiveness at Stake*, *supra* at note 272.

[277] GSM GSMA, *The Mobile Economy Latin America and the Caribbean 2017*, *supra* at note 268.

[278] *Id.*

PART FOUR: GLOBAL

coverage to almost 90% of Latin America's population and provide additional bandwidth for data-hungry applications.[279]

c. 4G Availability

4G availability, which is measured in terms of the percentage of time 4G users in a country have access to an LTE signal, is increasing in Argentina, Brazil, Chile, Colombia, Costa Rica, Mexico, and Peru. In all seven countries, availability scores rose by at least five percentage points year over year. Figure 20-4 illustrates the evolution of 4G in Latin America between 2016 and 2017.

Figure 20-4: 4G Evolution from 2016-2017

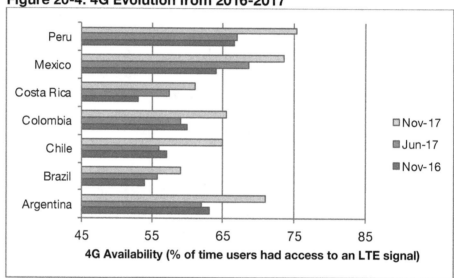

4G Availability (% of time users had access to an LTE signal)

Source: OpenSignal[280] and Summit Ridge Group, LLC analysis

Overall, 4G availability in Latin America has not surpassed the 80% mark, which generally used as the benchmark for a mature LTE country with widespread 4G service, but Peru is starting to get close to that mark, followed by Mexico. Operators in many countries are investing heavily in expanding their networks to make their 4G services more consistently accessible, but some countries are behind the curve, in particular, Brazil and Costa Rica.

d. 4G Speed

Several countries in Latin America boast powerful LTE network speeds. Four of the seven countries have 4G speed scores above the global average of 16.6 Mbps, with averaged 4G download speeds in excess of 20 Mbps in Mexico and Brazil. The Latin American speeds

---

[279] The 4th Annual Latin America Spectrum Management Conference.

[280] Kevin Pritchard, *The State of LTE in Latin America* OpenSignal (Nov.1, 2016) https://opensignal.com/blog/2017/11/01/the-state-of-lte-in-latin-america/.

are similar to the 2018 speeds for major U.S. carriers, reported by Wirefly to between 15 Mbps and 20 Mbps depending on the carrier, with an average speed of 19 Mbps.[281] However, average download speeds in Costa Rica is only 7 Mbps (only a few megabits faster than your typical 3G connection). 4G speeds in 2016 through 2017 are illustrated in Figure 20-5 below.

Figure 20-5: Evolution of 4G Speeds from 2016-2017

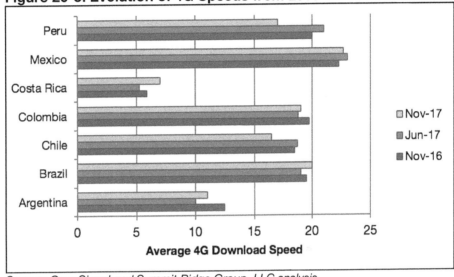

Source: OpenSignal and Summit Ridge Group, LLC analysis

As more customers sign up for 4G, networks become increasingly congested, causing average speeds to fall

Unlike availability, LTE speeds delivered the Latin American networks appear to be holding steady, although in a few cases speeds have decreased (but are still up to five times faster than 3G). This trend is often seen in developing markets. As operators roll out their initial LTE systems, those networks are often not heavily loaded. This is because most customers have not yet made the transition from 3G to 4G services. But as more customers sign up for 4G, networks may become increasingly congested, causing average speeds to fall. The expectation is for 4G to reach an equilibrium in Latin America, as operators balance network investment with customer acquisition. In particular, increased numbers of 4G users will cause speeds to fall, which will, in turn, trigger a wave of upgrades, which will cause speeds to increase. [282]

e. 4.5G Technology

The term "4.5G" was coined in 2018 to describe the evolution from

---

[281] Telecometitor, *In Latest Mobile Broadband Speed Comparison, Verizon Comes Out on Top*, Carl Weinstschenk, citing Wirefly data from 4Q17 to 1Q18 (Apr. 3, 2018) https://www.telecompetitor.com/wirefly-verizon-is-fastest-wireless-provider/.

[282] Id., *LTE Latin America OpenSignal.*

4G to 5G, just as 2.5G was used to describe carriers moving from GSM to GPRS, and then EDGE. 4.5G can be used to describe LTE-Advanced or carrier aggregation techniques such as MIMO, and LTE-U. Huawei has been using the term 4.5G for Latin America markets. Recent developments regarding 4.5G include an agreement between Telefónica and Huawei to deploy 4.5G Evolution for the first time in Latin America in Bogotá, Monterrey and Rio de Janeiro.[283]

9. 5G Technology

Mobile adoption and the use of data and Internet-oriented devices is rapidly growing in Latin America, thus making a case for the importance of data-intensive mobile services and widespread availability.[284] Latin America is therefore not immune to the hype surrounding the capabilities of 5G. However, the urgency to introduce 5G is limited due to the current build-out of 4G in Latin America.

The urgency to finance and implement the rollout of 5G is limited due to the build-out if 4G currently underway

Some industry observers expect the first 5G commercial launch in Latin America to be around 2019 and 2020, with deployment expected at the same time in the region's bigger markets. Industry observers anticipate 5G will begin to expand rapidly by the middle of the next decade to reach just under 50% penetration by 2025. This equates to over an estimated 300 million 5G connections in Latin America by 2025, which would be nearly 5% of the expected 5.9 billion global users.[285] 4G infrastructure is ready built for 5G requiring often only a software upgrade to the base station and an antenna change for the spectrum being used for 5G. The other cost is fiber being built to the neighborhoods and small cell installations.

Key factors affecting 5G deployment include the successful launch of 5G in US and Europe; a compelling business case for 5G in Latin America; the availability of affordable 5G smartphones; 5G frequency availability because Latin America, in general, does not have the same full spectrum use as the U.S. or Europe; and successful transition from 4.5G.[286] LTE-A will help in the preparation for 5G deployment.

In terms of 5G commercialization, the ITU divided 5G, and 3GPP

---

[283] Ian Channing, *Telefonica/Huawei Agree Latin American 4.5G Rollouts,* Developing Telecoms (Feb. 24, 2018) https://www.developingtelecoms.com/tech/wireless-networks/7630-telefonica-huawei-agree-latin-american-4-5g-rollouts.html.

[284] Gabriella Jeakins, *5G to Come to Latin America in 2012/2022, supra* at note 274.

[285] *5G in Latin America: A Region's Global Competitiveness at Stake, supra* at note 277.

[286] LTE and/or LTE-Advanced are generally equated with the 4G term; 4.5G is equated with the wireless technologies between 4G and 5G, in particular the technology between LTE-A and 5G (see: https://www.fiercewireless.com/special-report/meaning-4-5g-huawei-nokia-ericsson-qualcomm-weigh).

Release 15 for Non-Standalone 5G New Radio (NR), into three key drivers that will each be delivered in Latin America: eMBB, or "enhanced Mobile Broadband" for mobile handsets, and fixed broadband access (sometimes called "FBB") applications; ii) URLLC, or Ultra-Reliable Low-Latency Communications, which is used for autonomous vehicles, IoT, and industrial applications, and iii) MMTC, or Massive Machine Type Communications, which includes sensors and IoT. eMBB, URLCC, and MMTC were adopted by 3GPP in 2017 as the NR New Radio standard, which can include lower frequencies from 600 MHz to 6 GHz. These 5G network services being rolled out in Latin America are discussed below.

a. Regulatory Issues

Developing a spectrum strategy for 5G is a growing focus of regulators.[287] Countries in Latin America continue to develop national plans for the launch and rollout of 5G services. Key issues include the following:

- Ensuring that infrastructure and planning are in place when the market is ready for 5G.
- Deciding whether Latin America and Caribbean countries should follow the spectrum policies of U.S., Japan, and South Korea or if they should align with the bands shortlisted at WRC-15.
- Deciding the best use of spectrum below the mmW frequency bands.

b. Mobile Growth

In 2018, in Latin America, 106% of the total population had a mobile subscription compared to 108% in North America and 106% in China. For the first quarter of 2018, new mobile subscriptions in Latin America were anemic with a net loss of 1 million, compared to India adding 16 million and China 53 million. However, one study projects Latin America will experience strong mobile subscription growth in the future growing to 730 million by 2023 from 690 million in 2018, representing 14% of the total 2023 projected global subscriptions of 7.2 billion.[288] Latin America, with 730 million, is projected to leap far ahead of North America's 450 million in mobile subscriptions by 2023.

---

[287] The 4th Annual Latin America Spectrum Management Conference.

[288] Ericsson Mobility Report, *Latin America and the Caribbean* (June 2018) https://www.ericsson.com/assets/local/mobility-report/documents/2018/ericsson-mobility-report-june-2018.pdf (*Ericsson Latin America Mobility Report*).

PART FOUR: GLOBAL

Of the 5.4 billion LTE devices projected to be connected globally by 2023, there will be 550 million LTE voice connected smartphones, or approximately 10% of the total global in Latin America. Asia Pacific will dominate with almost 3.5 billion, while North America will have about 400 million, or around 15% of the total of Asia Pacific, and only 7% of the total global connections. By 2023, 75% of the 730 million mobile subscriptions in Latin America will be LTE, or 550 million, split between 4G and 5G, depending on growth curves. In North America, on the other hand, 400 million will be LTE split between 4G and 5G.[289]

c. Internet of Things (IoT)

Like the rest of the world, Latin America is ready to implement IoT solutions. One study projected that the IoT market in Latin America would grow to $44 billion by 2019.[290] Compared to the U.S., Latin Americans have only two connected devices compared to 11.5 for North Americans. IoT cellular devices are projected to reach 3.5 billion globally by 2023, with China driving the market with 2.2 billion in North East Asia, and Latin America has one of the smallest numbers by region.[291]

Recent developments in Latin America regarding IoT include a partnership between Telecom Argentina and Huawei to create a cloud core network and use network functions virtualization (NFV) to improve operational efficiencies and shorten the time-to-market of new products and services. This new cloud core network technology will allow Telecom Argentina to offer improved enterprise communications services as well as operations within IoT. Telecom Argentina's ability to provide IoT-related services will be crucial for its future success in the changing telecom market.

10. Satellite Telecommunications

Due to Latin America's size and geography, satellites play an integral role in reaching those outside of Latin America's main cities

Due to Latin America's size and geography, satellites play an integral role in reaching those living outside of Latin America's main cities.[292]

---

[289] Ericsson Mobility Report (June 2018) https://www.ericsson.com/assets/local/mobility-report/documents/2018/ericsson-mobility-report-june-2018.pdf.

[290] Micromarket Monitor, *Latin America Internet-of-Things (ioT) and Machine-to-Machine (M2M) Communications Market* http://www.micromarketmonitor.com/market/latin-america-Internet-of-things-iot-and-machine-to-machine-m2m-communication-4296836326.html.

[291] Ericsson Mobility Report, Latin *America and the Caribbean* (June 2018) https://www.ericsson.com/assets/local/mobility-report/documents/2018/ericsson-mobility-report-june-2018.pdf.

[292] W. Alegjanor Sanches, *Latin America's Space Programs,* The Space Review (Jan. 22, 2018) http://www.thespacereview.com/article/3413/1.

For remote areas, connectivity via satellite is often the only option.[293] Satellites are now providing a range of service to Latin American countries, and more countries in Latin America are seeking to develop their own satellite-building capabilities. Satellite operators with established operations in Latin America include SES, Intelsat, Eutelsat, Telesat, Hispasat, and Star One.

Companies with Latin American space programs have enjoyed multiple accomplishments in recent years.[294] Bolivia and Peru have new satellites in orbit that support telecommunications and surveillance projects, while Argentina, Central America, Colombia, Ecuador, and Mexico have domestically constructed their own platforms. From a regulatory perspective, Brazil is looking to revamp its space program, and Paraguay is attempting to jumpstart its space program. In general, aside from the loss of a Mexican satellite and the delay in replacing Chile's FASat Charlie (Sistema Satelital para Observación de la Tierra, or SSOT) satellite, the past several years have witnessed more space-related successes than failures.

a. Technical Developments in Latin America

Business models for serving residential markets that have been successful in the U.S. are not necessarily viable in Latin America. The need for a satellite-based solution exists in Latin America, but the big question is if there is enough volume of potential users with sufficient money to afford the service. To date, initiatives to reach residential consumers in Latin America using satellite have not been successful.

However, only until recently are companies with significant consumer experience and advanced high throughput satellites entering the Latin American market. Therefore, it is still unclear whether satellite service will be a viable alternative to serve the consumer market in the region.

In Brazil, Hughes' Jupiter satellite service's initial rollout went well. However, the rate of growth in the residential segment seems to have slowed down in its second year of service. The marketing of capacity to Small and Medium Enterprises (SMEs) with basic connectivity needs is an option if the residential market falls short of expectations. However, demand from SMEs will not be enough to consume the

PART FOUR: GLOBAL

---

[293] Mauricio Segovia, *Satellite Industry Fights for Better Future in Latin America*, Satellite Today (Apr. 5, 2018) https://www.satellitetoday.com/business/2018/04/05/3-trends-in-the-satellite-industry-that-will-impact-latin-america-2018/.

[294] Bernardo Schneidrman, *Market Briefs, The Latin American Satellite Market*, Satellite Markets & Research (Aug. 2015) http://www.satellitemarkets.com/pdf2015/latin-american-marketbrief.pdf.

capacity available for the region's residential market initiatives.

b. Technical Developments in Latin America

Brazil, Argentina, Mexico, Ecuador, Chile, Peru, Venezuela, Bolivia, and Nicaragua are working with ISRO[295] to develop and build satellites after ISRO proved it is capable of achieving even inter-planetary missions cost-effectively, in addition to having a reliable program.

B. Mexico

Mexico is the second largest telecom market in Latin America with 112 million users an 85% penetration rate of its 131 million population. As of 2018, Telcel, owned by América Móvil, serves 78 million users, Movistar, owned by Spain's Telefónica, serves 26 million and AT&T serves 12.5 million. dominate the mobile telecom market in Mexico. Other wireless participants include Totalplay, Cablevision, and Axtel. As of June 30th, 2017, Telcel claimed a 66% share of the Mexican mobile market, followed by Movistar at 23%, and AT&T at 11%. Market shares in Mexico's mobile telecom market have changed little since 2010.

Mexico's regulatory authorities are determined to introduce further price competition into the Mexican telecom market by lowering barriers to entry for mobile operators

Mexico's regulatory authorities are determined to introduce further price competition into the Mexican telecom market by lowering the barriers to entry for mobile operators. To further this goal, the ALTÁN Consortium, a group of telecom companies and investors, was awarded a license in November 2016 to develop a wholesale 4G LTE network to cover more than 90% of Mexico's population within the next seven years. 4G is reported to be available to 77% of the country with speeds of 23 Mbps.

1. Regulatory Developments

Mexico's President, Enrique Peña Nieto, signed a constitutional amendment on June 10, 2013, transforming the government's role in telecommunications.[296] The amendment set three distinct roles:

- Created the Instituto Federal de Telecomunicaciones (Federal Telecommunications Institute—IFETEL), a regulatory agency with constitutional status, the state reasserted its position as telecom regulator;

---

[295] ISRO is the Indian Space Research Organization, the space agency of the Government of India.

[296] Alejandro Madrazo, *Telecommunications: Mexico's New Reform,* Americas Quarterly (Summer 2013) http://americasquarterly.org/content/telecommunications-mexicos-new-reform.

- The amendment also mandates that the federal government set up a nonprofit, public service organization to broadcast provide objective information and to broadcast product content independently; and
- A wholesale-only 4G network was authorized, called Red Compartido, and provided with 90 MHz of 700 MHz spectrum and 18,000 km of fiber. The ALTÁN Consortium won the bid for the project. ALTÁN is required to cover 30% of the population by 2018, which it did, 50% by 2020, and 92% by 2024. The network started operating in March 2018.

In July 2014, President Nieto passed new rules for the telecommunications and broadcasting industries. The law included provisions designed to curb the power of América Móvil and Telcel.[297] In particular, the law prevented América Móvil and Telcel from charging interconnection fees. However, Mexico's Supreme Court ruled 2017 that the law was unconstitutional and that only IFT could instead set rates.[298] The ban imposed on Telcel to charge for termination services on its network – commonly referred to as the "Zero Rate" – was reversed by the IFT in November 2017. New IFT-mandated interconnection rates took effect in January 2018.[299]

In February 2017, Mexico's transport and communications ministry (SCT) unveiled its Conectividad Digital project, which provided the public policy guidelines for telecom-related matters. The projects in the plan include the Mexico Conectado initiative to bring free broadband Internet Wi-FI access to public places; the development of a national fiber backbone; Red Compartida; a satellite communications policy; and the national spectrum program.[300]

---

[297] Reuters, *Mexico's President Signs Telecoms Reform Rules into Law* (July 14, 2014) https://www.reuters.com/article/us-mexico-reforms/mexicos-president-signs-telecoms-reform-rules-into-law-idUSKBN0FJ2DU20140714.

[298] Diana Goovaerts, *Should AT&T Worry in the Wake of Mexican Court's America Mobil Decision?* ECN Magazine (Aug. 18, 2017) https://www.ecnmag.com/blog/2017/08/should-t-worry-wake-mexican-courts-america-movil-decision.

[299] TeleGeography, *IFT Scraps Telcel 'Zero Rate' Interconnection Rule* (Nov. 3, 2017) https://www.telegeography.com/products/commsupdate/articles/2017/11/03/ift-scraps-telcel-zero-rate-interconnection-rule/.

[300] Wallace Porter, *Mexico Communications Ministry Presents Digital Connectivity Program*, (Feb. 17, 2017) https://subscriber.bnamericas.com/en/news/ict/mexico-comms-ministry-presents-digital-connectivity-program/.

2. Spectrum

a. 2.5GHz Spectrum Auction

The IFT announced on February 8, 2018, that it will auction 120 MHz of spectrum in the 2.5 GHz band from, 2500-2690 MHz.[301] The auction's purpose is to promote the use of the 2.5 GHz band for the mobile services. The auction was originally scheduled to take place in March 2018 but is now expected to be completed in November 2018. The band has been divided into four FDD blocks of 10 MHz each and two TDD blocks of 20 MHz each.

The initial rules for the 2.5 GHz auction indicated that any operator could participate.[302] In response to competitors calling for strict limits placed on América Móvil's participation, the IFT later clarified that no operator would be restricted from the auction but that spectrum caps had been established. América Móvil already has 60 MHz of the 2.5 GHz band that they acquired from Grupo MVS, which may make América Móvil ineligible for the auction.

b. 600 MHz Spectrum Band Reallocation

The IFT has also announced its intention to relocate 48 digital television channels in the 614-698 MHz band.[303] This relocation will make Mexico one the first countries use 600 MHz band for mobile.[304]

3. Fiber

The SCT also announced a plan for state-owned Telecomm to add 35,000 km of fiber to the 20,000 km it is inheriting from state power company CFE.

4. Undersea Cable

Several undersea cables reach Mexico, notably the 10,000-kilometer Pan-American Crossing cable. Owned by Level 3, it stretches from

---

[301] Federico Hernandez Arroyo, *IFT Announces 2.5 GHz Auction* (Apr. 4, 2018) https://www.internationallawoffice.com/Newsletters/Telecoms/Mexico/Hogan-Lovells-BSTL-SC/IFT-announces-25-GHz-auction.

[302] Julia Love, *Mexico Telecoms Regulator Says All Can Participate In Spectrum Auction,* Reuters (Feb. 8, 2018) https://www.reuters.com/article/us-mexico-telecoms/mexico-telecoms-regulator-says-all-can-participate-in-spectrum-auction-idUSKBN1FT0EQ.

[303]TeleGeography, *Mexican 600MHz Spectrum Likely to be Available by 1Q19* (June 13, 2018) https://www.telegeography.com/products/commsupdate/articles/2018/06/13/mexican-600mhz-spectrum-likely-to-be-available-by-1q19/.

[304] entirely, *Mexico: IFT Releases 600 MHz Band as Mexico Becomes First Country to Release Frequency Band* (June 15, 2018) https://www.entirety.biz/mexico-ift-releases-600-mhz-band-as-mexico-becomes-first-country-to-release-frequency-band/.

Grover Beach, California to Tijuana and Mazatlán on the Pacific coast of Mexico before continuing down to Costa Rica and Panama. Level 3 also extended its long-haul network from Monterrey to McAllen, TX.

Other undersea cables serving Mexico include the ARCOS cable, the Maya-1 cable, and the América Móvil Submarine Cable System-1. The ARCOS cable connects the entire Caribbean region and has touch points that include Cancun and Tulum. The Maya-1 cable, which also serves Cancun, is a joint venture between Verizon, AT&T, Tata Communications, Telmex, and a dozen other firms. In 2014, América Móvil activated it Submarine Cable System-1, via Cancun. This cable extends from Jacksonville, Florida to Rio de Janeiro, Brazil.

Figure 20-6 shows Mexico mobile subscriptions compared to other Latin American countries.

Figure 20-6: Mexico Leads All but Brazil in Mobile Subscriptions

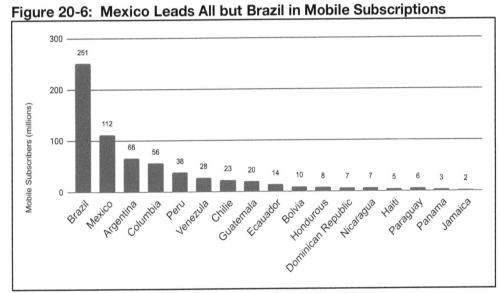

Source: Summit Ridge Group, LLC analysis

C. Brazil

The telecom market in Brazil... is the largest in Latin America

The telecom market in Brazil, which grew by 5.9% during the twelve months before September 4, 2017, is the largest telecom market in Latin America and the 5th largest globally.

The number of mobile subscribers grew to 251 million users by 2018. As of 2017, mobile Internet was accessible to 98% of Brazil's population via 3G and 4G. However, 4G was available only 61% of the time and had average speeds of 20 Mbps as reported by OpenSignal in 2018.

PART FOUR: GLOBAL

Telefonica S.A., América Móvil, Oi, and GVT dominate the Brazilian telecom market. Other industry participants include CTBC, TIM Cellular S.A. (TIM), and Sercomtel. Companies such as Telefonica Brasil (a subsidiary of Telefonica, S.A.) and Claro (a subsidiary of America Movil) that focus on Brazil's postpaid mobile market are considered more resilient than companies such as Oi and TIM that concentrate more on Brazil's shrinking prepaid market.

1. Regulatory Developments

The primary legislation governing telecommunications in Brazil is the 1997 General Law of Telecommunications or LTG. [305] The LGT was enacted in 1997 as a result of the denationalization of telecom activities in Brazil. It provides the key definitions relating to telecoms and establishes the basis for the organization of telecom activities. It also created ANATEL, the Brazilian regulatory agency.

The governmental agency responsible for regulating the telecom sector in Brazil is the Brazilian Telecommunications Agency (Agência Nacional de Telecomunicações - ANATEL), which is linked to the Brazilian Ministry of Communications. ANATEL mission is to promote the development of telecommunications in the country. ANATEL is administratively independent and financially autonomous.

At the top of [ANATEL]'s agenda is the re-auction unused 700 MHz spectrum licenses

ANATEL is the agency responsible for regulation, inspection, and granting of authorizations required for telecom activities in Brazil. ANATEL also has the authority to impose administrative sanctions for violations of Brazilian telecom laws and regulations. [306]

2. Spectrum

Juarez Quadros, president of the ANATEL, revealed that of the 58 regulatory initiatives that he expects to approve by year-end 2018, 20 are related to spectrum management. Quadros' spectrum management initiatives are particularly focused on the introduction of 5G technology. High on regulator's agenda is the re-auction of unused 700 MHz spectrum licenses. Anatel also intends to evaluate the 3.5 GHz band for 5G use by ensuring that there are no interference issues.

a. 700 MHz plan and 3.5 GHz spectrum

ANATEL initially auctioned the 700 MHz band in September 2014, generating a total of BRL 5.85 billion (USD $1.4 billion), which was

---

[305] LGT is Brazilian Federal Law No. 9,472 of 1997, as amended.

[306] TechinBrazil, *Overview of ANATEL*(Oct. 9, 2015) https://techinbrazil.com/overview-of-anatel.

well below ANATEL's BRL 7.71 billion target (USD $1.8 billion).[308] While Vivo, TIM Brasil, and Claro all won nationwide spectrum blocks, Oi did not participate in the auction. Likewise, regional operator Algar Telecom acquired spectrum within its own footprint. Sercomtel did not acquire spectrum. Another concession – nationwide barring the Algar/Sercomtel operating regions – also went unsold. [309]

b. Allocation of 2300-2400 MHz band for mobile use

Brazil's National Telecommunications Agency (Agencia Nacional de Telecomunicacoes, Anatel) is set to authorize spectrum in the 2300 MHz - 2400 MHz band for mobile use as per Resolution No. 688. The spectrum is to be revoked from Auxiliary Broadcasting and Related Services (Servicos Auxiliar de Radiodifusao e Correlatos, SARC) and Replay TV (Repeticao de Televisao, RpTV) license holders. The introduction of the 2300-2400 MHz band means that mobile operators in Brazil now have a total of 997 MHz of bandwidth at their collective disposal. [310]

3. Undersea Cables

- The Seabras-1 cable was completed in September 2017 and connects the U.S. and South America through New York rather than Florida.
- The Monet cable was completed in May 2018 and connects Brazil and the U.S. through Boca Raton, Florida.
- The BRUSA cable, scheduled for completion in mid-2018, will connect Brazil and the U.S. via Virginia Beach, Virginia.
- The Tannat cable between Brazil and Uruguay.
- A new cable between Brazil and Angola to be deployed by iAngola Cables, a state-owned telecommunications company based in Angola.

PART FOUR: GLOBAL

---

[308] *Anatel Reiterates 700MHz Plans; also Evaluating 3.5GHz Spectrum* (Mar. 21, 2018)
https://www.telegeography.com/products/commsupdate/articles/2018/03/21/anatel-reiterates-700mhz-plans-also-evaluating-3-5ghz-spectrum/.

[309] 5G Americas, *Status of the 700 MHz and 2.5 GHz Spectrum Bands in Latin America* (October 2017)
http://www.5gamericas.org/files/1315/0843/7824/700_MHz_y_25_GHz_Oct_2017_Final-EN.pdf.

[310] TeleGeography, *Anatel to Allocate 2300MHz-2400MHz Band for Mobile Use* (Nov. 28, 2017)
https://www.telegeography.com/products/commsupdate/articles/2017/11/28/anatel-to-allocate-2300mhz-2400mhz-band-for-mobile-use/.

- The Junior cable, which will connect San Paulo and Rio, is part of Google's Latin America network.
- The EllaLink cable, which will connect Madrid and Sao Paulo, is to be completed in 2019.

Figure 20-7 summarizes Brazil's mobile operator competitive environment.

Figure 20-7: Brazilian Users (millions) by Mobile Operator

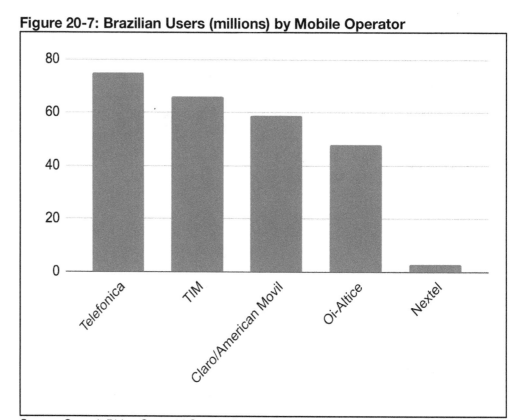

Source: Summit Ridge Group LLC analysis

D. Argentina

Though numerous operators are licensed to provide telecom services in Argentina, broadband competition is considered insufficient. The provision of both broadband and mobile services is dominated by a few key players, including Movistar, owned by Spain's Telefónica, serves 21 million users, Personal, owned by Telecom Argentina, serves 21 million, Claro, owned by América Móvil, serves 83 million, and Nextel Argentina, owned by Grupo Clarín, serves 1.8 million users. Other participants in Argentina's telecom market include Arlink and Arsat.

Argentina has the second-most developed broadband markets in

South America after Chile.[310] Telefonica de Argentina, Telecom Argentina, and Grupo Clarin dominate this market.

In September 2017, Grupo Clarín agreed to a merger of its Cablevisión unit, Argentina's largest pay-TV provider and the country's leading broadband provider, and Telecom Argentina.[311]

ARSAT-1 and ARSAT-2 satellites were launched in October 2014 and September 2015, respectively. ARSAT-3 was canceled. The satellites provide a range of services across Argentina and regional countries. Both are part of the Argentine Geostationary Telecommunications Satellite System (AGTSS).[312] ARSAT-1 and ARSAT-2 were designed and developed by the Argentine company INVAP and are operated by Argentine satellite operator ARSAT (Empresa Argentina de Soluciones Satelitales Sociedad Anonima).

Argentina has also expanded its undersea cable connectivity. Argentina developed a local link to the Atlantic Cable System (ACSea) in partnership with Brazil.

1. Regulatory Developments

Argentina has one of the most advanced telecom infrastructures in Latin America. However, significant additional investment is still required to update services in rural areas. Mobile revenue accounts for more than two-thirds of total telecom revenue. Moreover, the proportion of Mobile Revenue continues to rise while the proportion of fixed-line revenue declines. The government embarked on a large-scale National Broadband Plan, and in August 2016 the state-owned infrastructure operator, ARSAT (Empresa Argentina de Soluciones Satelitales S.A.), launched a USD $160 million project to extend broadband services to approximately 1,200 rural communities. By mid-2017 this project was 60% complete. Argentina's Congress passed the Argentina Digital Act in December 2014 to replace the

PART FOUR: GLOBAL

---

[310] Henry Lancaster, *Argentina: Telecoms Infrastructure, Operators, Regulations-Statistics and Analyses*, BuddeComm (Dec. 15, 2017) https://www.budde.com.au/Research/Argentina-Telecoms-Infrastructure-Operators-Regulations-Statistics-and-Analyses.

[311] Matthew McLaughlin, *Shaking up the Argentinian Telecom Space*, Seeking Alpha (May 28, 2018) https://seekingalpha.com/article/4177628-shaking-argentinian-telecom-space.

[312] Aeropace Technology, *ARSAT-1 Telecommunications* Satellite (2015) https://www.aerospace-technology.com/projects/arsat-1-telecommunication-satellite/.

country's Telecommunications Law and Decree No. 764/2000.[314,315]

ENACOM, the Ente Nacional de Comunicaciones (National Entity for Communications) is Argentina's telecom regulator. It replaced AFTIC and AFSCA in January 2016. In January 2018, ENACOM implemented a rule allowing companies to provide a "quadruple play" of mobile phone, land line, cable television, and Internet services, which had previously been prohibited.[316]

2. Spectrum

a. Auction of 2.5 - 2.6 GHz spectrum

Four different operators participated in Argentina's 2.5 - 2.6 GHz auction in July 2017. Bids were submitted by TeleCentro, a Buenos Aires-based cable company, Claro, a mobile incumbent, Movistar, a mobile incumbent that is a subsidiary of Telefonica SA, and Telecom Personal, a mobile incumbent. The winning bidders received the following:[317]

- Movistar was awarded block A, which comprises 30 MHz over six channels for FDD
- Claro was awarded 30 MHz for FDD mode
- Personal was allocated 40 MHz over eight channels, four in LTE-FDD mode and four in the LTE-TDD

The terms of the spectrum auction require the successful LTE-FDD winners to roll out 2.5 GHz within the following 12 and 48 months depending on location. The winning bid for the LTE-TDD block has a 48-month implementation deadline.

Nextel did not participate in the auction after acquiring 2.5 GHz spectrum holders Callibi, Infotel, Skyonline de Argentina, Netizen, and Eritown Corporation Argentina from co-owners WX Telecommunications and Greenmax Telecommunications in January 2017.

---

[314] *Argentina: Telecoms Infrastructure, Operators, Regulations- Statistics and Analyses, supra* note 311.

[315] Daniel F Di Paola, *Business Opportunities in Argentina: Telecommunications & Broadcasting,* Marval O'Farrell Mairal https://doingbusinessinarg.com/business-opportunities-in-argentina-telecommunications-broadcasting/.

[316] Reuters, *Argentina's Telecom Plans to Invest $5 billion Through 2020* (Jan. 31, 2018) https://www.reuters.com/article/argentina-telecoms-telecom/argentinas-telecom-plans-to-invest-5-bln-through-2020-idUSL2N1PR032.

[317] Telecompaper, *Movistar, Claro, Personal win Argentina 2.5 GHz Auction* (July 7, 2017) https://www.telecompaper.com/news/movistar-claro-personal-win-argentina-25-ghz-auction--1203034.

Pricing for the fifteen-year licenses was not disclosed. Before the auction, observers anticipated that bids from Telcom Argentina SA, Telefonica SA and Claro could reach $800 million.

Argentina is planning to auction 90 MHz of 4G spectrum to mobile telephone and Internet companies

b. 4G Spectrum Auction

In 2018, Argentina prepared to auction 90 MHz of 4G spectrum to mobile operators that could reach $800 million. The available spectrum will consist of 3G spectrum 60 MHz from 1890 to 1980 MHz returned by Arlink. In addition, 30 MHz of 4G spectrum returned from Arlink from 1745 to 1755 MHz, 2145 to 2155 MHz, 738 to 803 MHz. Airlink's parent company, Grupo America, failed to pay the USD $506 million license fee. [317]

3. Undersea Cables

GlobaNet announced in May 2018 plans to deploy a submarine cable to connect Rio de Janeiro and Sao Paulo in Brazil to Buenos Aires, Argentina.[318]

Telecom Argentina, Grupo Werthein, and Seaborn Networks announced in July 2018 that the ARBR submarine cable system between Argentina and Brazil would be landing in Telecom Argentina's cable landing station in Las Toninas, Argentina.[319]

Figure 20-8 shows the number of mobile subscriptions by operator in Argentina. It is clear from the graph that the market is evenly divided across the carriers.

PART FOUR: GLOBAL

---

[317] Eliana Raszewski, *Argentina Prepares 4G Spectrum Auction That Could Raise $800 Million*, Reuters (Mar, 16, 2018) https://www.reuters.com/article/us-argentina-telecoms/argentina-prepares-4g-spectrum-auction-that-could-raise-800-million-source-idUSKCN1GS1Y3.

[318] Henry Lancaster, *Argentina: Mobile Infrastructure, Broadband, Operators - Statistics and Analyses*, BuddeComm https://www.budde.com.au/Research/Argentina-Telecoms-Infrastructure-Operators-Regulations-Statistics-and-Analyses.

[319] Stephen Hary, *GlobeNet Plans Argentina to Brazil Submarine Cable*, Lightwave (May 7, 2018) https://www.lightwaveonline.com/articles/2018/05/globenet-plans-argentina-to-brazil-submarine-cable.html.

Figure 20-8: Argentina's Users by Mobile Operator

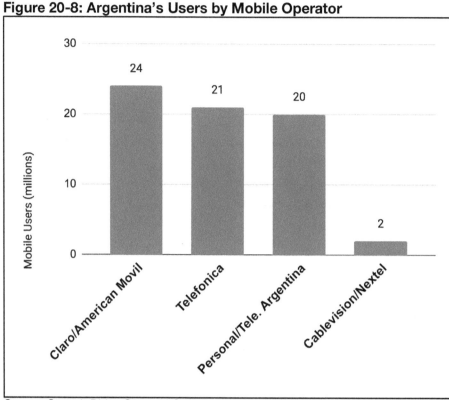

Source: Summit Ridge Group LLC analysis

4. Fiber

Argentina trails other Latin American countries when it comes to broadband network architecture using optical fiber, and calls are becoming louder to close this gap.[320]

5. Satellites

ARSAT-1 and ARSAT-2 satellites were launched in October 2014 and September 2015, respectively, to provide a range of services across Argentina and the rest of South America. Both are part of the Argentine Geostationary Telecommunications Satellite System (AGTSS).[321] ARSAT-1 and ARSAT-2 were designed and developed by the Argentine company INVAP and are operated by Argentine satellite operator ARSAT (Empresa Argentina de Soluciones Satelitales Sociedad Anonima). A third satellite, ARSAT-3, was canceled due to unsold capacity on ARSAT-2.

---

[320] Stefanie Eschenbacher, *How Argentina's Fiber Infrastructure Stacks Up Against the Rest of Latam* BNAmericas (Apr. 6, 2017) https://subscriber.bnamericas.com/en/features/ict/how-argentinas-fiber-infrastructure-stacks-up-against-the-rest-of-latam/?position=2048263.

[321] Aerospeace Technology, *ARSAT-1 Telecommunications Satellite* https://www.aerospace-technology.com/projects/arsat-1-telecommunication-satellite/.

E. Chile

Chile has one of the highest mobile penetration rates in South America

Chile's telecommunications sector, which has been fully privatized since the 1980s is considered the most modern and mature market in Latin America, although it is not the largest in terms of its 22.4 million users or 117% penetration. Broadband services and mobile telephone represent the telecom areas where investment demand is the highest. Chile is reported by OpenSignal to have 4G available 70% of the time compared to Canada's 82%. Throughput on 4G in Chile averages 17 Mbps compared to 16 Mbps in the U.S. and 36 Mbps in Canada.

Key factors driving the number of mobile subscribers include subscribers' ending multiple SIM card use and greater availability of LTE networks and services.[322] There are three large mobile operators equally dividing the market, Movistar, owned by Spain's Telefonica, Entel, and Claro each serve 7 million users. They each offer LTE-TDD using 2.6 GHz spectrum. Nextel Chile was purchased in 2017 and was re-branded as WOM and serves 1.7 million users. WOM has positioned itself as a new low-cost carrier, making a substantial spot in the market among its top competitors.

1. Regulatory Developments

The Ministry of Transportation and Telecommunications (MTT) is responsible for telecommunications regulation in Chile. MTT fulfills this role through the Undersecretariat of Telecommunications (SUBTEL),[323] which is responsible for coordinating, promoting, and developing telecommunications in Chile, which has transformed this sector into an engine for the economic and social development of the country.[324]

The primary law regarding Chile's communications sector is the General Telecommunications Law (GTL). GTL's general rules contain the following:

- A concept of telecommunications
- The principle of free and equal access to telecoms
- A classification of telecommunications services

---

[322] Henry Lancaster, *Chile: Mobile Infrastructure, Broadband, Operators- Statistics and Analysis*, BuddeComm https://www.budde.com.au/Research/Chile-Mobile-Infrastructure-Broadband-Operators-Statistics-and-Analyses.

[323] Subsecretaria de Telecomunicaciones, Subtel http://www.subtel.gob.cl/

[324] Alfonso Silva Cubillos and Eduardo Martin, *Telecoms and Media: Chile*, GettingTheDealThrough (July 2018) https://gettingthedealthrough.com/area/39/jurisdiction/3/telecoms-media-chile/.

PART FOUR: GLOBAL

- A general regulatory framework for the installation, operation, and exploitation of such services

Rules for the interpretation, application, and control of the GTL and its complementary rules, including: telecoms concessions, permits and licenses needed to provide telecoms services and the requirements and procedures applicable to their granting, tariffing processes for certain telecoms services; the fees for the use of spectrum, and various breaches and sanctions.

SUBTEL has five strategic goals:

SUBTEL has relied on "beauty contests" for the licensing of spectrum

- Bridging the digital divide and promoting social inclusion
- Increasing protection of telecommunications users
- Improving the quality of service in telecommunications
- Promoting competition to accelerate the advance of the information society
- Stimulating innovation and development of new information and communication technology.

SUBTEL assigned spectrum not based on auctions but on "beauty contests" as the FCC originally did in the U.S. when assigning spectrum for the first two cell phone companies. SUBTEL licensing included the 850 MHz band for 2G and, later, for 3G and 4G, the 700 MHz band and the 2.6 GHz band. Under this method of spectrum allocation, licenses are awarded after submissions of technical proposals; spectrum is auctioned only if there is a stalemate between submitted proposals. While Chile has achieved high levels of network development, there is concern that the required license obligations favored incumbents over new entrants. The additional license obligations also made it more difficult to sell or trade the license. [325]

a. 2017 Southern Fiber Optics Project

The Fibra Optica Astral (Southern Fiber Optics) project is a Chilean initiative to bring higher-level connectivity to the most southern and extreme areas of the country. During 2017, another land portion and also submarine portions of the project were awarded by Chile. This project is part of an initiative to bring higher level connectivity to the most southern and extreme areas of the country. Finally, in connection with the above, there have been some announcements and speculations of new submarine cable projects. For example, Google has announced that they will build a submarine cable

---

[325] GSMA Spectrum, *Best Practice in Mobile Spectrum Licensing* (Sept. 2016) https://www.gsma.com/spectrum/wp-content/uploads/2016/11/spec_best_practice_ENG.pdf.

connecting the U.S. and Chile, and Huawei has announced that they are analyzing the possibility of laying a submarine cable between China and Chile.

In March 2018, a new public bid process was announced regarding the deployment of land portions of the Southern Fiber Optics Project.

2. Spectrum

In January 2009, the Chilean Supreme Court ruled that no operator may concentrate more than 60 MHz in any band assigned for public mobile telephony services as a consequence of the 3G public bid.[326] At the time of this ruling, Entel had 60MHz and Movistar and Claro each had 55 MHz. A public bid for 3G later in 2009 resulted in Nextel's obtaining two concessions (licenses) of 30 MHz each and VTR's obtaining 30 MHz. VTR, at the time, was a subsidiary of Liberty Media.

A public bidding process took place in 2012, in Chile to grant public mobile operator licenses requiring 4G technology for delivering fixed or mobile services in the 2505-2565 MHz and 2625-2685 MHz bands. SUBTEL announced after a public auction that Claro, Entel, and Movistar were all awarded one of the three 40 MHz spectrum blocks granted through this public bid of the blocks A, B, and C, respectively.

A new public bidding process took place in Chile in 2014 for the granting of public telecommunication service concessions based on 4G technology. This was done for fixed or mobile data transmission public services in the 713-748 MHz and 768-803 MHz frequency bands. After a public auction, SUBTEL announced that Movistar, Entel, and Claro (the incumbents who participated in the 3G public bid in 2009) were each awarded one of the three spectrum blocks granted through this public bid of block A of 20MHz, B of 30MHz and C of 20MHz, respectively. Later in 2014, SUBTEL issued a technical rule reserving 20MHz of the 700 MHz band in favor of the Chile government for public safety purposes.

3. Undersea Cables

The Chilean government announced in June 2017 a project with China for an underwater fiber optic cable between the two countries. This

PART FOUR: GLOBAL

---

[326] Alfonso Silva Cubillos and Eduardo Martin, *Telecoms and Media: Chile, supra* at note 325.

would be the first cable to connect Asia with Latin America directly.[327] In January 2018, Google announced the construction of an undersea cable, Curie, between Chile and the U.S. from Los Angeles, California.

Figure 20-9 shows Chile's mobile competition by operator.

Figure 20-9: Chilean Mobile Competition by Operator

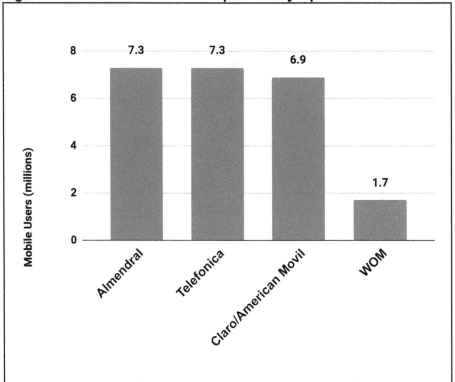

Source: Public data sources and Summit Ridge Group, LLC analysis

---

[327] Zhang Dongmiao, *Chile, China moving ahead with underwater fiber optic cable connection,* Xinhua (June 7, 2017) http://www.xinhuanet.com/english/2017-06/08/c_136349897.htm.

XXI. Europe

European countries have different agendas for allocating spectrum

European regulators have worked to pave the way for LTE and for 5G. Europe, which includes Western, Central and Eastern Europe, has a total of 1.105 billion mobile subscriptions as of 2018, with 525 million in Western Europe and 580 million in Central and Eastern Europe.[328] There are 54 nations making up Europe, and each has its own regulator although many work with the European Commission's CEPT and ESTI to standardize mobile operations. The nations and regulators assign spectrum and work to balance and provide incentives for creating competition through roaming rate regulation, MVNO regulation, and incentives to purchase spectrum licenses and build infrastructure.

There are more than 30 mobile operator competitors in Europe with each country having three to six competitors each. Figure 21-1 below shows the strong growth of mobile users by country and by operator.

Figure 21-1: European Operators by Country

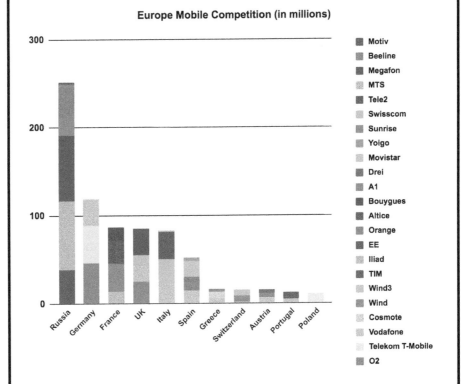

Source: Wikipedia and Summit Ridge Group, LLC analysis[329]

---

[328] Ericsson Mobility Report, June 2018.

[329] List of Mobile Network Operations in Europe, Wikipedia.
https://en.wikipedia.org/wiki/List_of_mobile_network_operators_of_Europe

Europe has 20% of the total 5.5 billion global mobile subscriptions. As estimated in Ericsson's 2018 Mobility Report, Europe had less than a net one million new mobile subscriptions, with the growth primarily from Central and Eastern Europe, which implies a mature market. Subscription penetration is 126% of the total population with little growth opportunity, compared to China which had 53 million new users in the same quarter. Figure 21-2 below gives a sample of the competitive diversity across Europe.

Figure 21-2: Mobile Operators in 2018

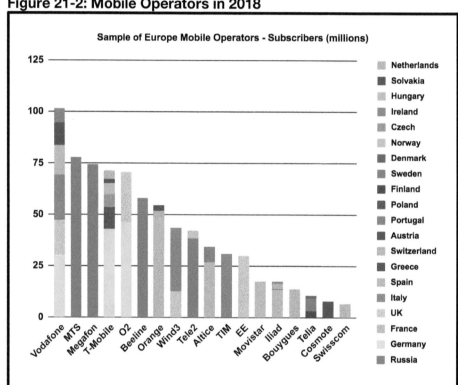

Source: Wikipedia and Summit Ridge Group, LLC analysis[330]

Europe is quickly evolving its mobile infrastructure from WCMDA and HSPA to LTE, with close to half of the subscribers using LTE. It is projected that 83% of Central and Eastern Europe will be using LTE and 5% will be on 5G by 2023. Western Europe will move much faster to 5G with 21%, or more than 100 million, using 5G by 2023. Data use per smartphone in Western Europe is 4 GB per month which is on par with the U.S. rate, and by 2023 the Western European rate is expected to increase to 25 GB per smartphone. In spite of the dramatic increase in data used projected for Western Europe, the U.S. is projected to leap ahead with 5G with the average U.S. smartphone consuming almost 50 GB by 2023. IoT connections in 2018 are

---

[330] *Id.*

approximately 200 million and are projected to increase to around 490 million in 2023. Europe will represent only 20% of the nearly 3.5 billion IoT connections in North East Asia projected for that same year.

Innovative bands for mmW are being considered for 5G, as they are in the U.S., including the W-band ranging from 92-115 GHz and the D-band ranging from 130-175 GHz. In November 2012, the European Commission authorized 120 MHz of spectrum in the 2 GHz band, which is a paired band that includes 1920-1980 MHz and 2110-2170 MHz and previously allocated for 3G UMTS services, to be cleared for 4G services by June 30, 2014. Now that the clearing processes has been completed, Europe's Radio Spectrum Policy Program (RSPP) is working to make over 1200 GHz of spectrum available for 4G services by 2020. [331]

Europe is also preparing for LSA spectrum sharing using a model similar to the FCC's CBRS. As in the U.S., Europe is also exploring the use of unlicensed spectrum for Wireless Access Systems and Radio Local Area Network, or WAS/RLAN, in the 5.925-6.425 GHz band. [332]

PART FOUR: GLOBAL

---

[331] European Commission, *Radio Spectrum Policy Program: The Roadmap for Wireless Europe* (Mar. 20, 2018) https://ec.europa.eu/digital-agenda/en/rspp-roadmap-wireless-europe.

[332] DIGITALEUROPE, *Whitepaper on 5925-6425 MHz (6 GHz) Wireless Access Systems / Radio Local Area Network (WAS/RLAN)* (Feb. 2018) http://www.digitaleurope.org/DesktopModules/Bring2mind/DMX/Download.aspx?Command=Core_Download&EntryId=2611&language=en-US&PortalId=0&TabId=353

Figure 21-3: Mobile Spectrum in Select EU Countries (MHz)

Band	Germany	Spain	France	Italy	UK
700 MHz	60		60	75*	
800 MHz	60	60	60	60	60
900 MHz	70	70	70	70	70
1500 MHz	40			40	
1700/1800 MHz	140	150	150	140	143
1900 MHz	35	15	15	20	35
2 GHz	120*				
2.1 GHz	120	120	120	120	120
2.3 GHz					40
2.6 GHz	190	140	190	150	190
3.4 GHz					150
3.6 GHz	300*	200		200*	
3.7 GHz	100*				195
26 GHz				1000*	
Total	**1,135**	**755**	**665**	**1,875**	**1,003**
* Indicates spectrum pipeline					

Source: BNetzA, SESIAD, ARCEP, Ofcom, and Summit Ridge Group, LLC analysis

EU countries allocate spectrum at a national level

Europe has a unique challenge in that EU leaders seek to create a unified wireless telecom market with standardized prices at the wholesale level. However, countries in the EU generally allocate spectrum at a national level. Different countries have different agendas for allocating spectrum. Some use it for raising revenue, while others want to make it available to as many people as cheaply as possible. Some governments focus on innovation by encouraging competition; others prefer fewer competitors to ensure more efficient spectrum use. But these varying strategies of spectrum allocation are at times inconsistent with the uniform wholesale pricing the EU leaders seek.[333] Furthermore, as newer LTE technologies require larger spectrum blocks to be efficient, the trade-off between competition and efficiencies becomes even more complex. Despite these challenges, the European Conference of Postal and Telecommunication Administrations (CEPT) has ensured strong

---

[333] Coleago, *Toward a Single E.U. Market* (Mar. 14, 2013) http://coleago.wordpress.com/2013/03/14/towards-a-single-eu-telecoms-market.

Aggregate wireless capital expenditures in Europe are not keeping pace with those in the United States

technical coordination within the EU. Moreover, the EU has the power to force its members to comply with EU policies to which their countries are signatories, which include most communications regulation.

Another challenge European operators face is different regulatory regimes in each country. Additionally, there is greater uncertainty over long-term spectrum rights than in the U.S. These challenges make cross-border consolidation and achieving economies of scale difficult, Consequently, the two largest operators in the U.S., AT&T and Verizon, are each larger than the three largest European operators combined.[334]

LTE infrastructure build-out will drive CAPEX in Western Europe and Central Europe through 2023, and 5G will require further spending. Western European operators will be under similar challenges as U.S. operators who will have to justify new 5G CAPEX expenditures with increased subscriber additions or increased ARPU. European Operators as a whole are projected to spend USD $100 billion in CAPEX between 2017 and 2020, averaging $33 billion per year, with an average 20% of revenue going to infrastructure. Total operator revenue during the same period will hover around $165 billion per year. Total mobile infrastructure CAPEX decreased from $28 billion per year in 2013 to $25 billion in 2017 and is projected to remain flat through 2020. Determining CAPEX for 5G will be difficult because the 4G base stations used for sub 1 GHz cannot be repurposed for 5G using spectrum from 3 GHz to the mmW bands.

European operators are pressing the regulators for speeding up the process of allocating new spectrum and spectrum sharing in an open letter to the regulators. 5G may be slower to come to market than in the U.S., but in 2017 Telecom Italia Group rolled out an LAA aggregation 4.5G service delivering up to 700 Mbps in seven cities including Rome and Milan, using Samsung and Sony phones. Customers in these same cities could receive 1 Gbps fiber service in their homes.[335] In addition to LTE-U type of 5G services, trials are being conducted in Europe for mmW at 28 Gbps. The trial in London

---

[334] GSMA, *Mobile Wireless Performance in the EU & the U.S.*(May 2013)
https://www.gsma.com/newsroom/wp-content/uploads/2013/12/GSMA_Mobile_Wireless_Performance_Report_2013.pdf.

[335]Telecom Italia, *TIM speeds up with ultrabroadband and launches 1,000 Mb fibre* (June 26, 2017)
http://www.telecomitalia.com/tit/en/archivio/media/note-stampa/market/2017/NS-TIM-1000-Mega.html.

delivered 1 Gbps service as a fixed wireless service into a home over several hundred meters.[336] As mentioned before, such mmW service has the possibility of replacing a customer's fixed wired broadband service in their home, especially if it is bundled with their mobile service. The revenue being paid to the wired broadband provider could be shifted to the mobile provider increasing ARPU for users.

1. Shared Spectrum in the 2.3-2.4 GHz band

Europe has taken a slightly different approach to spectrum sharing than the U.S. As outlined in Chapter VIII.K, the U.S. has employed a three-tiered system called the Spectrum Access System (SAS) to the CBRS 3.5 GHz band. The ECPTA's European Communications Committee (ECC) has opted to use the Licensed Shared Access (LSA) system for their spectrum sharing.[337] LSA is used in the 2.3-2.4 GHz band where incumbent users, like defense agencies, are protected. Incumbent users are different in each of the European countries, and the database must be able to provide information to the base stations – called Reconfigurable Radio Systems or RRS in LSA -- to protect the different country agency incumbents in the differing geographies with different boundaries, spectrum, and power limits. LSA ensures a certain level of guarantee in terms of spectrum access and protection against harmful interference for both incumbents and LSA licensees, thus allowing them to provide a predictable quality of service.

Europe has taken a different approach to spectrum sharing than the United States

The ECC has identified the 2.3-2.4 GHz band and the 3.6-3.8 GHz band for shared spectrum usage between incumbents and new wireless broadband communication services.[338] Starting in 2015, European countries on an individual basis began conducting LSA tests and trials in the 2.3-2.4 GHz band. It is likely that the exact implementation of LSA will differ from country to country in order to adapt to national circumstances. National LSA systems have been developed in Italy (2.3 GHz), France, Finland (2.3 GHz LSA and 3.5 GHz CBRS), Russia (700 MHz), the Netherlands (2.3 GHz), and Spain. In the U.K. sharing is called TV White Spaces.

---

[336] Arquiva, *Arqiva and Samsung Kick off UK's First 5G Fixed Wireless Access* Trial (July 25, 2017) https://www.arqiva.com/news/press-releases/arqiva-and-samsung-kick-off-uks-first-5g-fixed-wireless-access-trial/.

[337] CEPT, Electronic Communications Committee, *ECC Report 205: Licensed Shared Access (LSA)* (Feb. 2014) https://www.ecodocdb.dk/download/baa4087d-e404/ECCREP205.PDF.

[338] CEPT, Electronic Communications Committee, Report 254, *Operational guidelines for spectrum sharing to support the implementation of the current ECC framework in the 3600-3800 MHz range* (Nov. 18 2016) http://www.erodocdb.dk/Docs/doc98/official/pdf/ECCREP254.PDF

a. LSA, LAA, and SAS

LAA, or Licensed Assisted Access, is used to assist operators to aggregate or use license-exempt spectrum

LSA is different from the FCC's CBRS SAS database because it does not include concepts such as opportunistic spectrum access or general authorized access (GAA) users.[339] The LSA system is based on two tiers, not three: incumbents and LSA licensees. Both tiers of users have exclusive access to the spectrum while they are using it. To achieve this, the incumbent uses a database indicating when the LSA licensee can access the spectrum in a given geographic area, a given frequency band, a given period of time. This means, however, that a mobile network operator is required to vacate the band at a given geographic area, frequency range, or period of time for when the incumbent requires access to the spectrum. Like the SAS in the U.S., the LSA uses a similar database – however because of the nature of the Navy radar incumbent that moves, the U.S.'s SAS is connected to sensors that detect when and where the Navy ships are located. While satellites, the Navy, and fixed WISP wireless are the incumbents in the U.S., incumbents in Europe include amateur radio, mobile video paths, aircraft systems, and wireless camera systems.

LAA, or License Assisted Access, is used to assist operators to aggregate or use license-exempt spectrum. LAA assists in keeping the handset on the licensed spectrum for control data and they using the license-exempt spectrum transmitting the main data, like video.

2. Viasat vs. Inmarsat

The European Aviation Network (EAN) is an integrated satellite and air to ground connectivity network across the EU built by Inmarsat and Deutsche Telekom. To build the EAN, Deutsche Telekom installed approximately 300 ground towers, and Inmarsat used its S-band licensed spectrum in the 2 GHz range to host the satellite, which sparked outrage from rival satellite company Viasat. The S-band satellite is controversial because, according to Viasat, Inmarsat abused the conditions of its original license.

When the Inmarsat license was initially granted in 2009, its defined purpose was for satellite-based mobile services, not ground-based stations to deliver in-flight broadband connectivity. In October 2017, UK telecom regulator, Ofcom, announced that it would allow Inmarsat

---

[339] For more details on the differences between LSA and SAS, *see*, Markus Dominik Mueck, Srikathyayani Srikanteswara, and Biljana Badic, *Spectrum Sharing: Licensed and Shared Access (LSA) and Spectrum Access System (SAS)*, Intel Corp (Oct. 2015) https://www.intel.com/content/dam/www/public/us/en/documents/white-papers/spectrum-sharing-lsa-sas-paper.pdf.

PART FOUR: GLOBAL

to use its license for its airline broadband service. Viasat argued that Inmarsat violated their license because they did not proceed with developing a satellite-based mobile phone network when they received the license in 2009, instead intentionally saving it to develop an in-flight broadband service. Viasat insists that Inmarsat should either be compelled to comply with the original conditions of the license or else the spectrum should be retendered.

In December 2017, Viasat initiated legal actions against Ofcom to dispute their decision, along with teaming up with Eutelsat to file objections on a country-by-country basis to disrupt EAN. Additionally, Viasat and Eutelsat contended that they are trying to prevent Inmarsat from gaining a monopoly in the billion-dollar market for in-flight Internet services. On March 14, 2018, the Brussels Court of Appeal revoked approval of Inmarsat's use of terrestrial towers for the EAN. Despite this decision, EAN is still on schedule to launch commercial service by early 2019.

3. 5G in Europe

The EU is working to prevent Europe from falling further behind the U.S., China, and Korea in the race to 5G. To lay the groundwork for the deployment of 5G across Europe, the EU, European Parliament, and European Commission have agreed to set a 20-year time span on 5G spectrum licenses, compared to 10 to 15-year terms for prior licenses in most EU countries. The reason for the long license term extension was to encourage investment. This begins the process for holding 5G spectrum auctions, which are expected to be completed by 2020. The EU countries plan to use the 3.6 GHz mid-band and 26 GHz mmWave bands for 5G. Widespread commercial 5G use is scheduled for 2025.

The sizable delay in Europe [for 5G]... is contributed to regulatory inertia

The sizable delay in Europe, compared to countries leading the way to 5G, is attributed to regulatory inertia by national regulators who have so far been unsuccessful in coordinating the auctions of countries' spectrum to reduce regional divisions, among other regulatory coordination issues. Also contributing to a lack of coordination is that carriers do not have the continental scale needed to invest in widespread 5G networks due to the EU's strict competition laws that have made it difficult for carriers to expand into other European countries. This is not the first time Europe has encountered difficulties rolling out the next generation of mobile networks. A delayed and fragmented assignment of radio spectrum also led to a lag in 4G deployment.

The European Commission's 5G Action Plan[340] proposes to bring uninterrupted 5G coverage to all major European urban areas by 2025, along with setting deadlines for the development of a deployment roadmap by the end of 2017, spectrum assignments by 2019, and a development of global 5G standards by 2019. Additionally, the EC has launched the European Broadband Fund, which is a combination of private and public investments, to support network deployment throughout the EU. Although the UK has voted to leave the EU, the official Brexit departure date is not until March 29, 2019, so it is expected that the UK will still follow the 5G Action Plan.

A. United Kingdom

1. Regulatory Bodies

The U.K. has more than 90 million mobile subscribers served by four mobile companies – EE, 02, Vodafone, and 3 -- with infrastructure and 104 MVNOs. a The Office of Communication, or 120 Ofcom, is the independent communications regulator in the UK.[341] Ofcom's specific statutory duties are divided into five main areas:

- Ensuring the optimal use of radio spectrum. This includes monitoring the airwaves to identify cases of interference and taking action against illegal broadcasters and the use of unauthorized wireless devices
- Ensuring that a wide range of electronic communications services, including high-speed data services, are available throughout the UK
- Ensuring there are numerous TV and radio service providers of high quality and broad appeal
- Securing the universal service obligation on postal services within their jurisdiction
- Applying adequate protection for audiences against offensive material and privacy issues

2. Brexit

Control and management of spectrum has remained the exclusive property of the state, so Brexit should not hurt the UK's spectrum usage. However, as previously mentioned, the EU allocates spectrum at a national level. Cross-border usage requires coordination at an

---

[340] European Commission, *5G Action Plan* https://ec.europa.eu/digital-single-market/en/5g-europe-action-plan.

[341] More information about Ofcom can be found at: https://www.ofcom.org.uk/home.

PART FOUR: GLOBAL

international level through the ITU, as well as at a European level.[342] Thus, the UK's vote to leave the EU in 2017, commonly referred to as "Brexit," caused serious concerns regarding the implications this move could have for the state of the UK's telecom industry, given the cross-border nature of digital services.

Historically, the UK has held a strong influence over EU telecom rules, and many of the EU's current policies are incorporated in British law. Although after the UK's formal exit from the EU, the UK would be free to change its laws. The region has been a strong advocate for removing unnecessary regulation, and as a result of their departure from the EU it is expected that the EU may have a more regulation-heavy approach to telecom regulations in the future. This will affect the UK, home to the world's largest number of pan-European media companies, by forcing them to continue following EU rules in order to access the EU single market.

3. Spectrum

Currently, auctions are the primary market took for the allocation of spectrum

Auctions are the primary market tool for the allocation of spectrum. The auction process in the UK is designed to promote competition and coverage. The most recent auction was for spectrum in the 2.3 GHz and 3.4 GHz bands. The auction generated $1.5 billion USD in proceeds. Ofcom's next major auction is for the 700 MHz band and is expected to take place in late 2018 or early 2019. Figure 21-4 below illustrates the 2.3 GHz and 3.4 GHz band plans based on the final auction results.

Figure 21-4: 2.3 GHz and 3.4 GHz Band Plans

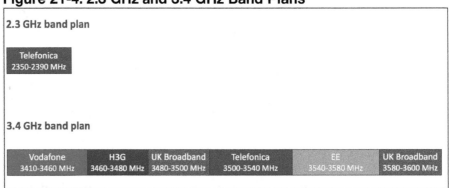

Source: Ofcom

---

[342] Broadband Stakeholder Group, *Implications of Brexit on the Digital Communications Sector* (Apr. 2017) http://www.broadbanduk.org/wp-content/uploads/2017/04/Implications-of-Brexit-on-the-digital-communications-sector-FINAL.pdf.

4. 5G

The European Commission's 5G Action Plan proposes to bring uninterrupted 5G coverage to all major European urban areas by 2025, along with setting deadlines for the development of a deployment roadmap by the end of 2017, spectrum assignments by 2019, and a development of global 5G standards by 2019. Additionally, the EC has launched the European Broadband Fund, which is a combination of private and public investments, to support network deployment throughout the EU. Although the UK has voted to leave the EU, the official departure date is not until March 29, 2019, so it is expected that the UK will still follow the 5G Action Plan.

B. Germany

1. Regulatory Bodies

There are 114 million mobile users in Germany, a 140% penetration rate. 02, owned by Telefonica, serves 46 million, Vodafone, serves 30 million, and Telekom, owned by Deutsche Telekom, serves 43 million. In Germany, the federal legislator is the main regulator of telecommunications. The federal legislator is strongly influenced by EU regulations. The Bundesnetzagentur, or Federal Network Agency, (BNetzA)[343] monitors telecommunication companies and ensures that they comply with the German Telecommunications Act.

BNetzA's responsibilities include: i) Ensuring the liberalization and deregulation of the telecom market through non-discriminatory access and efficient use-of-system charges; ii) Securing the efficient and interference-free use of spectrum frequencies and protecting public safety interests; iii) Administering frequencies and telephone numbers; and iv) Detecting radio interference.

2. Spectrum Allocation

In June 2017, BNetzA released a draft proposal for a 5G spectrum auction. The auction will include two segments of 60 MHz of paired spectrum in the 2 GHz band and 300 MHz unpaired spectrum from the 3.6 GHz band. Although the auction was originally scheduled for 2018, disagreements between Germany's transport ministry and BNetzA over the conditions under which bidders will be allowed to participate in the auction have delayed the auction until early 2019. The German government plans to use the proceeds of the auction to upgrade Germany's national broadband network.

---

[343] Bundesnetzagentur, BNetzA
https://www.bundesnetzagentur.de/EN/Home/home_node.html

The most recent spectrum auction was held in June 2015. Spectrum in the 700 MHz, 900 MHz, 1500 MHz, and 1800 MHz bands were auctioned for the development of 4G networks. The auction resulted in proceeds of USD $5.9 billion, valuing the spectrum at USD $0.27 per MHz/pop. Germany plans to have a 5G spectrum auction in 2019.

3. 5G

Germany is just above Colombia in 4G availability at 67% and averages speeds of 22 Mbps far below the Netherlands' 42 Mbps, as reported by OpenSignal. Nevertheless, the German mobile market's value is the largest in Europe. Mobile network providers invested heavily in their 4G LTE networks. In Germany, telecom giant Deutsche Telekom launched the first, new 5G radio antennas in Europe at two locations in downtown Berlin in early May 2018. The antennas fully support the new communications standard and lay the foundation for a nationwide 5G rollout, scheduled for 2020. Germany is focusing on the 3 GHz spectrum band for initial 5G deployment, and the antennas are currently operating in frequencies in the 3.7 GHz band.[344]

4. Gigabit Germany Initiative for the Future

The Ministry of Transport and Digital Infrastructure has adopted the Gigabit Germany Initiative for the Future, with the objective to invest €100 billion to create a high performance, gigabit speed broadband network by 2025.

C. France

1. Regulatory Bodies

There are five different government bodies involved in the regulation of technology, media, and telecommunications in France:

- ARCEP [345] is an independent government agency that oversees electronic communication and postal services. ARCEP defines the regulatory framework, allocates radio frequencies, and ensures universal service.
- The Superior Audiovisual Council (CSA) is the regulatory authority responsible for setting rules for broadcasting content and allocating frequencies by granting licenses to radio and television operators.

---

[344] Ryan Daws, *Deutsche Telekom switches on the first 5G antennas in Europe*, Telecomstech News (May 3, 2018) https://www.telecomstechnews.com/news/2018/may/03/deutsche-telekom-5g-antennas-europe/.

[345] ARCEP https://www.arcep.fr/

- The Data Protection Authority (CNIL) ensures the protection of personal data.
- The High Authority for the Distribution of Works and the Protection of Copyright on the Internet (HADOPI) protects intellectual property rights over works of art and literature on the Internet.
- The National Frequencies Agency is entrusted with the management of the entire French radio frequency spectrum. It apportions the available spectrum, which is either allocated to governmental agencies (i.e. aviation, defense, space) or to independent authorities, ARCEP and the CSA, who allocate spectrum to mobile providers, radio operators, and television operators via license.

2. 5G

Although preparation for 5G had a slow start, France has gathered some momentum in the past year

With 75 million mobile users and 114% penetration, France has a strong mobile industry and is ready for 5G. There is 4G availability 68% of the time, as reported by OpenSignal. France has four carriers Orange, serving 32 million, Altice, or SFR, serving 26 million, Bouygues Telecom, serving 14 million, and Iliad, or Free Mobile, serving 13 million. Under ARCEP supervision and following the framework outlined by the EC, 5G deployment is being prepared with at least one major city in France to have commercial services by 2020. Although preparation for 5G had a slow start, France has gathered some momentum in the past year. ARCEP announced in January 2018 that it would release temporary frequency authorizations to conduct 5G trials in the 3400-3800 MHz band and 26 GHz band. ARCEP intends to use the feedback on the use of 5G networks from these initial trials to make decisions on the allocation procedure for future 5G licenses. France released a 5G roadmap reaffirming that 5G is a national priority. It will: i) Launch 5G pilot projects in the regions; ii) Allocate new frequencies; iii) Support 5G infrastructure; iv) Deploy 5G commercially in at least one major city by 2020; v) Provide 5G coverage on main transport roads by 2025; and vi) Ensure transparency of the 5G rollouts to keep the public informed

D. Spain

1. Regulatory Bodies

Spain has 52 million mobile users and a 110% penetration rate. There are four carriers: Movistar-Telefonica, serving 18 million users, Orange, serving 16 million, Vodafone, serving 14 million, and Yoigo, serving 4 million.

PART FOUR: GLOBAL

The national regulatory authorities that develop and enforce the telecom laws are: 1) the National Markets and Competition Commission which supervises market competition and supervise the operators' obligations, to promote fair competition and maintain the right number of operators, and the resolve of disputes between operators,[346] and, 2) the State Secretariat of Information Society and the Digital Agenda (SESIAD) which is responsible for proposing general policies and regulations on electronic communications and information, the promotion and development of telecom infrastructure and services, and the management and control of spectrum, including the processing and granting of spectrum licenses for private spectrum use.[347]

2. Spectrum Policy

The SESIAD may limit the concessions in certain frequency bands in order to guarantee the efficient use of the spectrum

In 2017, Royal Decree 123 was passed with the intention of making spectrum use and spectrum assignment more flexible, along with promoting services and technological neutrality. It also creates a regulatory framework for the possibility of sharing spectrum among various titleholders in the same geographical area. The decree outlines the procedure to attain administrative authorization or concession to make private use of spectrum in Spain. The SESIAD may limit the licenses in certain frequency bands in order to guarantee the efficient use of the spectrum. SESIAD grants licenses through auctions.

Spain's 4G has high availability, delivering 4G 85% of the time and delivering 31 Mbps, far above the 16 Mbps delivered in the United States. Spain is moving forward now with 5G infrastructure. In July, Spanish authorities held a 5G auction for spectrum in the 3.6-3.8 GHz band, for a total of 200 MHz, divided into 40 blocks of 5 MHz each. The 5G spectrum licenses' term is 20 years. The auction generated $508 million USD in proceeds.

E. Italy

1. Regulatory Bodies

In recent years, the Italian telecommunications sector has undergone a significant reconfiguration. The two authorities tasked with the regulation of the IT, media, and telecommunications sectors in Italy are:

---

[346] National Markets and Competition Commission https://www.cnmc.es/en.
[347] More information about SESIAD can be found at:
http://www.mincotur.gob.es/telecomunicaciones/en-US/Paginas/index.aspx.

- The Italian Communications Authority (AGCOM) [348] - an independent administrative body that regulates and supervises the electronic communications, broadcasting, and publishing sectors in Italy. SGCOM ensures fair competition among operators by preventing monopolies and protects consumers by ensuring minimum standards of quality
- The Ministry of Economic Development's (MISE) [349] Department of Communications manages spectrum by approving the national frequency allocation plan and by issuing the related tender procedures in coordination with AGCOM

MISE... divides spectrum into frequency bands and assigns each band to services and users. AGCOM... determines the locations of radio stations and the frequencies assigned to each of them

Italy has a long history in wireless spectrum with Guglielmo Marconi first experimenting with wireless in the country in 1894, in the small town of Pontecchio, Italy. Now in 2018, Italy has 100 million mobile users with a 165% penetration rate. Four mobile operators serve the country, TIM, or Telecom Italia, serving 31 million users, Wind Tre, owned by Hutchinson, serving 29 million users, Vodafone, serving 22 million users, and Iliad, serving 1 million users.

2. Spectrum Policy

The MISE and AGCOM are responsible for the management of Italian spectrum. The MISE defines the national frequency allocation plan, which divides spectrum into frequency bands and assigns each band to services and users. AGCOM adopts the national frequency assignment plan, which determines the locations of radio stations and the frequencies assigned to each of them. The final allocation of frequencies and the granting of related rights of use is made by the MISE, following a call for applications by network operators. The allocation and assignment of radio frequencies is executed through competitive auctions. Auctions have been held for spectrum in the 800 MHz, 1452-1492 MHz, 1800 MHz, 2000 MHz, 2600 MHz, and 3.5 GHz bands.

Recently, Italy has followed European trends and has made the Italian regulatory framework concerning spectrum use more flexible, with the intention being to promote spectrum sharing, not necessarily limited to a particular frequency band, as a spectrum management tool. Most recently, the MISE has been pursuing spectrum sharing between licensed and unlicensed operators in the 2.3 GHz band using the

---

[348] AGCOM https://www.agcom.it/.

[349] MISE http://www.sviluppoeconomico.gov.it/index.php/en/.

License Shared Access (LSA) approach.

AGCOM initiated an inquiry regarding the future development of 5G mobile services and the use of frequency bands above 6 GHz to insure that there would be sufficient spectrum for 5G. AGCOM addressed the spectrum allocation methods involved in delivering 5G related to the development of 5G services, including licensing and spectrum sharing. The goals were to identify new bands to assigned to 5G and define a regulatory framework for their efficient allocation and use. The 5G process was approved by MISE in July 2018.

3. 5G

Italy's 4G infrastructure is available 70% of the time, compared to 90% in the U.S., as reported by OpenSignal, and it delivers 25 Mbps speeds, compared to Norway which delivers 41Mbps speeds. Italy is now planning, as all nations are, to move to 5G.

MISE is planning to hold a 5G spectrum auction for 75 MHz in the low-Band 700 MHz band, 200 MHz from mid-band 3.6-3.8 GHz, and 1 GHz from mmW 26.5-27.5 GHz. The 700MHz band will be sold in six paired 5MHz blocks, with two paired 10 MHz blocks reserved for a new competitor. Two blocks of 80 MHz spectrum and two blocks of 20 MHz will be sold in the 3.6-3.8GHz band, with a spectrum cap of 100MHz per operator, while the mmW 26.5-27.5 GHz band will be split into five lots of 200 MHz each.

MISE announced in August 2018 that seven carriers would participate in the auction: TIM, Wind Tre, and Iliad, and fixed broadband operators Fastweb, Vodafone Italia, Linkem, and Open Fiber. Italian authorities expect to raise at least $2.9 billion USD in the auction, significantly higher than the proceeds of recent 5G spectrum auctions in Spain and the UK.[350] This high projection is attributed to the fact that Italy's auction includes spectrum from the 700 MHz band, which is very desirable to mobile providers due to its ability to provide wide area coverage.

The 5G auction of 700 MHz involves relocating TV stations. However, two TV stations are considering legal actions against Communications Regulatory Authority and the mobile operators announced they do not want to participate in the auction because they claim the 700 MHz spectrum price is set too high and if sold would not be available until 2022.

---

[350] Reuters, *Italy to Auction 5G Frequencies by End-September* (May 23, 2018) https://www.reuters.com/article/us-italy-telecoms-5g-auction/italy-to-auction-5g-frequencies-by-end-september-idUSKCN1IO2OO.

XXII. Middle East and North Africa (MENA)

A. Middle East

Mobile wireless in the Middle East is growing rapidly, but spectrum dynamics vary widely there due to the variety of political regimes and levels of economic development. For this reason, generalizations are difficult. However, the comparatively young population of the region is a key factor driving increased demand for mobile broadband service. Several multinational wireless operators have emerged that may influence greater uniformity in the region's telecom industry over time. It is expected that by 2022, more than two-thirds of the telecommunications revenue will come from mobile services.

One major difference between the Middle East and the OECD ITU regions it that the former is characterized by high rates of pre-paid users

One major difference between the Middle East and the OECD ITU regions is that the former is characterized by high rates of pre-paid users. Users of pre-paid SIM cards are not tied to contracts and can easily change providers. As a result of low switching costs, the Middle East market is extremely price-competitive. This may explain why mobile operators are leaders at mobile advertising,[351] a technique to enhance revenue without the need for increasing subscriber rates.

1. Saudi Arabia

The Kingdom of Saudi Arabia is the largest in terms of capital volume and spending. Saudi Arabia has 26 million mobile users with a 161% penetration rate. STC (Saudi Telecom Company) the state-owned mobile firm, serves 20 million users, Mobily, owned by Etisalat (which globally has 167 million subscribers), serves 15 million, and Zain serves 11 million. OpenSignal reported in 2018, that 4G was available 76% of the time, compared to Japan's 92%, and that 4G speeds were only 10 Mbps compared to Norway's 41 Mbps. From 1998 to 2005, the Saudi Telecom Company (STC) was the only mobile operator. In 2005 that the CITC opened up competition.

a. Regulatory Agency

Established in 2001, the Communications and Information Technology Commission (CITC) was created to ensure that a proper framework and to establish regulatory procedures throughout the industry. These

---

[351] Alawaba Business, *Middle East Spending on Mobile Ads Goes Through the Roof* (Dec. 9, 2012) http://www.albawaba.com/business/mideast-mobile-ads-455486.

PART FOUR: GLOBAL

included encouraging fair competition, providing transparent rules for regulators, utilizing spectrum efficiently, and protecting the public, the mobile users, and the investors.

b. Spectrum

CITC auctioned, in 2017, 60 MHz to four operators in the 700 MHz and 1800 MHz bands. In February 2018, Saudi Arabia had their second spectrum auction where 80MHz was assigned to three operators (in the 700, 800, and 1800 MHz band.

Figure 22-1: February 2018 Spectrum Auction Results

No.	Operator	Spectrum Sold	Amount Spent for License
1	Zain	20 MHz of 800 MHz	$26.6 million USD
2	Mobily	10 MHz of 1800 MHz	$8 million USD
3	STC	50 MHz of 700/1800 MHz	$415 million USD

Source: Public data sources and Summit Ridge Group, LLC analysis

c. 5G

In February 2018, CITC issued temporary licenses to the operators for 5G trials in the mid-band ranges include 3.6-3.8 GHz Nokia is a major player and has partnered with Mobily and STC in the developing and launching of the 5G network. STC has plans to roll out a 5G network by the end of 2018.

2. Israel

Out of all the countries in the Middle East, Israel has one the most developed telecommunications network. In fact, the telecom sector accounts for approximately 2 percent of Israel's GDP. As of 2017, Israel had 10.3 million mobile users and a 125% penetration rate. Cellcom serves 28 million users, Partner serves 2.7 million, Pelephone serves 2.3 million, and Golan serves 0.8 million subscribers.

b. Regulatory Agency

The Ministry of Communications was established in 1971 after it separated from the post office, becoming an independent regulator. As a result, the Ministry was able to integrate the telecom infrastructure into the economy, thus providing a positive economic impact. The normal functions of the Ministry involve supervision of all operators throughout the telecom, postal and banking sectors. For the telecom sector, this involves managing frequency, facilitating licenses, and ensuring there is a fair competitive marketplace that is in the best interest for the users and investors.[352]

c. Spectrum

Currently, the 850 MHz, 900 MHz, 1800 MHz, and 2100 MHz bands are being used for mobile technology. In 2015, 40 MHz in the 1800 MHz band was auctioned off to six mobile operators. This is shown in Figure 22-2 below.

Figure 22-2: 2015 Spectrum Auction Results

No.	Operator	Spectrum Sold	Amount
1	Pelephone	15MHz of 1800MHz	$24.3 m USD
2	Parner	5MHz of 1800MHz	$8.49 m USD
3	Cellcom	5MHz of 1800MHz	$8.24 m USD
4	HOT Mobile	5MHz of 1800MHz	$8.75 m USD
5	Golan Telecom	5MHz of 1800MHz	$8.62 m USD
6	Xfone	5MHz of 1800MHz	$8.37 m USD

Source: Public data sources and Summit Ridge Group, LLC analysis

B. North Africa

The recent development of Northern Africa has allowed for growth, comparatively.

1. Algeria

Algeria has a large and advanced mobile infrastructure serving 43 million mobile users and a 72% penetration rate. The mobile operators are Djezzy, serving 18.6 million users, Mobilis, serving 13 million, and Oordedoo, serving 11.7 million users. Algeria is also part of the 4,500 km Trans-Saharan fiber network.[353] OpenSignal reported, in 2018, that Algeria's 4G networks delivered the second lowest throughput with an average 8.6 Mbps, just above India's 6 Mbps, the lowest. In terms of average availability of 4G, Open Signal reported

---

[352] Israeli Ministry of Communications,
https://www.gov.il/he/Departments/about/aboutministerofcommunication.

[353] Henry Lancaster, *Algeria: Telecoms, Mobile, and Broadband- Statistics and Analyses*, BubbeComm(Nov. 29, 2017) https://www.budde.com.au/Research/Algeria-Telecoms-Mobile-and-Broadband-Statistics-and-Analyses/?r=51.

PART FOUR: GLOBAL

that Algeria ranked the lowest of all countries at 41% availability, below El Salvador's 45%, the second lowest.

2. Egypt

Egypt is one of the most well-developed countries in terms of mobile user population. As of 2018, there were 100 million mobile users which is a 105% penetration rate. Vodaphone serves 38 million users, Orange 33 million, Etisalat serves 24 million, and WE serves 1.6 million users. Egypt's 4G network delivered 17 Mbps on average, which is higher than experienced by OpenSignal in the U.S.; however, the average 4G availability reported was 45%, fourth above Algeria, at the lowest.

Many fiber cables run through Egypt to get to the Middle East. The MENA subsea cable came into commercial use in late 2015, augmenting the country's considerable international bandwidth.[354]

a. Regulatory Agency

The National Telecom Regulatory Authority (NTRA) is an independent organization whose main focus is to create an equal, competitive, fair environment that fosters growth through innovation.[355] Their main competencies include:

- Testing and certifying telecommunication and broadcasting equipment to ensure compliance
- Ensuring the distribution of telecom services to all regions of the country, even the parts still in development
- Ensuring the security of telecommunication networks
- Managing the radio spectrum efficiently and effectively

b. Spectrum

Telecom Egypt paid $797 million USD for 5 MHz in the 900 MHz band and 2x5 MHz in the 1800 MHz band. The regulator held firm came to an agreement with operators Orange and Etisalat, who received 10 MHz each and Vodafone, who received 5 MHz. The total sale for the spectrum amounted to over $1.9 billion USD.

---

[354] Henry Lancaster, *Egypt: Fixed Broadband, Digital Economy and Digital Media-Statistics and Analyses,*BubbeComm (Aug. 2, 2017) https://www.budde.com.au/Research/Egypt-Fixed-Broadband-Digital-Economy-and-Digital-Media-Statistics-and-Analyses/?r=51.

[355] NTRA: http://www.tra.gov.eg/en/Pages/ntra-in-brief.aspx.

XXIII. Sub-Saharan Africa

Africa is a highly underserviced continent from a telecommunications perspective. In some areas, landline telephony is poorly developed. Investors have avoided the region due to its poverty and concerns over corruption and its overall business climate. However, over the past 10-15 years, many African countries have increased the transparency of their regulatory regimes and become more open to foreign investment. The African telecom market has been proactive in improving its networks. As a result, capital expenditure for telecommunications hardware and software has been steadily increasing. With low levels of existing wireline infrastructure, service providers often bypass wireline telecom systems to transmit signal across its final segment to the customer with mobile and fixed wireless broadband. Cisco reported that in 2016 Africa had the highest growth rate of 96% in mobile data traffic and forecast a compounded annual growth rate of 65% between 2016 and 2021.

In the mid-1990s, only 1% of the population owned a telephone in Sub-Saharan Africa.[357] Starting in 1990, there were only two countries that offered mobile cellular service and had only 10,000 subscribers. By 1995, over half the countries offered mobile cellular service to 500,000 subscribers. This parabolic upward trend continued through 2015, when over 750 million subscribers are serviced across the region. Overall, the mobile penetration had reached over 75% in 2015. Regarding the number of pay TV subscribers in Sub-Saharan Africa, there will be a 74% increase between 2017 and 2023 to reach 40.89 million.[358] However, the Sub-Saharan Africa Pay TV Forecasts report estimates that subscriber growth will outstrip revenue progress. Pay TV revenues will climb by 41% to $6.64 billion by 2023, up by $2 billion on 2017.

In order for Africa to build-out their telecom network, they must first expand their infrastructure

In order for Sub-Saharan Africa to build-out their telecommunications network, infrastructure first must be expanded. A major problem that many sub-Saharan countries have is lack of electricity. Only approximately 20% of the Sub-Saharan African population has

PART FOUR: GLOBAL

---

[357] EM Compass, *Creating Mobile Telecom Markets in Africa* (Sept. 2016) https://www.ifc.org/wps/wcm/connect/95f1e831-fc48-49e4-804f-d92b710882dc/EMCompass+Note+19+Mobile+Telecoms+SSA+9-30+Final.pdf?MOD=AJPERES.

[358] Telecom-Week, *Sub-Sahara Africa Pay TV Forecasts* (Jan 2018) .https://www.africantelecomsnews.com/Products/Sub-Saharan_Africa_Pay-TV_Forecasts.html.

compared to about 50% in South Asia and more than 80% in Latin America. Of these, 71% of homes in urban areas and only 12% of homes in rural areas have access to electricity. Notably, two-thirds of the total population live in rural areas, further complicating and raising the expense of extending the electrical grid to more homes. Network operators need to build-out these networks and the cost of deployment of each network segment increases on a cost-per-user metric. First, beginning with the initial investment and international landing point, not to mention the additional costs for installation, as they would need diesel generators in many locations and additional equipment to reach these locations due to the lack of infrastructure. In addition, network operators would need to continue progressing through their network including the last-mile segment. The last-mile accounts for 45-60% of the total cost of network segments.[358] A viable solution for providing power would involve a decentralized grid, where solar energy units could provide power both to the customer and the network infrastructure. This problem of obtaining low-cost power for last mile networks could cost Sub-Saharan Africa more than 25% of its future users.[22]

Mobile telephones account for over 90% of all telephones in Sub-Saharan Africa. Approximately 99% of these mobile phones are prepaid.[359] Due to the lack of a fiber network, more than 95% of Internet access is also through mobile phones. Sub-Saharan Africa mobile Internet penetration in 2016 was 26% and is projected to grow to 38% by 2020.[23]

As of 2017, the top six countries with the highest GDP accounted for 62.7% of the region's total GDP. Rounding out the top 3 were Nigeria, South Africa and Egypt, respectively. It appears that there is a direct correlation between the country's GDP and the amount of telecommunications infrastructure development occurring within the country. The region supports more than 40 mobile operators. Almost all Foreign Direct Investment (FDI) funding for telecom goes to these developing countries. This has not been the case for Sub-Saharan Africa in the past. Many investors have been wary due to political and macroeconomic instability, lack of public transparency, corruption, and weak governance. With limited operators, telecoms are able to

Due to a lack of a fiber network, more than 95% of Internet access is through mobile phones

---

[358] GSMA, *The Mobile Economy Sub-Saharan Africa 2017* (2017) https://www.gsmaintelligence.com/research/?file=7bf3592e6d750144e58d9dcfac6adfab&download.

[359] Henry Lancaster, Africa: Mobile Network Operators and MVNOs BubbeComm (Apr. 25, 2018) https://www.budde.com.au/Research/Africa-Mobile-Network-Operators-and-MVNOs.

obtain the spectrum that is being released at a discount.

As terrestrial fiber back-haul continues to grow, major players like Facebook and Google are becoming increasingly active developers. Google plans to build metro networks in both the eastern and western regions of Africa, with their newly established company, CSquared, acting as the operator. In addition, Facebook is investing in fiber optic cable in Eastern Africa. Fiber-to-the-Home or Fiber-to-the-Premises (FTTH/FTTP) has been growing, especially in urban areas, due to the increase in demand from the users and decreased cost to install.

A. Western Africa

1. Nigeria

Nigeria is Africa's largest mobile market

Nigeria is Africa's largest mobile market, more than twice the size of South Africa's market, with 81% penetration and 158 million mobile subscribers.[360] Nigeria has five mobile operators. MTN serves 63 million users, Airtel serves 31 million, Glo Mobile serves 31 million, 9mobile serves 24 million, and Visafone serves 2 million.[361]

a. Regulatory Agency

The Nigerian Communications Commission (NCC) is an independent regulatory agency for the telecommunication industry in Nigeria. The NCC is regarded as one of the most prominent regulatory agencies in Africa. They are developing programs in order to accelerate the adoption and use of information and communications technology (ICT). Ultimately, the NCC's goal is to achieve a rich communications environment that is on par, in terms of quality, with the rest of the world.[362]

b. Spectrum

As of 2013, Nigeria was the only country in Sub-Saharan Africa to successfully conduct a spectrum auction. Since then, several countries have followed, though not all countries are conducting auctions.[363] In late 2013 the NCC announced a spectrum auction for 30 MHz in the 2.3 GHz spectrum band. Bitflux won the auction and paid a total of $23 million USD. It was not until 2016 that the 2.6 GHz

---

[360] GSMA, *The Mobile Economy Sub-Saharan Africa 2017, supra* at note 361.

[361] "Telecoms and Media: *Africa* Getting The Deal Through (July 2018) https://gettingthedealthrough.com/area/39/jurisdiction/18/telecoms-media-nigeria/.

[362] NCC https://www.ncc.gov.ng/about-ncc/who-we-are

[363] Steve Song, T*he Failure of Spectrum Auctions in Africa,* Many Possibilities Apr.21, 2017) https://manypossibilities.net/2017/04/the-failure-of-spectrum-auctions-in-africa/

PART FOUR: GLOBAL

band was put up for auction in Nigeria. Of the 14 lots of 2x5 MHz spectrum (140 MHz of spectrum in total) put up for auction, only 6 lots were sold. One operator, MTN Nigeria, won the six lots and paid $96 million USD for the 60 MHz of spectrum. These spectrum licenses are valid until 2021.

2. Ghana

Ghana was one of the first countries in Africa to liberalize and connect to the Internet

Ghana was one of the first countries in Africa to liberalize and connect to the Internet. Ghana is benefitting heavily from telecommunications, where the value of products and services produced by the information and communication sector surged 239% since 2012.[364] As of 2017, Ghana has 36 million unique mobile subscribers and a 140% penetration rate.[365] Five mobile operators provide service. These include MTN serving 16.3 million subscribers, Vodafone serving 9.1 million, Tigo serving 4.9 million, Airtel serving 4.8 million, and Glo serving 1.4 million.

a. Regulatory Agency

The National Communications Authority (NCA) is the overarching regulatory body in Ghana. They have numerous duties, including granting licenses and ensuring fair competition.

b. Spectrum

In 2015, Ghana auctioned 800 MHz spectrum, offering 2 lots of 2x10 MHz, a total of 40 MHz. Only MTN paid $67 million USD for the spectrum.[366]

3. Senegal

a. Regulatory Agency

The Agency for Telecommunications and Postal Regulations (ARTP) is an independent authority in Senegal that oversees the telecommunications and postal sectors. To ensure fair and healthy competition they have specifications for operators and supervise the operators' activity. As of 2017, Senegal has four operators and 16 million mobile subscribers and a 115% penetration rate.[367]

---

[364] Matthew A. Winkler, *African Economic Growth Rides on Wireless Rails*, Bloomberg (Nov. 13, 2017) https://www.bloomberg.com/view/articles/2017-11-13/african-economic-growth-rides-on-wireless-rails.

[365] GSMA, *The Mobile Economy Sub-Saharan Africa 2017*, supra at note 361.

[366] Henry Lancaster, *2015 Ghana: Telecoms, Mobile, and Broadband*, BubbeComm (Mar. 31, 2015) https://www.budde.com.au/Research/2015-Ghana-Telecoms-Mobile-and-Broadband.

[367] GSMA, The Mobile Economy Sub-Saharan Africa 2017, supra at note 361.

In 2015, Senegalese regulators announced an invitation to apply for LTE spectrum in the 700 MHz, 800 MHz, and 1800 MHz bands. Due to the high reserve price, there was a standoff between ARTP and the operators. The standoff ended when the regulator decided to negotiate a deal with Sonatel, the former fixed incumbent operator, to pay $53 million USD for 2x10 MHz of spectrum in the 800 MHz band and 2x10 MHz in the 1800 MHz band. The agreement was for a 20-year lease license though with the provision that Sonatel achieves 70% coverage within five years and 90% coverage within ten years.

B. Eastern Africa

Mozambique was one the first countries in the eastern African region to start a telecommunications reform. Even so, the mobile and fixed penetration rates have remained low in comparison to the rest of the region. In 2016, there was an 11 percent growth in the national telecommunications market.[368] Mozambique also planned to hold an auction for the 800 MHz spectrum, but the reserve price was set too high.

1. Kenya

Kenya has the fourth largest mobile telecommunications market in Africa[369] with 39 million mobile subscribers and a 79% penetration rate.[370] After several investments to their network infrastructure and access to 4 new submarine cables, the pricing rates in Kenya subsequently decreased due to wholesale pricing being introduced.[371] This resulted in cheaper pricing for customers, leading to a rise in subscriptions.

a. Regulatory Agency

The Communications Authority of Kenya was established in 1999 to ensure the development of the country's information and

---

[368] Matshelane Mamabolo, *11% Growth in Mozambique's Telecoms Sector*, ITWeb Africa (Jan. 9, 2018) http://www.itwebafrica.com/telecommunications/909-mozambique/242249-11-growth-in-mozambiques-telecoms-sector

[369] GSMA, *The Mobile Economy Sub-Saharan Africa 2017*, *supra* at note 361.

[370] Elixi RR, *Spectrum Management in Africa* (2015) https://www.elixirr.com/wp-content/uploads/2015/08/spectrum_management_in_africa.pdf

[371] Henry Lancaster, *Kenya: Fixed Broadband Market- Statistics and Analysis*, BubbeComm (May 9, 2018) https://www.budde.com.au/Research/Kenya-Fixed-Broadband-Market-Statistics-and-Analyses/?r=51.

communication sectors.[372] Their duties include the following:

- Regulating tariffs for communication services
- Licensing all systems and services in the communications industry and monitoring these licenses to ensure compliance
- Managing the country's spectrum resources and making sure they are allocated in a manner best suited for the country

b. Spectrum

Kenya... assigns spectrum rather than holding an auction

Kenya has been making strides recently by assigning spectrum rather than holding an auction. This change follows a deal made between the Kenyan government and Safaricom, which had Safaricom building the government a national police communications network and paying $56.2 million USD in exchange for access to 2x15 MHz of 800 MHz spectrum. They were able to assign licenses for the 800 MHz band to allow for immediate use.

2. Uganda

Uganda is an emerging country that is in a good position to excel in the telecom industry. This is due to a growing economy where the people are become familiarized with technology. As stated earlier, major players like Google and Facebook have been developing networks in eastern Africa. Facebook, in particular, is building fiber networks, specifically in northern Uganda, in a partnership with BCS and Airtel Telecom.[373] Before liberalization, there was only one operator.[374] As of 2018, Uganda had 22 million mobile subscribers and a 65% penetration rate and is served by four mobile operators.[375]

a. Regulatory Agency

The Uganda Communications Commission (UCC) is an independent regulator established in 1997 in order to help develop modern communications infrastructure.[376] They facilitate a range of functions including the following:

- Licensing and standards

---

[372] Kenya Communications Authority http://www.ca.go.ke/index.php/what-we-do.

[373] Steve Song, *African Telecoms Infrastructure in 2017*, Many Possibilities (Jan. 10, 2018) https://manypossibilities.net/2018/01/africa-telecoms-infrastructure-in-2017/.

[374] ICT, "National Spectrum Management Policy for Uganda" http://www.ict.go.ug/sites/default/files/Resource/Spectrum%20Management%20and%20Licensing%20Policy%202017.pdf.

[375] GSMA, *The Mobile Economy Sub-Saharan Africa 2017*, *supra* at note 361.

[376] More information on the UCC can be found at: http://www.ucc.co.ug/about-ucc/

- Spectrum management and policy regulation
- Tariff regulations
- Rural communications development
- Research and development

b. Spectrum

As of 2016, there was approximately 650 MHz of spectrum available to mobile operators in Uganda.

C. Southern Africa

1. South Africa

As of 2018, South Africa is the second largest market in Africa and has 73 million mobile subscribers and a 148% penetration rate.[377] South Africa has had telephone lines since its inception in 1876 with the Bell Telephone Company. It was not until 1991 that Telekom was created and took over from the South African Postal Service. The telecom industry had always been state-owned and operated, even with Telekom, until 1997. There are four mobile operators in South Africa: Vodacom serving 42 million mobile users, MTN serving 31 million, Cell C serving 16 million, and Telkom serving 4 million. Before 2009, broadband growth was difficult due to high costs caused by limited global supply. In 2009, however, this changed with the first international submarine cable being brought to Africa.[378]

In 2009 the first international submarine cable was brought to Africa

a. Regulatory Agency

The Independent Communication Authority of South Africa (ICASA) is an independent regulator that was formed in 2000. It promotes competition, the digital agenda, and improvement to stakeholder and customer experience. The ICASA grants and monitors licenses, develops regulation, and manages radio frequency spectrum.[379]

b. Spectrum

South Africa planned to have spectrum auctions since 2010 in the 2.6 GHz, 3.5 GHz, and 800 MHz spectrum bands but all of their attempted plans failed. South Africa plans to hold an auction for 5G spectrum in the mid-band 3.5 GHz and in the high-band in March 2019. They

---

[377] GSMA, *The Mobile Economy Sub-Saharan Africa 2017*, *supra* at note 361.

[378] Henry Lancaster, *South Africa- Fixed Broadband Market- Statistics and Analysis*, BubbeComm (Nov. 7, 2017) https://www.budde.com.au/Research/South-Africa-Fixed-Broadband-Market-Statistics-and-Analyses/?r=51.

[379] ICASA, https://www.icasa.org.za/pages/vision-mission-and-values

wanted to use a different approach where they planned to create a wholesale-only Wireless Open Access Network or WOAN. South Africa seeks to have the mobile operators purchase 30% of WOAN. In this network, operators would not have to build the infrastructure so they could dedicate their resources towards being competitive and providing the best service. The idea has only been tested in Mexico and Rwanda as of 2017 but the results have not been favorable in either case. As of 2017 there has not been any resolution.

Figure 23-1: Summary of Spectrum Auctions in Africa

No.	Country	Spectrum Sold	Amount
1	Nigeria	30 MHz of 2.3 GHz &80MHz of 2.6GHz	$119 million USD
2	Ghana	20MHz of 800MHz	$67.5 million USD
3	Kenya	60MHz of 800MHz	$75 million USD
4	Senegal	20MHz of 800MHz & 20MHz of 1800MHz	$53 million USD
5	Egypt	40MHz of 900/1800 MHz	$1.9 billion USD
6	Rwanda	10MHz of 800MZ	PPP to cover 95% of the pop. with LTE in three years
Mozambique attempted to auction off spectrum 800MHz band			
South Africa attempted to auction spectrum but is currently in a standstill			

Source: Public data sources and Summit Ridge Group, LLC analysis

XXIV. Asia Pacific and Greater China

The Asia-Pacific market is forecasted to account for 47 percent of global mobile traffic by 2021, the largest share of traffic of any region.[380] Both companies and governments in the region are particularly concerned about developing spectrum-efficient ways of operating mobile services.

The Asia-Pacific market is forecasted to account for 47% of global mobile traffic by 2021

Operators in the region have been making more consistent capital expenditures to improve spectral usage than companies in Europe, North America and Latin America. Interestingly, major Asian countries are now beginning to allocate the 700 MHz band to mobile wireless, a move that the U.S. recently completed.

A. India

1. Regional Overview

In terms of the number of mobile connections, the Indian telecommunications network is the second largest in the world after China. The telecom industry is considered to be an important tool for the development of India as a whole. In the endeavor to transform India into a digitally empowered and knowledgeable society, the Indian government has launched the ambitious Digital India program. This program's projected cost is approximately $17 billion USD and has been implemented in phases during its 2014 to 2018 timeline.

The Indian telecom network is the second largest in the world after China

India is the second largest telecom market with over 1.18 billion mobile users as of 2018, and is growing at a rate of over 2% per month.[381] As of the first quarter of 2018, India was the fastest growing market for mobile applications. This growth is possible due to India's having the lowest call tariffs in the world, which is a result of extreme competition between many mobile operators. A new mobile connection can be activated with a monthly commitment of only US$0.15.[382] Currently, there are ten mobile network operators, with five operators controlling over 87% of the market and each of the five

---

[380] *Cisco Visual Networking Index (VNI) Global Mobile Data Traffic Forecast Update 2016-2021, supra* at note 175.

[381] Highlights of Telecom Subscription Data as of March 31, 2018 is https://www.trai.gov.in/sites/default/files/PRNo56Eng23052018.pdf

[382] International Business Publications, *India Telecom Laws and Regulations Handbook,* page 52 (2013) https://books.google.com/books/about/India_Telecom_Laws_and_Regulations_Handb .html?id=TeqRAAAAQBAJ.

PART FOUR: GLOBAL

holding more than a 9% market share. Moreover, two of the five major players – Vodafone (with 19% and 223 million users) and Idea (with 18% and 221 million users) – are planning a merger, which will create the largest telecommunications company in India with over a 36% market share. Bharti Airtel, the largest carrier, with 30% market share and 345 million users, will soon acquire Tata Docomo with 27 million users and plans to invest over $20 billion by 2020 in order to develop its network infrastructure. Developing these networks will allow for continued growth with telephones where the current mobile penetration is 36% and is expected to grow at an exponential rate.[383] The rapid growth within the telecom sector will force India to develop their power grid and further their infrastructure in order to supply the necessary channels needed to sustain growth in this network. In the Draft National Digital Communications Policy 2018,[384] the Department of Telecommunications in India predicted by 2025 that their digital economy will surpass one trillion USD.

2. Telecom History

India has one of the oldest telecom sectors in the world. In 1850, the first experimental electric telegraph line was started between Calcutta and Diamond Harbour. It was not until 1927 that radio broadcasting began, although by 1930 it was taken over by the government.[385] In 1959, India began broadcasting television. The Internet became accessible in 1995 as well as the first mobile phone call occurred not one year after the first spectrum auction was offered. Spectrum auctions only offered bandwidth in the 900 MHz band until 2001 when spectrum in the 1800 MHz band became available. The spectrum that was auctioned off in 2001 was used as a pricing benchmark for the 2G spectrum auction, which took place in 2008. Following the 900 MHz spectrum auction in 2008 was the 2010 auction, where 3G and 4G spectrum were auctioned off at a much higher price.

a. Liberalization

Liberalization of the Indian telecommunication industry started in 1981. The DoT had a strong grip over most of the telecom industry. They were also part of the India Post & Telecommunication

---

[383] Statistics.com, *Share of mobile phone users that use a smartphone in India from 2014 to 2019* (2018) https://www.statista.com/statistics/257048/smartphone-user-penetration-in-india.

[384] Indian Government, *The Draft National Digital Communications Policy 2018* www.dot.gov.in/sites/default/files/DNDCP2018.pdf (*Draft National Digital Communications Policy 2018*).

[385] Prasar Bharti, *Growth and Development*, All India Radio http://allindiaradio.gov.in/Profile/Growth%20and%20Development/Pages/default.aspx

Department until 1985 when they separated. In 1986, the DoT would lose its complete control over India's telecom services sector when Mahanaga, Telephone Nigam Limited (MTNL) and Videsh Sanchar Nigam Limited (VSNL) were formed to operate telecom services in urban areas. As a result of the Liberalization-Privatization-Globalization policies that the government agreed to, private investments in the value-added services sector were allowed. Subsequently, foreign direct investments (FDI) began occurring, allowing up to 49% investment in a company to come from FDI. It was not until after 2000 that government regulation loosened up even more, allowing up to 74% of investments to come from FDI. In addition, the government reduced the spectrum license fees, which allowed operators to lower their rates and becoming more competitive. This enabled more middle-class families to afford mobile services and resulted in a growth in users. It was not until 2002 that the Indian government decided to lower its stake in VSNL, which allowed for even more FDI.

b. Foreign Direct Investments

Foreign companies began investing more money into India's telecom sector as soon as they were allowed to. As of March 2016, India has received a total of $371 billion USD in FDI dating back to 1991.[386] Just in the first three months of 2016, the industry received $10.55 billion USD in investments. Figure 24-1 below shows how FDIs began increasing after 2000, with the bulk of FDI resulting after 2005.

Figure 24-1: Amount of Foreign Direct Investment in India

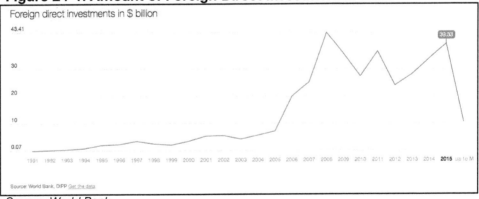

Source: World Bank

Indian spectrum regulation has had a checkered history

---

[386] Aprameya Rao and Kishor Kadam, *25 Years of Liberalization: A Glimpse of India's Growth in 14 Charts*, FirstPost (July 7, 2016) https://www.firstpost.com/business/25-years-of-liberalisation-a-glimpse-of-indias-growth-in-14-charts-2877654.html.

PART FOUR: GLOBAL

3. Spectrum

India's spectrum regulation is evolving to match the strong growth. It granted 2G licenses in the 900 MHz spectrum in 2008, but the Indian Supreme Court canceled the licenses in early 2012 over concerns of corruption. Following the tainted 2008 auction, India has held six successful spectrum auctions. This includes the following: the 2010 auction selling 3G 1900 MHz spectrum; the 2012 auction for 2G services in the 800 and 1800 MHz bands; the 2014 auction for 2G services in the 900 MHz and 1800 MHz bands; the 2015 auction of spectrum in the 800 MHz, 900 MHz, 1800 MHz, and 2100 MHz bands; and the 2016 auction for a total of 2354 MHz of spectrum.

India has the least amount of spectrum assigned to mobile services when comparing it to other global competitors in 2016

India had the least amount of spectrum assigned to mobile services when comparing it to other global competitors in 2016. However, India is in one of the best positions to excel due to their underutilization of the 700 MHz band. Prior to 2016, the 700 MHz band was only used for Over the Air (OTA) channels, but after the 2016 spectrum auction, the 696-806 MHz spectrum is now used for digital dividend spectrum. The 2015 auction raised $17 billion USD. The auction continued into 2016 but only 40%, or 965 MHz of 2355 MHz offered, was auctioned off due to high pricing. Spectrum sold included 800 MHz, 1800 MHz, and 2300 MHz. There were no bids for the low-band 700 MHz and 900 MHz spectrum. India's spectrum allocations are described in Figure 24-2 below.

Figure 24-2: India's Spectrum Allocation

Bands Available for Mobile Phone Services			
Band (MHz)	**Frequency (MHz)**	**Uses**	**Duplexing Scheme**
700	703-748/758-803	4G-LTE	FDD
800	824-844/869-889	4G-LTE	FDD
900	890-915/935-960	4G-LTE	FDD
1800	1710-1785/1805-1880	3G/4G-LTE	FDD
2100	1920-1980/2110-2170	3G	FDD
2300	2300-2400	4G-LTE	TDD
2500	2500-2690	4GLTE	TDD

Source: Telecom Regulatory of India, "Consultation Paper on Auction of Spectrum in 700 MHz, 800 MHz, 900 MHz, 1800 MHz, 2100 MHz, 2300 MHz, 2500 MHz, 3300-3400 MHz and 3400-3600 MHz bands." August 28, 2017.

a. 2G Spectrum Scandal

A case, dismissed by the lower courts, was appealed to the Supreme Court of India after the 2010 auction to determine if the auction of 2008 spectrum was legitimate. It was not until February 2012 that the Supreme Court ruled to cancel all of the 122 spectrum licenses granted during the 2008 spectrum auction on account that the allocation of the spectrum did not follow usual procedures, favored those competitors who had previously obtained licenses, and set the price of the spectrum to 2001 auction price.[387] Following the Indian Supreme Court's ruling, the government first allowed unsuccessful bidders to offer service in the 900 MHz band. Later, it reversed itself and ordered a new spectrum auction for 2013. Any charges that had been brought against those involved in the 2010 scandal were dropped in 2017.[388] This turbulent history has made international investors reluctant to enter the Indian market.

b. Future Spectrum

India is now planning the nation's largest spectrum auction with a planned sale of more than 3000 MHz of frequencies in multiple bands, including spectrum intended for 5G from the 700 MHz, 800 MHz, 900 MHz, 1800 MHz, 2100 MHz, 2300 MHz, 2500 MHz, 3300 – 3400 MHz and 3400 – 3600 MHz bands.[389]

4. 5G/Fiber

Due to rapid and continuous growth, low spectrum allocation, and interconnectivity issues, Indian cellular networks are facing traffic congestion problems

Due to rapid and continuous growth, low spectrum allocation, and interconnectivity issues, Indian cellular networks are facing traffic congestion problems, especially in urban areas. Mobile providers have not yet achieved wide-scale deployment of 4G networks and are still working to expand 3G networks in India. Although India intends to auction off spectrum for 5G, they will not have a dedicated plan until 2019 or 2020.[390] For 5G deployment, India is considering spectrum in the 25-30 GHz range for commercial 5G networks. They are also considering the 37 GHz, 39 GHz, and 42 GHz frequency bands. They

[387] Guru Acharya, *India: Case Study on the Supreme Court Ruling on the 2G Spectrum Scam*, SSRN(Apr. 30, 2012) https://ssrn.com/abstract=2048719.

[388] Aamir Khan *2G Spectrum Case Judgement: What the Court Said in its Verdict*, The Times of India (Dec. 21, 2017) https://timesofindia.indiatimes.com/india/2g-case-what-the-court-said-in-its-verdict/articleshow/62191725.cms.

[389] Charley Lewis, *Lessons From Spectrum Auctions: A Benchmark Approach*, SSRN (June 12, 2018) https://ssrn.com/abstract=3185752.

[390] Phil Harpur, *India- Mobile Infrastructure, Broadband, Operators' Statistics and Analysis*, BuddeComm https://www.budde.com.au/Research/India-Mobile-Infrastructure-Broadband-Operators-Statistics-and-Analyses.

PART FOUR: GLOBAL

are still in the midst of rolling out 3G and 4G, which ultimately resulted from the spectrum scandal during the issuance of the 2G licenses. India is also looking to permit the sharing of spectrum to optimize utilization of spectrum.

In addition, India is planning one of the largest rural fiber rollouts in the world. India is trying to connect over 600,000 villages by broadband to their new initiative, BharatNet, which will soon become the pillar for emerging technologies such as IOT, cloud, and 5G.[391] The Department of Telecommunications in India expects that an additional 500 million Internet users will be online by 2023 as a result.

5. Satellite

India has an active space program through the Indian Space Research Organization (ISRO) run by the government. It is one of the few companies to have its own launch capabilities. Foreign companies have long complained of difficulty accessing the Indian market, particularly for media applications. India has opted for the use of both the GSM and CDMA technologies in the mobile sector.

6. Wi-Fi In India

In 2017, Facebook launched Express Wi-Fi, where they are working with Bharti Airtel to launch 20,000 additional online hotspots. Additionally, Facebook is working with local ISP's and entrepreneurs to allow the entrepreneurs to resell Internet access, which will allow more devices to connect to the Internet.[392]

7. Regulatory Bodies

The Telecom Regulatory Authority of India (TRAI) was established in 1997 to regulate telecom services, including fixation or revision of tariffs for telecom services. The TRAI's main objective is to provide a level playing field between operators by providing a fair and transparent policy environment.[393]

The Telecom Disputes Settlement and Appellate Tribunal (TDSAT) was established in 2000 to take appealed cases from the TRAI. These cases involved the following:

- Disputes between licensor and licensee
- Disputes between two or more service providers

---

[391]Draft National Digital Communications Policy 2018.

[392] Frederic Lardinois, *Facebook's Express Wi-Fi Launches Commercially in India*, TechCrunch (May 4, 2017) https://techcrunch.com/2017/05/04/facebooks-express-Wi-Fi-launches-commercially-in-india/.

[393] For more information about the TRAI, see: https://www.trai.gov.in/about-us/history.

- Disputes between service provider and a group of customers
- Appeals of the TRAI's decisions

The Telecom Commission is part of The Department of Telecom (DoT), which falls under the department of the Ministry of Communications, which is run by the Indian government.[394] The Telecom Commission has numerous responsibilities including:

- Formulating the policy of the DoT for approval by the Government
- Preparing the budget for the DoT for each financial year and getting it approved by the government
- Implementing government policy in all matters concerning telecommunications

The TRAI acts as an advisor to the Telecom Commission by providing suggestions they believe would benefit India. In the past, many of the suggestions that the TRAI made to the Telecom Commission were disregarded. In recent years, however, the Telecom Commission has begun to take the suggestions from the TRAI. Though ultimately, the DoT approves the decisions made by the Telecom Commission.

a. Net Neutrality

Until recently, there were not any laws governing net neutrality. It was not until November 2017 that the TRAI made recommendations for net neutrality. In July 2018, the TRAI suggestion on net neutrality was approved by the Telecom Commission. Service providers can no longer discriminate against Internet content.[395] This includes blocking, throttling or granting them higher speed access.[396]

B. China

China is the largest market in the Asia Pacific region with 1.5 billion mobile subscribers as of June 2018. Manufacturers and operators from all over the world came to China because it has the largest market for radio equipment. Huawei is now the largest

China... has elected to primarily use time division duplexing (TDD) for its LTE standards as opposed to the frequency division duplexing (FDD)

---

[394] DoT, http://www.dot.gov.in/profile.

[395] ESN Economic Bureau, *Net Neutrality in India Gets Telecom Commission Nod, No More Throttling of Internet*, Indian Express(July 12, 2018) https://indianexpress.com/article/technology/tech-news-technology/net-neutrality-gets-telecom-commission-nod-5255681/.

[396] TRAI's Recommendations on Net Neutrality, https://trai.gov.in/sites/default/files/PR_No.100of2017.pdf.

telecommunications equipment manufacturer, overtaking Ericsson in 2012. China, one of the fastest growing economies, has elected to use LTE-TDD for its LTE standard as opposed to the LTE-FDD, which the U.S. has predominately used prior to 3.5 GHz CBRS. LTE-TDD may provide greater flexibility as it will not need paired frequency bands for uplink and downlink. This flexibility is likely to be important as China has only allocated 227 MHz of spectrum to mobile broadband. China Mobile, however, indicates it will also operate an LTE-FDD network in parallel to its LTE-TDD network.[397] According to a recent study by Analysys Mason, China is currently holding a narrow lead in the race to 5G thanks to a combination of industry momentum and government support. The country's five-year plan aims for a broad commercial launch by 2020. Each of China's providers has committed to this timeline, and all major wireless providers have conducted considerable 5G trials and committed to 5G commercial launches. The Chinese government has committed to opening significant amounts of both mid-band and high-band spectrum, promising at least 100 MHz of mid-band spectrum in the 3.4-3.6 GHz band and 2 GHz of high band spectrum for each wireless provider.[398]

China's "Big 3" collectively surpassed 1.1 billion 4G subscribers by the end of June 2018

1. Market Structure

The Chinese market is dominated by three mobile operators: China Mobile, serving 910 million users, China Telecom, serving 287 million, and China Unicom, serving 305 million. China's "Big Three" collectively surpassed 1.1 billion 4G subscribers by the end of June 2018. The growth of the Chinese mobile market is shown in Figure 24-3 below.

---

[397] Benny Har-Even, Telecoms, "China Mobile to Operate TDD and FDD LTE in Tandem CEO Reveals,"January 22, 2013, http://www.telecoms.com/75811/china-mobile-to-operate-tdd-and-fdd-lte-in-tandem-ceo-reveals.

[398] CTIA, *The Global Race to 5G,* https://www.ctia.org/the-wireless-industry/the-race-to-5g.

Figure 24-3: Chinese Mobile Subscriber Growth

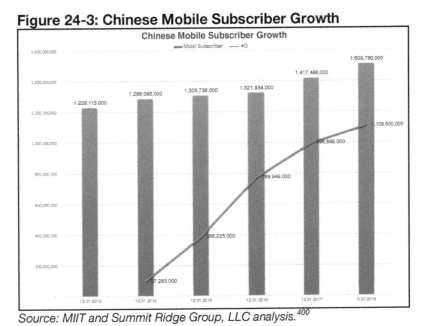

Source: MIIT and Summit Ridge Group, LLC analysis.[400]

The past several years witnessed dramatically fast development of 4G industry and high-speed mobile Internet traffic growth. China (as well as Japan and South Korea) are targeting 2020 for 5G commercial launches.

2. Regulatory Bodies and Spectrum

The major industry regulatory authorities in China include the following:

- The Ministry of Industry and Information Technology (MIIT) – regulates the telecoms business and grants operational licenses for telecoms business.
- The National Development and Reform Commission (NDRC) – has jurisdiction over project approval and pricing for telecoms services and IT industry planning and policy.
- The Ministry of Commerce (MOFCOM) – has the authority to approve foreign investment projects and regulates e-commerce.
- The State Administration for Industry and Commerce (SAIC) – responsible for industrial and commercial registration for enterprises and for the issuance of business registration licenses. The SAIC also oversees consumer rights protection, online advertising, and fair competition.

[400] Ministry of Industry and Information Technology (July 19, 2017) http://www.miit.gov.cn/n1146312/n1146904/n1648372/c5735472/content.html.

PART FOUR: GLOBAL

- State Administration for Press, Publication, Radio, Film and Television (SAPPT) – merged from the former State Administration for Radio, Film and Television and the former General Administration for Press and Publication in 2013, the SAPPT has a broad jurisdiction over the approval and administration of publications activities (including those via the Internet); the administration of radio and television broadcasting; the transmission of audio and video content; and content censorship.

- The Ministry of Culture (MOC) – has jurisdiction over the cultural industry, including the responsibility for pre-approving online transmission of "cultural products," which includes online gaming, Internet cultural activities and online music. The MOC was dissolved on March 19, 2018 and its responsibilities were assumed by the Ministry of Culture and Tourism.

- The State Oceanic Administration (SOA) – regulates the laying of underwater cables and pipelines.

- The Ministry of Housing and Urban-Rural Development (MOHURD) – has jurisdiction over the approval process for construction and engineering design activities that relate to the telecoms sector.

Spectrum use is allotted on a centralized basis

Spectrum use is allotted on a centralized basis. The MIIT reviews the telecom resource applications submitted by each telecom operators and decides whether to allocate the resources within 30 days. Unlike an auction price or "beauty contest" China has uses annual use fee with exception for certain types of licenses. Operators are required to pay a fee that is periodically reviewed by the government. Permits from SAPPT are required for cable television broadcasting, installation of satellite receiving equipment, video-on-demand services and provincial radio management. Telecom resources are not tradable, nor can they be leased to any third party without prior approval by the government.[401]

As part of China's 13th Five-Year Plan, the MIIT released a capital expenditure target of 2 trillion yuan (USD $289.3 billion) for telecommunications infrastructure investments between 2016 and 2020.[402]

---

[401] Telecoms Regulation and the Administrative Regulation for Radio (July 13, 2017) http://www.miit.gov.cn/n1146295/n1146557/n1146624/c5727360/content.html.

[402] The U.S.-China Economic and Security Review Commission's (USCC) report on China's 13th Five-Year Plan, https://www.uscc.gov/Research/13th-five-year-plan.

China launched the Overall Plan for Promoting Triple Network Convergence for telecommunications, Internet, and broadcasting networks in 2010 for a five-year initial trial period. Then, in September 2015 the State Council issued the Triple Network Convergence Promotion Plan. In May 2016, MIIT issued a Basic Telecommunications Services (BTS) License to China Broadcasting Television and Internet Company, which allowed the company to provide nationwide Internet data and telecommunications services. This is expected to further promote the triple-network convergence process and the involvement of cable television networks in general telecom services. The fragmentation of cable networks in China has also added challenges to the three-network convergence.

The fragmentation of cable networks in China has also added challenges to the three-network convergence

3. Use of TDD in China

China has been a strong promoter of LTE-TDD technology in both 3G and 4G networks, and now in creating 5G networks, for the following reasons:

- CDMA-TDD and LTE-TDD are more cost-efficient.
- Unlike FDD, which requires a pair of channels, TDD can be operated in higher frequency ranges and require less frequency bandwidth than FDD.

Specifically, in China, the CDMA-TDD model has been used as the standard for the 3G mobile network system. CDMA is classified into two mainstream technologies: CDMA2000 and CDMA-TDD. The CDMA-TDD is referred to as TD-SCDMA (Time Division – Synchronous Code Division Multiple Access) and was extensively developed by Siemens and the China Academy of Telecommunications Technology.

China's main carrier, China Mobile, was the only carrier in the world to deploy CDMA-TDD networks for 3G. The other two smaller operators focus primarily on FDD. China Mobile, China Unicom and China Telecom use 250 MHz, 193 MHz and 110 MHz spectrum respectively. The frequency allocation in China is shown in Figure 24-4 below:

PART FOUR: GLOBAL

Figure 24-4: Frequency Allocation in China

Operator	System	Uplink	Downlink	Bandwidth	Total
China Mobile	GSM900	889-909 MHz	934-954 MHz	40 MHz	250 MHz
	GSM1800	1710-1735 MHz	1805-1830 MHz	50 MHz	
	3G TDD	1880-1915 MHz	2010-2025 MHz	50 MHz	
	4G TD-LTE	2320-2370 MHz		50 MHz	
		2575-2635 MHz		60 MHz	
China Unicom	GSM900	909-915 MHz	954-960 MHz	12 MHz	192 MHz
	GSM1800	1735-1750 MHz	1830-1845 MHz	30 MHz	
	FDD-LTE	1750-1765 MHz	1845-1860 MHz	30 MHz	
	3G/FDD-LTE	1940-1965 MHz	2130-2155 MHz	50 MHz	
	TD-LTE	2320-2370 MHz		50 MHz	
		2555-2575 MHz		20 MHz	
China Telecom	CDMA/LTE	825-835 MHz	870-880 MHz	20 MHz	110 MHz
	FDD-LTE	1765-1780 MHz	1860-1875 MHz	30 MHz	
	3G/FDD-LTE	1920-1940 MHz	2110-2130 MHz	40 MHz	
	TD-LTE	2635-2655 MHz		20 MHz	

Source: MIIT and Summit Ridge Group, LLC analysis.

4. 4G and 5G Deployment

China developed its 4G market. For example, 206 million of China Unicom's 304 million users are on 4G. China will also have a well-developed 5G market by 2023. However, with the trade war with the U.S. providers like Huawei and ZTE may cause China to lose the lead.

With the ongoing trade war with the U.S. and market pressures from Huawei and ZTE, some believe that China may lose its lead in 5G

As with many other countries, spectrum is one of the most important issues related to 5G deployment in China. Spectrum will remain a critical but scarce resource in the 5G era and governments around the world are facing strong pressure to free up more spectrum for broadband wireless networks.

In late 2017, the Chinese government decided to allocate 5G spectrum from 3300-3400 MHz, for indoor use only, and 3400-3600 MHz and 4800-5000 MHz for outdoor use. [402] The C-band will be the key 5G band. Between 2017 and 2018, China's 5G research and development trial is mainly focusing on technology, while product trials will be implemented between 2019 and 2020. The 5G system needs to support aggregation of frequency bands. Low and medium bands will be used for 5G coverage and capacity while high frequency bands would be used for 5G capacity and back-haul. At the same time, cooperation with the ITU is important to ensure global harmonization of the 5G spectrum. On July 1, 2018, operators including China Mobile and Chndomestic roaming charges across

---

[402] www.miit.gov.cn/n1146295/n1652858/n1652930/.../content.html

harmonization of the 5G spectrum. On July 1, 2018, operators including China Mobile and Chndomestic roaming charges across provinces. As a result, consumers in China will be the biggest beneficiaries and it is also a sign that operators are willing to provide better prices for 5G implement preparation.

5. Satellites

China launched the first satellite, the Dong Fang Hong I in 1970

China launched the first satellite, the Dong Fang Hong I in 1970. Since then, China has launched over 200 satellites for military, communication, scientific and other purposes. By August 31st, 2017, China ranked 2nd worldwide with 203 operating satellites (The U.S. has 786 in total, while Russia has 139).[403] AsiaSat is the first regional commercial satellite operator in Asia. It is based in Hong Kong and has been providing service for 53 countries and areas. Other Chinese satellite operators include APT Satellite and Asia Broadcast Satellite (ABS), which are also based in Hong Kong.

The national space monitoring network consists of two state monitoring stations in Beijing and Shenzhen. The stations monitor emissions from GSO satellites in the L, S, C, X, Ku and Ka bands, as well as monitoring emissions from non-GSO satellites in the L, S and X bands.[404]

C. Japan

Japan is one of the most developed telecommunication markets in the world. As of 2014, the broadband penetration rate had reached 100%. The telecommunications industry in Japan is dominated by Nippon Telegraph and Telephone East Corporation (NTT East) and Nippon Telegraph and Telephone West Corporation (NTT West) for optical data services and by three major telecom operators: NTT DOCOMO, KDDI Corporation (KDDI), and Softbank Corp (Softbank).

When Japan-based Softbank completed its acquisition of Sprint it added pressure for harmonization of U.S. and Asian spectrum policies, particularly for hardware and handset standards. Harmonization would likely increase economies of scale and purchasing power for wireless operators' over their suppliers.

PART FOUR: GLOBAL

---

[403] Includes 144 LEO, 8 MEO and 51 GEO satellites. *See: UCS Satellite Database,* Union of Concerned Scientists https://www.ucsusa.org/nuclear-weapons/space-weapons/satellite-database#.W2bUzthKi9Y.

[404] Haim Mazar. *Radio Spectrum Management,* John Wiley & Sons, Ltd, 2016, 315.

1. Regulatory Bodies and Spectrum

The Ministry of Internal Affairs and Communications (MIC) is responsible for allocating frequency spectrum to private telecommunications operators by considering the business plans submitted by telecom carriers. It also administers the Telecommunication Business Act, the Radio Act and the Wire Telecommunications Act. Of the 35 countries in the Organization for Economic Cooperation and Development (OECD), Japan is the only country that does not use auctions to allocate new spectrum. Their selection method has drawn criticism because it allows the MIC to exercise control over the market and opens the MIC to accusations of favoritism and political manipulation. 2G mobile service that used the Personal Digital Cellular (PDC) system was used from March 1993 to 2012 in Japan and was then discontinued. 3G based on IMT-2000 has been used in Japan since 2001.

3G mobile service and 4G are widely used in Japan. For 5G spectrum allocation, Japan will revise this process to establish a more transparent, fair, and efficient spectrum allocation framework that will introduce some features of spectrum auctions. In addition, the MIC has taken steps to eliminate anticompetitive practices such as SIM card locking and automatically renewing two-year contracts. They are hoping new competition will drive down mobile plan prices, which currently charge some of the highest rates in the world.

2. 5G Deployment

Japan's main current focus is to achieve widespread 5G deployment by the 2020 Tokyo Olympic Games

Japan's current focus is to achieve widespread 5G deployment by the time of the 2020 Tokyo Olympic Games. Both wireless carriers and the government are committed to reaching this goal, with mobile providers investing in 5G trials and Japan's government pledging to release mid-band and high-band spectrum by early 2019 to follow the national 5G roadmap policy adopted in 2016.[405] Currently, carriers are performing a large-scale pre-commercial field trial using spectrum within the 3.7 GHz, 4.5 GHz, and 28 GHz ranges. Japan has also been focused on the improvement and expansion of free, public Wi-Fi accessibility in an effort to increase the number of foreign visitors and to accommodate the massive number of visitors expected during the Olympic Games.

Operators around the world are conducting or are planning to conduct 5G trials as shown in Figure 24-5. As one of the global leaders in mobile communications in the past decades, Japan is once again

---

[405] CTIA, *The Global Race to 5G, supra* at note 403.

leading the innovations in 5G world.

The Japanese government and the three main mobile service providers in Japan have announced their intent to offer 5G services by 2020, and specifically by the 2020 Tokyo Olympics. In pursuit of this goal, Japanese company NTT DOCOMO and Chinese vendor Huawei have announced that they will collaborate with Tobu Railway to trial a 5G millimeter wave system at Tokyo Skytree Town. This is part of a broader push for 5G field trials advocated by Japan's ministry of Internal Affairs and Communications (MIC). Both NTT DOCOMO and KDDI, two of the three main providers in Japan, began testing 5G networks in May 2017. The Japanese government is looking to introduce new players into the market for 5G services through the new spectrum allocation process.

The Japanese government and the three main mobile providers have announced their intent to offer 5G services by 2020

Figure 24-5: Countries Where Operators are Testing Potential 5G Technologies

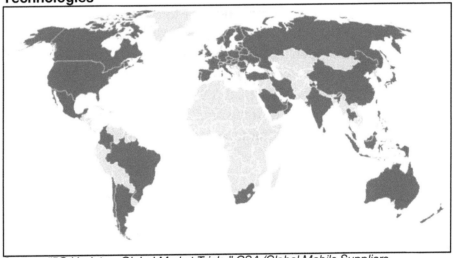

Source: "5G Update – Global Market Trials," GSA (Global Mobile Suppliers Association), April 2018.

2. Satellites

SKY Perfect JSAT Group is a leading satellite operator in the Asia-Pacific region and it is also the only satellite operator in Japan. As of July 2017, SKY Perfect JSAT has a fleet of 17commercial satellites.

D. South Korea

South Korea is one of the most advanced countries for communications in the world. According to the Cisco VNI, South Korea experienced acceleration in mobile traffic growth in 2016, while most other countries experienced strong but tapering growth compared to previous years. [406] Korea Telecom, LG U+ and SK Telecom collectively provide nearly 100% of the population with mobile services.

1. Regulatory Bodies and Spectrum

The telecommunications and Internet businesses are primarily regulated by the following laws and regulators: [407]

- The Telecommunication Business Act (TBA)
- The Act on Promotion of Information and Communications Network Utilization and Information Protection (ICNA)
- The Radio Waves Act (RWA)
- Ministry of Science and ICT (MSIT) – executive ministry under the authority of the Prime Minister
- Korea Communications Commission (KCC) – a regulatory agency directly under the authority of the President

Auctions are used by MSIT to assign radio frequencies. South Korea's 5G spectrum auction kicked off in June 2018 and SK Telecom and KT each won 100MHz of the 3.5GHz spectrum, while LG Uplus clinched 80 MHz. All three secured 800MHz of the 28 GHz spectrum. In total, the companies paid 3.6183 trillion won for the spectrum, 340 billion won higher than the starting price of 3.3 trillion won. They can use the 3.5GHz spectrum for the next 10 years and 28 GHz spectrum for five years.

2. 5G

South Korea is very well positioned in the race to 5G, ranked directly after China in readiness. This is due to strong wireless provider commitment and augmented by the Winter Olympics earlier 2018, which provided a perfect outlet for early investment, research, and trials. The Pyeongchang Winter Olympics served as a world stage for major companies like Samsung and Intel to showcase the technological capabilities 5G has to offer using 26.5-29.5 GHz spectrum. KT Corporation, South Korea's largest telecom firm, offered the first 5G Olympic Games in the world by providing users the opportunity to watch 360-degree games in HD video with a 5G equipped table or VR headset.

The three major mobile operators in South Korea, SK Telecom, KT, and LG U+, have recently announced that they will be working in

---

[406] *Cisco Visual Networking Index (VNI) Global Mobile Data Traffic Forecast Update 2016-2021, supra* at note 175.
[407] Telecoms, Media & Internet 2018 – South Korea

cooperation to launch their 5G networks together in March 2019 during "Korea 5G Day." The networks hope their unity will make South Korea the world's first 5G country. Launching their 5G networks at the same time will also avoid unnecessary competition that would exacerbate marketing costs.

At the first economic minister's meeting in 2017, South Korea included in the "K-ICT spectrum plan" the new 5G allocations of 1,000 MHz bandwidth within the 28 GHz band and 1,300 MHz bandwidth within 3.5 GHz band until 2018. South Korea has also completed their 5G spectrum auction by June 2018. 280 MHz of spectrum in the 3.5 GHz band and 2400 MHz of spectrum in the 28 GHz band were made available in a simultaneous block auction. SK Telecom and KT each won 100 MHz of spectrum in the 3.5 GHz band and LG Uplus won 80 MHz. In the 28 GHz band, the three operators won 800 MHz each. The 3.5 GHz licenses are for ten years and the 28 GHz licenses are for five years. The MSIT announced that the providers may begin using the spectrum on December 1, 2018.

3. Satellites

South Korea's satellite operator, KT Sat, has 3 satellites in orbit. Although it has not been very aggressive in pursuing new sources of revenue, KT Sat aims to triple its revenue by 2025 and propel itself to one of the world's largest operators.

E. Indonesia

Indonesia is currently focused on the rapid deployment of infrastructure

Indonesia's mobile industry is one of the largest globally with 417 million users. Indonesia is currently focused on the rapid deployment of infrastructure. To move the project forward, the president of Indonesia issued a Presidential Regulation that outlined projects with national strategic importance in 2016. The project most significant to the telecommunications industry is the East Palapa Ring broadband project. This project involves the construction and installation of an underwater fiber optic infrastructure that will provide Internet access to 57 cities in eastern Indonesia. Prior to 2014, rural areas, particularly in eastern Indonesia, had a lower connectivity than urban. This, in turn, caused a major developmental gap. The government is taking active measures to improve connectivity by setting targets and increasing the use of Internet-based public services as outlined in the 2014-2019 Indonesian Broadband Plan.

The major operators in Indonesia include state-owned Telkomsel

PART FOUR: GLOBAL

serving 193 million users, Indosat Ooredoo serving 96 million (with 95 million pre-paid), Hutchison 3 Indonesi serving 64 million users, XL Axiata serving 51 million, and Smartfren serving 12 million.

1. Regulatory Bodies and Spectrum

Indonesia's telecommunications sector is highly regulated. Industry jurisdictions include the following:[408]

- Minister of Communication and Information Technology (*MCIT*) – the regulatory entity that requires an operator to obtain radio frequency spectrum license prior to initially using spectrum.
- Indonesian Telecommunication Regulatory Authority (*Badan Regulasi Telekomunikasi Indonesia* BRTI) – in charge of regulating, supervising and managing Indonesia's telecommunications networks and services. It is required to file an annual report to Indonesia's Sector Ministry.
- Indonesian Broadcasting Committee (*Komisi Penyiaran Indonesia* KPI) – responsible for establishing and supervising the implementation of broadcasting standards, regulations and guidelines.

Auctions are used in Indonesia to allocate new spectrum. In October 2017, Indosat Ooredoo, Tri and XL Axiata submitted bid documents to participate in the auctioning of two blocks of unallocated 2100 MHz spectrum. Telkomsel is not allowed to participate in the auction because it won the 2300 MHz spectrum for $74 million. Like China, Japan, Malaysia and India, Indonesia is also a member of the ITU. Therefore, allocation of spectrum is managed in accordance to the ITU's radio regulations.

2. 5G Deployment

The MCIT has announced that they will make available spectrum in the 3.5 GHz, 26 GHz, and 28 GHz bands for 5G trials. Indonesia has plans to build a "5G Experience Center" at the Asian Games 2018 (Aug 18, 2018 – Sep 2, 2018). Telkom had submitted a proposal to the regulator on the frequencies to use and the location of the tests.

3. Satellites

Telkom and Indosat are the major satellite operators in Indonesia,

---

[408] Telecoms, Media & Internet 2018 – *Indonesia,* International Comparative Legal Guides (July 11, 2017) https://iclg.com/practice-areas/telecoms-media-and-internet-laws-and-regulations/indonesia.

each with 2 commercial satellites in orbit.

F. Malaysia

Telephone services were introduced in Malaysia after the World War I to help run the government's administrative system. Malaysia now has 40 million mobile subscribers, a 130% penetration rate. The major operators in the country include Digi serving 11.7 million users, Maxis serving 10.9 million, Celcom serving 9.6 million, U Mobile serving 6.1 million, and Yes 4G serving 0.7 million, Unifi Mobile serving 0.5 million, and ALTEL serving 0.7 million.

By 2016 Malaysia exceeded both Japan and the U.S. in mobile cellular subscriptions by reaching 140.8 per 100 inhabitants

The growth rate for telecommunications increased dramatically in Malaysia, even outpacing regional neighbors. For example, by 2016 Malaysia exceeded both Japan and the U.S. in mobile subscriptions by reaching 140 per 100 inhabitants. The Malaysian mobile operators are now focused on broadband 4G LTE-A and 5G deployments to boost broadband penetration in the country. A comparison of fixed-telephone, mobile and Internet users of Asia-Pacific Countries and the U.S. is demonstrated below in Figure 24-6.

Figure 24-6: Fixed-Telephone, Mobile & Internet Subs: 2016 (per 100 pop)

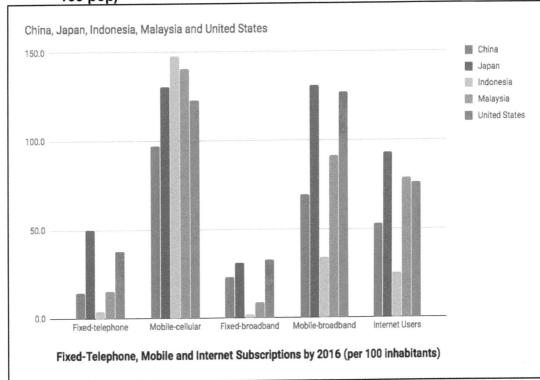

Fixed-Telephone, Mobile and Internet Subscriptions by 2016 (per 100 inhabitants)

Source: Statistics from governments and Summit Ridge Group, LLC Analysis.

PART FOUR: GLOBAL

1. Regulatory Bodies and Spectrum

The Energy, Telecommunications and Posts Ministry is responsible for the formulation of policies and the planning of the future long-term course of the telecommunications sector.[409]

Malaysian Communications and Multimedia Commission (MCMC) – responsible for the supervision of the telecommunication sector. It replaced Malaysian Telecommunications Department (*Jabatan Telekom Malaysia*) as the new regulator in accordance with the Communications and Multimedia Act 1998.

In keeping with the evolving industry, MCMC continues to carry out studies and research. In collaboration and partnership with institutes of higher learning, it is aimed at providing reliable information to foster an informed industry. In 2017, MCMC signed an agreement with the Telecom Regulatory Authority of India (TRAI). MCMC and TRAI also agreed to cooperate in international and regional forums such as the Association of Southeast Asian Nations (ASEAN), Asia-Pacific Telecommunity (APT) and the ITU.

2. 5G Deployment

5G is expected to be used widely in Malaysia by 2022-2023. Celcom has carried out Malaysia's first 5G trial with Ericsson in February 2017 by using 28 GHz spectrum. The trial featured 5G radio prototypes, robotic control, connected environment, virtual reality, Internet of Things (IoT) applications and 4K video streaming. Malaysia's MCMC sold in a "beauty contest" two 5 MHz blocks for USD $50 million each in the 700 MHz spectrum. Carriers were limited to four blocks. At the same time, operators were reassigned 2100 MHz. MCMC previously sold 900 MHz spectrum 1800 MHz for USD $660 million.

3. Satellites

The satellite operator in Malaysia is MEASAT Satellite Systems Sdn. Bhd, which owns and operates the MEASAT (Malaysia East Asia Satellite) and AFRICASAT spacecraft.[410] It provides satellite services to over 150 countries representing 80% of the world's population across Asia, the Middle East, Africa, Europe and Australia.

G. Australia

Australia has identified meeting unprecedented growth in demand for

The telecom sector in Australia is currently transitioning to the wholesale only, government owned National Broadband Network, which will replace legacy

---

[409] *National Telecommunication Policy of Malaysia* (1994-2020), Malaysia Government http://unpan1.un.org/intradoc/groups/public/documents/apcity/unpan002712.pdf.
[410] MEASAT Satellite System – Wikipedia, https://en.wikipedia.org/wiki/MEASAT_Satellite_Systems

mobile broadband and next generation services as a priority for the next decade. The telecommunications sector in Australia is currently transitioning to wholesale only, government-owned National Broadband Network (NBN), which will replace legacy copper networks.

1. Regulation

The Australian Communications and Media Authority (ACMA) is the converged regulator for the Internet, broadcasting, telecommunications, and radio communications sectors. The key responsibilities of the ACMA include the following:

- Licensing and regulating telecom carriers, mobile service providers and content service providers
- Licensing and regulating spectrum allocations
- Regulating television and radio broadcasting and content
- Regulating telecommunications and radio communications equipment
- Regulating telephone and email marketing and online content

Australia has 33 million mobile subscribers spread across three operators. The mobile operators are Telstra serving 17.4 million users, Optus serving 9.6 million, and Vodafone serving 6 million. 4G coverage is solid. Australia is reported by OpenSignal to have 86% availability for 4G service, one of the best covered 4G countries and 36 Mbps per second average throughput, far exceeding the U.S.

2. Spectrum Allocation

Currently, the ACMA allocates spectrum licenses via auction. The licenses are issued for a maximum of 15 years and are technology neutral. This gives licensees the freedom to operate any type of equipment for any purpose, contingent on compliance with license conditions and technical standards. However, the Australian government is in the process of streamlining the current spectrum management system for a simpler and more flexible framework that aligns with the government's broad policy of deregulation. In May 2017, the Australian government released a draft of the new mobile communications bill on spectrum pricing and Commonwealth held spectrum auction for 700 MHz. TPG purchased the 2 x 10 MHz block for USD $910 million and Vodafone the purchased 2 x 5 MHz lot for USD $206 million. The reforms intend to support new, innovative technologies and services, such as 5G and IoT, while providing

PART FOUR: GLOBAL

certainty of spectrum access rights for users and reducing the regulatory burden on spectrum users.

3. 5G Deployment

The Australian Competition and Consumer Commission (ACCC) released the Communications Sector Market Study[411] in April 2018. In the report, the ACCC anticipates that the three major mobile network providers Telstra, Optus, and Vodafone will begin to launch 5G services by 2020. The ACCC also noted that 5G networks are expected to use higher frequency spectrum than current 4G networks, specifically within the 3.4-3.7 GHz spectrum bands.

---

[411] *The Communications Sector Market Study Final Report*, Australian Competition & Consumer Commission (April 5, 2018) https://www.accc.gov.au/publications/c ommunications-sector-market-study-final-report

XXV. Russia and CIS

A. Russia and the CIS

1. Regional Commonwealth in the field of Communications

The Regional Commonwealth in the field of Communications (RCC) was established on December 17, 1991 in Moscow by the Communications Administrations of eleven countries: Azerbaijan, Armenia, Belarus, Kazakhstan, Kyrgyzstan, Moldova, Russia, Tajikistan, Turkmenistan, Uzbekistan, and Ukraine. The RCC was designed to carry out the cooperation of the newly established Commonwealth of Independent States (CIS) in the fields of communications, including networks and the means to provide telephone communication, data transmission, TV broadcasting, and radio broadcasting. The activities of the RCC are guided by the current legislation of the CIS member countries, the decisions of the RCC board and the ITU. The RCC has defined the following goals:

- To improve regulation and increase efficiency of wireless spectrum and satellite orbits
- To maintain the balance of interests between existing and new allocations to different wireless services
- To consider both technical and economic opportunities in the development of wireless communications
- To strengthen regional and international cooperation in the development of radio communication equipment and systems

B. Russia

The telecom sector in Russia is heavily regulated and is often driven by political and lobbying efforts

Russia has a strong mobile market with 248 million users, a 171% penetration rate. MTS serves 77 million users, Megafon serves 75 million, Beeline serves 58 million, Tele2 serves 38 million, and MOTIV serves 2.5 million. Recent trends in Russia's telecom market include increasing legislative pressure on market players, restricting foreign investment, and strengthening state control over operators, media, and consumers. Between 2012 and 2018, the Russian government set objectives to further develop the sector. These objectives include:

- Achieve penetration rate of over 90% for broadband services, allowing fast access to Internet for people living in 250 towns and villages
- Ensure that every year over 20 million citizens get access to 4G mobile Internet
- Have venture investments in the IT sector of over USD $1.2 billion
- Make average growth of the IT sector three times higher than Russian GDP growth

1. Regulatory Body

The main regulator of the telecommunications sector is the Ministry of Communication and Mass Media of the Russian Federation (Minsvyaz). [413] The Ministry is responsible for developing and implementing national policy and legal regulation on the following topics:

- Telecommunications, including the allocation and conversion of radio frequency spectrum
- Mass media, including electronic media, development of the Internet, television and radio broadcasting, and related topics
- Publishing, printing, and distribution of printed media
- Information technology, including the creation of government information resources and promotion of access to such resources
- Personal data processing and Internet governance

2. Spectrum Policy

The Communication Law in Russia establishes that electromagnetic spectrum shall be allocated by the State Commission for Radio Frequencies (SCRF), which is an inter-agency coordinating body under Minsvyaz. There has been a gradual movement to align Russian regulations on frequency allocation with international regulations. Currently, the state has priority on all frequency allocations. Spectrum licenses are typically assigned for a term of ten years or less.

3. 5G

In July 2017, SCRF awarded spectrum to mobile operator MegaFon

---

[413] Russian Ministry, http://minsvyaz.ru/en/ministry/common/

for 5G testing in the 3.4 GHz, 25.25 GHz, and 29.50 GHz bands.[414] The following January, Rostelecom, another mobile operator, became the second Russian operator to gain clearance for 5G trials in the 3.4 GHz, 24.5 GHz, and 29.5 GHz bands. This is an unusual situation because only two of Russia's four operators were approved for 5G trials. The other two operators, MTS and Beeline, requests to begin 5G trials were denied due to concerns that trials in the spectrum frequencies requested would interfere with Roscosmos space agency, operations and the Federal Protective Service. MegaFon and Roscosmos have committed to a cooperation agreement to jointly develop a 5G network to minimize the cost of deploying the next-generation standard. Pilot projects in Moscow and St Petersburg are currently in progress.

C. Ukraine

1. Market Structure

Ukraine's mobile infrastructure is being modernized through considerable investment. There are 61 million mobile users, a 142% penetration rate, served by four operators: Kyivstar serves 25 million mobile users, Vodafone serves 21 million, Lifecell serves 11 million, and Intertelecom and Tribmob serve 2 million. The Ukraine telecom industry is in transition following the privatization of the monopoly held by state-owned fixed-line provider Ukrtelecom in 2011.

2. Spectrum

In the mobile market, Ukraine's deployment of new technologies is significantly behind schedule

In the mobile market, Ukraine's deployment of new technologies is significantly behind schedule. An auction for LTE spectrum was held in March of this year for 2x75 MHz of spectrum in the 1800 MHz band. The auction was organized by the National Commission for State Regulation of Telecommunications and Informatization (NCCIR) and raised a total of $204 million USD. The winners were the three leading Ukrainian mobile operators: Kyivstar, Vodafone Ukraine, and Lifecell. All the licenses are valid for 15 years, nationwide.[415] This was the second spectrum auction held for LTE. The first was held earlier in 2018 for spectrum in the 2600 MHz band, where 15-year licenses

---

[414] Juan Pedro Tomas, *Russian Regulator Fails to Award Spectrum for 5G Testing*, RCR Wireless (Jan. 8, 2018) https://www.rcrwireless.com/20180108/5g/russian-regulator-fails-to-award-spectrum-5g-testing-tag23

[415] Ian Channing, *Ukrainian Spectrum Auctions Concluded*, Developing Telecoms (Mar. 9, 2018) https://www.developingtelecoms.com/business/regulation/7710-ukrainian-spectrum-auctions-concluded.html

were won by the same three operators.

Figure 25-1: Regional and Global MHz Identified for IMT

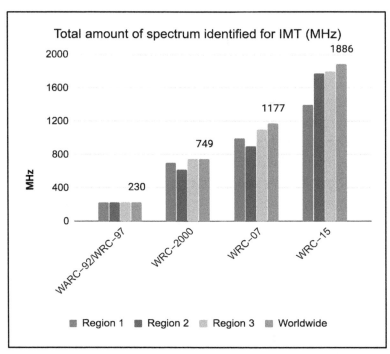

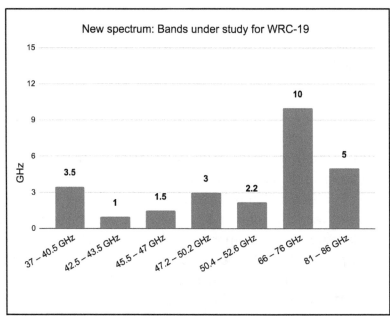

Source: ITU[417] and Summit Ridge Group, LLC analysis

[417] Information Session by ITU-R and ITU-T, *5G roadmap: challenges and opportunities ahead*,ITU (July 2017) https://www.itu.int/en/ITU-D/Conferences/GSR/Documents/GSR2017/IMT2020%20roadmap%20GSR17%20V1%202017-06-21.pdf

PART FIVE: VALUATION

XXVI. Spectrum Valuation Overview

This chapter is intended to provide a summary-level overview of spectrum valuation. It is impossible to fully explain the nuances of spectrum valuation in a single chapter.

Historically, spectrum price volatility, particularly for less desirable spectrum, has been very high.

Spectrum has three dimensions of value: 1) the financial benefits for the licensee; 2) the indirect economic benefits to society; and 3) the social benefits such as improved access to emergency services. This chapter will focus only on the first dimension of value, while acknowledging the other values may be much higher. A complete analysis, even of the financial value to the licensee, is beyond the scope of this paper. Rather, this chapter will introduce the process. Summit Ridge Group has extensive experience in spectrum valuation and is available for more detailed consultations.

Summit Ridge Group believes that strict regulation and rapid demand growth has made spectrum a scarce resource in the U.S. and other parts of the world.[418] Historically, spectrum license price volatility, particularly with less desirable spectrum, has been very high. When estimates for demand increase, the value of less desirable spectrum spikes on the expectation that well-financed service providers will soon develop the spectrum. As demand estimates fluctuate downward, spectrum prices plummet on doubts that the spectrum will ever be put to profitable use. However, there are analytical frameworks for considering spectrum value.

Spectrum licenses are intangible assets

Spectrum licenses are intangible assets, which technically cannot be considered property since the licensee must explicitly waive ownership claims over the acquired spectrum. For valuation purposes, spectrum licenses can be treated as quasi-property. There are three approaches to consider when evaluating the commercial value of spectrum – the income, market, and cost approach. These approaches seek to answer the following questions: How much value does the spectrum add? What is the market price? and What would it cost to replace? Additionally, policymakers often use econometric modeling to gauge general valuation levels for auction estimation or tax purposes.

Industry custom is to describe spectrum pricing in units of price per

---

[418] The debate over what role government regulation should play in the process is far from settled. In general, European policymakers favor a more significant and more deliberate government role in spectrum management than its counterparts in the U.S. Spectrum is, in theory, infinite since cell sizes can be made smaller and smaller. However, such an infrastructure build-out becomes cost-prohibitive.

MHz/PoP, i.e. the price divided by the number of megahertz, divided by the population covered. While not all MHz or populations are equal, this calculation provides a consistent comparison of prices across transactions.

A. Standard of Value and Level of Value

Before starting work on a valuation, the appraiser must identify some basic premises, including the standard of value to be used and the level of value.

1. Standard of Value

The term "value" is ambiguous and must be defined in a valuation project via a specific standard of value, sometimes called the premise of value. The standard of value refers to the assumed circumstances of the valuation. Fair Market Value, for example, refers to the amount the subject asset would sell for in the open market.[419] This is appropriate for some circumstances, but not others. For example, a factory may spend a large amount of money on a custom-designed piece of metal needed as part of its unique manufacturing process and that requires a great deal of labor to install. This piece of metal may be very valuable to the factory owner, but it may have minimal resale value as it is of almost no use to anyone else other than for scrap purposes. If the goal is to measure the price at which the factory owner might sell the asset, the fair value[420] might be a more appropriate method of valuing the asset. If the goal is to measure the unique value the piece of metal creates for a specific factory, investment value might be a more appropriate standard of value. Likewise, a company can be valued as a going concern or liquidation value each giving very different results.[421]

In each case, the appraiser determines the standard of value based on the purpose of the valuation and the relevant circumstances. In some cases, such as tax valuations, financial reporting valuations or valuation of economic damages, the required standard of value may

---

[419] The full definition of Fair Market Value is contained in IRS Revenue Ruling 59-60: https://www.fdic.gov/regulations/examinations/trustmanual/appendix_e/e_rulings.html

[420] Fair Value is defined in Financial Accounting Standards Board's ASC 820: https://asc.fasb.org/imageRoot/00/7534500.pdf.

[421] For a more in-depth explanation of the various standards of value see: Shannon P. Pratt, *Opinion of the College on Defining Standards of Value*. Valuation, Vol. 34, No. 2 (June 1989) http://www.appraisers.org/docs/default-source/college-of-fellows-articles/defining-standards-of-value.pdf.

be prescribed in the relevant regulations and/or case/law.

2. Level of Value

The level of value refers to two things – control and marketability. A controlling interest in an asset may be worth more than a minority interest. A party with controlling interest may be able to make changes in the way it is used to increase value. A party with a controlling interest has little risk of being taking advantage of by their partners. On the other hand, if an asset is being well managed there may not be a premium associated with owning a controlling interest versus a minority interest.

The second aspect of level of value is marketability. An asset that can easily be sold is generally worth more than an asset that is difficult to sell. This is because most people prefer, all else equal, the flexibility of being able to quickly convert their investment into cash than needing to go through a potentially long and expensive sales process. To accept the risk and effort of tying-up their money in an investment that is hard to sell, buyers will require a discount compared to the price they would pay if it were easy to sell. The amount of the discount involves an analysis of the specific circumstances of the asset and is beyond the scope of this chapter.

B. Income Approach

1. Description

The income appraisal method predicts future benefit streams (usually cash flows) that a licensee might generate using the acquired spectrum. The predicted cash flow in excess of the costs required to generate revenue (including the cost of spectrum, equipment, labor, and the normalized cost of capital) are discounted for risk and the time value of money. The result is the intrinsic value of the spectrum license. The most common version of the income approach is called the discounted cash flow (DCF) method.

2. Application

The DCF method is most useful when used internally since accurate and reliable estimations of future revenues and growth are needed. This is often the case with stable industries.

For licenses with established uses such as radio broadcasting, industry metrics are used to estimate the potential value of a license – a critical element for starting the business. This is called the Greenfield Method, which is essentially a DCF analysis starting from scratch. Another version of the income appraisal method is called the

The income method is most useful when used internally since accurate and reliable estimations of future revenues and growth are needed

Multi-Period Excess Earnings Model (MPEEM). The MPEEM can be used to value a critical business intangible. It examines the return a business earns, subtracts the portions attributable to other supporting assets, and discounts the remainder. A complete description of the MPEEM models is beyond the scope of this text,[422] but Summit Ridge Group professionals have experience in applying it and explaining the methodology to clients and in legal proceedings.

3. Challenges

The DCF and MPEEM methods are very sensitive to the projections and discount rates. Small changes in assumptions can result in large differences in valuation. With early-stage companies, particularly those with new technologies or business models, long-term projections are typically somewhat speculative.

C. Market Approach – Comparable Transactions

1. Description

Spectrum is one of the few intangible assets where relevant market comparables are often available

The market approach is based on historical data rather than predicted future data. It is called the market comparable method and is based on the logic that an asset is worth what buyers have previously paid for similar assets, e.g., the price paid for similar licenses. A valuation estimate is determined by applying the relevant metrics from prior transactions to the spectrum license being appraised. Most intangible assets are unique so relevant market comparables are unavailable. Spectrum, however, is one of the few intangible assets where relevant market comparables are often available.

2. Application

While the pricing standard is generally "price per MHz/PoP," for satellite orbit slots and secondary licenses, valuation professionals use different pricing standards. They are usually considered in terms of the price paid for other licenses in the same band. When using comparable transactions, a valuation professional must consider and adjust for industry-specific regulatory and technical issues. This can be a significant challenge. The market comparable method is the primary method used by audiences like courts or public market investors with limited industry data to scrutinize the assumptions in a DCF model. The market approach is usually the best option if relevant

PART FIVE: VALUATION

---

[422] MPEEM
http://www.kpmg.com/CN/en/IssuesAndInsights/ArticlesPublications/Newsletters/Defini ng-Issues/Documents/Defining-Issues-O-1008-33.pdf

comparables are available and cash flow uncertainty makes income-based approaches difficult.

3. Challenges

Direct comparables are often rare, so appraisers usually must make adjustments to the closest available comparables. But it is often difficult to find principled methods for making the adjustments. When comparing auction results between countries, for example, seemingly small differences can have a large difference in expected auction outcomes, making adjusting challenging. Additionally, the market changes rapidly, particularly for non-prime spectrum, limiting the value of comparables.

D. Cost Approach - Replacement Method

1. Description

The third method is based on the principle that something is worth no more than what it costs to replace it with something of equivalent functionality. For example, if a mobile operator loses spectrum, it can, for a price, replace that capability with additional cell splitting. This method called the Optimal Deprived Valuation Method (or the "With and Without Method"). It would estimate the loss of value to the company if the spectrum were taken away and replaced by the most economical alternative means for replicating the functionality of this spectrum.

2. Application

The most obvious way for a mobile operator to adapt to losing spectrum is by further dividing existing cell sites in the remaining spectrum into smaller cells to increase reuse. The cost of this provides an approximate value of the spectrum. Figure 26-1 below shows the FCC projections for the cost savings to the wireless industry of providing 500 MHz of additional spectrum.[423]

Under the cost approach technique, the value of spectrum is the difference in costs between current or planned spectrum and the next best alternative

---

[423] For additional analysis of the trade-off between additional spectrum and capital expenditures, *see* Robert J. Shapiro, Douglas Holtz-Eakin, & Coleman Bazelon, *The Economic Implications of Restricting Spectrum Purchases in the Incentive Auctions*, (April 30, 2013)
http://www.sonecon.com/docs/studies/EconImplicationsSpectrumAuctions.pdf.

Figure 26-1: Cost Savings of Additional Spectrum

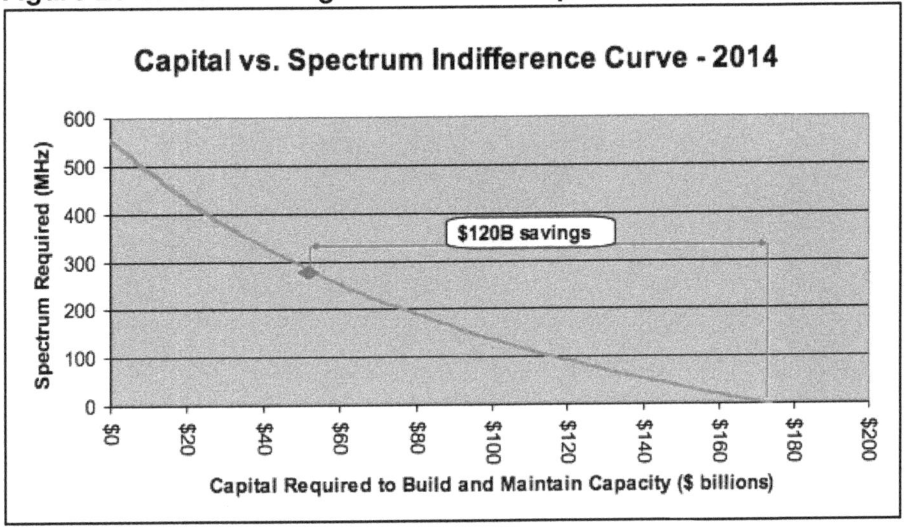

Capital vs. Spectrum Indifference Curve - 2014

$120B savings

Source: FCC

Using the cost approach, the value of spectrum is the difference in costs to a company between its current or planned spectrum and the next best alternative. The Optimal Deprived Valuation Method is most applicable for developed businesses trying to sell spectrum for which there is a clear alternative replacement at a known cost.

3. Challenges

This method is not a viable method for businesses that would need to shut down when faced with spectrum reduction. It is also often difficult to predict the most efficient manner for a company to respond to the loss of an asset, or to predict the replacement cost of a comparable asset.

E. Econometric Modeling

This method analyzes statistical differences between variables and a sample of other assets. It is useful when determining a general value for a class of assets than for a particular asset. Regulators often use it to estimate aggregate auction proceeds or to set tax levels. Business valuation professionals evaluating a particular asset generally do not use it.

F. Other Considerations

The valuation drivers of these methods are related. When valuing spectrum, buyers generally will not pay more than the market price, nor will they pay more than it would cost to replicate the functionality using another technology method. Assuming those conditions are

Regulators often use econometric modeling to estimate auction proceeds or to set tax levels. Business valuation professionals evaluating a specific asset generally do not use it

PART FIVE: VALUATION

met, their valuation will focus on the potential return to a business using the spectrum. This return depends on many factors: the network construction cost, the number of customers that the spectrum can support, FCC regulation, topography, availability of equipment, and required battery life.

The cost of building a network largely determines the economic feasibility of adopting a specific frequency. The cost of using a specific frequency is, in turn, determined by the availability of equipment developed for that spectrum, the supply of towers and the spectrum's cost. The cost of spectrum varies according to its physical propagation characteristics in the region, the costs to build a network using it as well as strategic issues such as the equipment vendor support needed to make a spectrum range valuable for commercial use. With more equipment vendor support, more equipment becomes available, and the specific frequency becomes cheaper and easier for operators to build-out.

Service providers generally will not pay more than the market price for spectrum, nor will they pay more than the cost of replicating the functionality using another technology method

The number of customers that can be supported by the frequency is also significant. The more customers it can support, the more valuable the spectrum. This is partially dependent on the propagation qualities of frequency and the local geography in terms of the needs of the buyer.

G. Valuation Challenges

1. Business Environment Can Change

Industries are dynamic. The numbers of players change, significantly influencing profitability. Industry dynamics can also impact the number of potential buyers, affecting the liquidity of the market in which a license is sold. There is often uncertainty about the future demand for services using the spectrum. Strategic issues are also significant, particularly with new LTE technologies for which operators prefer large (15 or 20 MHz) swaths of contiguous spectrum. A license holder with spectrum in the middle of a more substantial holder's otherwise contiguous swath may have significant economic leverage.

Wireless operators normally prefer licensed spectrum to shared spectrum

Demand growth can also change significantly. For example, the demand for wireless broadband is currently growing rapidly. Wireless operators are investing in new technology to accommodate this growth. However, should growth slow markedly, reverse, or be absorbed by unlicensed spectrum, the value of wireless broadband spectrum could dramatically decline. This is particularly true for spectrum towards the higher or lower ends or traditional use for a given application. It's much like real estate at the edge of town. It the town grows, in increases in value quickly, but if the town shrinks, it's value rapidly falls.

2. Technological Change Risk

The communications industry is a technology industry, which by nature is constantly in flux. Change increases or decreases the value of spectrum depending on the situation. Currently, there is a perceived shortage of spectrum, which increases pricing as new technologies encourage wireless users to use more data-intensive applications. Other new technologies such as dynamic spectrum access radios and associated databases promise to significantly increase the supply of spectrum through sharing, depressing spectrum license valuation. Wireless operators usually prefer licensed spectrum to shared spectrum because the availability of licensed spectrum is guaranteed for their customers. However, the alternatives of unlicensed spectrum and technical improvements in cognitive radio technology may limit the price operators will pay for licensed spectrum.

3. Financial Market Risk

Markets change rapidly – even more rapidly than technology. This impacts the theoretical value of a spectrum license as the cost of capital changes. It also affects a buyer's access to capital as financing windows open and close. Typically, the cost of capital and access to capital markets improves or deteriorates at roughly the same time, thus compounding the challenge.

4. Regulatory Risk

Regulatory changes are often difficult to predict, both in terms of substance and the timing of those changes

The telecommunications industry is highly regulated, particularly with respect to spectrum. Regulatory authorities can increase the supply of spectrum thus lowering demand for spectrum at a given price-point. They also can change license terms, enforcement terms, and grant or deny waivers for terms such as build-out requirements and control many other factors that impact value. Regulatory changes are often difficult to predict, both regarding the substance and the timing of those changes. Figure 26-2 shows general ranges for the impact of common regulatory factors.

PART FIVE: VALUATION

Figure 26-2: Impact of Common Regulatory Factors

Driver	From (worst)	To (best)	Impact on cost to serve subscribers
Infrastructure/ Spectrum Sharing	No site/spectrum sharing allowed	Active site and spectrum sharing encouraged	-35% to -40%
Coverage obligations	High coverage requirements	No coverage requirements	-25% to -35%
Industry structure	Multiple players	Economically viable number of players	-20% to -30%
Spectrum license fees	High fees	No fees	-15% to -30%

Source: ITU[424] and Summit Ridge Group, LLC analysis

Spectrum above 2 GHz or below 300 MHz has less value due to its difficulty with range and building penetration issues. However, as cell sites get smaller and new technology improves building penetration, spectrum near or above 2 GHz becomes more valuable

5. Internal Strategic Issues

Spectrum licenses can have value specific to the bidder due to its individual strategic issues. Spectrum may have value in blocking a competitor in combination with existing spectrum, avoiding a site build-out, tax considerations, and many other complex issues.

H. General Valuation Observations

Many factors influence the value of spectrum. Detailing all of them is outside the scope of this report. However, a few significant considerations follow.[425]

1. Frequency Band is Critical

For terrestrial mobile wireless use, the most valuable spectrum is between 300 MHz and 1 GHz since lower frequencies have better penetration qualities and travel further. However, spectrum between 1 GHz and 2 GHz has become valuable as well. Lower frequencies are in highest demand for rural areas due to the larger circumference of the area reached by waves. But in urban areas higher frequencies are often sufficient for high population density because the waves need not travel great distances.

---

[424] *Exploring the Value and Economic Valuation of Spectrum*, International Telecommunications Union – Broadband Series, April 2013.

[425] For additional information on spectrum valuation *see,* Bazelon, Coleman and McHenry, Giulia, *Spectrum Value* (Mar. 31, 2012). 2012 TRPC. SSRN: http://ssrn.com/abstract=2032213 or http://dx.doi.org/10.2139/ssrn.2032213

Not only is the lower circumference of the area reached by higher frequency waves no longer a disadvantage, but their improved data capacity also becomes an advantage in urban areas. High frequencies enable spectral efficiency to increase for high-volume data applications. Since the demand for data-intensive services used on devices like smartphones and tablets has risen rapidly, the value of spectrum at the upper end of the spectrum rage has also increased.

Spectrum rights above 2 GHz or below 300 MHz have less value due to difficulties with range and building penetration issues. However, as cell sites get smaller and newer technology improves building penetration, spectrum near or above 2 GHz becomes more valuable, particularly in urban areas where cell sites are the smallest. There is an ongoing movement to redeploy some of the satellite spectrum in the lower portion of the C-band (3.7 GHz) to Wi-Fi and other terrestrial wireless applications. A description of the coverage of various frequencies is in Figure 26-3 below.

Figure 26-3: Coverage Difference Between Frequencies

Frequency (MHz)	Cell radius (km)	Cell area (km2)	Relative Cell Count
450	50.0	7,850	1
900	25.0	1,964	4
1800	12.5	491	16
2100	10.7	360	22
2500	9.0	254	31
3000	7.5	177	44
3600	6.25	123	64
4200	5.35	90	87

Source: Wikipedia and Summit Ridge Group, LLC analysis

The area covered by a cell is proportional to the square of its frequency

As the table above indicates, the area covered by a cell is proportional to the square of the frequency. Thus, at 2 GHz, approximately four times as many cell sites are needed than at 1 GHz. The above table assumes the antenna size scales with wavelength. This is not always the case. If the antenna size is fixed, operators will experience less geographical coverage loss as a carrier moves to higher frequencies.

PART FIVE: VALUATION

Moreover, other factors such as geography, antenna height and power regulation and other factors can also limit coverage and thus limit the ability of larger cells to utilize their theoretical full coverage areas.

2. Wider Bands of Paired Contiguous Spectrum Are More Valuable

To be efficient, newer spectrum protocols, including various spread spectrum technologies, require broader swaths of spectrum. Without a broad swath, spectrum rights are generally less valuable.[427]

a. Blocks of Contiguous Spectrum Valuable

Broader swaths of spectrum allow inter-cell distances to be larger and improve efficiencies in the carriage of signal from network node nearest the origin to the node nearest the destination (also known as "trunking"). While 3G spectrum reaches its maximum spectral efficiency with blocks of 5 MHz of contiguous spectrum, LTE spectrum needs two blocks of 15 or 20 MHz to be most efficient depending. With 5 MHz swaths, the spectrum is approximately 25% as efficient as 20 MHz swaths for LTE services.

Reorganizing spectrum nationally into wider and more efficient swaths requires significant changes to the current system. It is analogous to replacing country roads with a major interstate highway. Ownership of spectrum by many smaller entities impedes the ability to conduct the spectrum swaps necessary to create larger blocks. At the same time, most national regulators are often loath to limit the number of competitors for fear of anti-trust issues.[428]

b. Value of Pairing

In addition to the issue of large contiguous blocks, spectrum often needs to be "paired," i.e., allocated in two pieces that are separate enough to avoid interference but close enough that the propagation characteristics do not materially change. This allows one block to be used for the "uplink" (from the handset to the base station) and the other for the "downlink" (from the base station to the handset). With a block of spectrum for each of the two transmission directions, the

With a block of spectrum for each of the two transmission directions, the spectrum can be used more efficiently

---

[427] Thomas W. Hazlett & Roberto E. Munoz, *What Really Matters in Spectrum Allocation Design* (April 2010)
https://www.researchgate.net/publication/46454377_What_Really_Matters_in_Spectrum_Allocation_Design

[428] Regulators in the Netherlands have concluded that higher efficiencies in spectrum sharing can be achieved via a separation of infrastructure providers (who own and build-out the spectrum), and service providers (who provide the service).

spectrum is used more efficiently. Closely spaced spectrum pairs (small duplex gaps) are more desirable because the propagation differences between the uplink and downlink are minimized. However, it is often easier for regulators to find larger blocks to allocate if they are further apart (large duplex gaps). As large blocks are generally more valuable than small blocks, regulators face a tradeoff.

Some of the latest spread spectrum technologies such as LTE-TDD, however, do not benefit from pairing, so the enhanced value associated with paired spectrum may decline over time.

3. Hardware Availability Must Be Considered

Hardware availability is an important consideration, particularly in price-sensitive applications, including most consumer markets. Operators resist paying high prices for spectrum for which there is little equipment available or if the hardware market is not price-competitive. They are legitimately concerned that a lack of competitively priced hardware will make it more difficult for them to attract customers or force them to pay greater device subsidies to get customers. The challenge of available hardware is more common with small amounts of spectrum. Without adequate spectrum, hardware manufacturers may believe demand will be insufficient even if the spectrum is of high quality. A significant driver behind efforts at international harmonization is a desire to increase hardware availability. Manufacturers are more likely to develop hardware for spectrum if there is a global market as opposed to only a domestic one.

A significant driver behind efforts at international harmonization is a desire to increase hardware availability

On the other hand, operators sometimes seek to limit hardware strategically. In the 700 MHz band, In the U.S., Verizon and AT&T have tried to limit handsets so that they do not work on the A Block generally owned by smaller operators. They were seeking to effectively "lock" their hardware to their own spectrum and, at the same time, make it difficult for smaller operators to have cost-effective handsets without economies of scale.

4. Geography Is Critical

The spectrum crunch is largely an urban phenomenon

In general, demand for wireless services is much greater in urban areas. The more populous a given area, the higher the density of use and the more spectrum needed. As a result, spectrum crunch is largely an urban area phenomenon. In fact, the FCC indicated in 2010 that the then existing 608 MHz of wireless spectrum in the U.S. was

PART FIVE: VALUATION

sufficient for most rural areas.[429] Urban spectrum is, therefore, more valuable than rural spectrum. A license that covers urban areas is likely worth considerably more than one in rural areas. Additionally, licenses for large areas are priced lower than licenses for smaller territories since smaller license territories allow buyers to more narrowly bid for territories that they need most for their businesses. For very large territories, the cost of the required build-out restrains the bidding level. For example, few companies have the resources to finance a national build-out. So, a nationwide license should sell for a discount on a price per MHz/PoP basis than the aggregation of smaller regional licenses covering the country.

5. Supply and Demand Considerations

In addition to the current supply-demand dynamics that drive the analysis above, we must also consider future supply and demand. While short-term mismatches are possible, the FCC is moving on several fronts to allocate additional spectrum to the areas most in demand. Although, as described in Chapter VII.H of this *Handbook*, the FCC reallocation process can take years, it would be a mistake to blindly assume that the current scarcity in certain markets will continue indefinitely. Regulatory processes, although slow, often tend to overcompensate when they finally begin to move.

It would be a mistake to blindly assume that the current scarcity in certain market will continue indefinitely

In addition to the macro issues of supply and demand, there are company-specific issues to consider. In the 700 MHz band, in the U.S., Verizon and AT&T are under regulatory and political pressure to reduce or maintain their spectrum at current levels particularly in the lower bands. Current rules, called "spectrum screens," generally limit operators from making further acquisitions once they control more than 33% of the spectrum in a given geographical area. With these deep-pocketed players out of the bidding in certain spectrum license auctions, demand may be lower, resulting in a reduced price.

6. Auction Rules

Policymakers designing auctions must balance the desire to attract multiple bidders to ensure a competitive auction against the desire that each operator have enough bandwidth to operate efficiently. This is often difficult to achieve.

Auctions for identical spectrum in similar countries can yield price differentials of over an order of magnitude

As a result of the difficulty in balancing these interests, prices in spectrum license auctions vary widely. Auctions for identical spectrum

---

[429] FCC Staff Technical Paper, *Mobile Broadband: The Benefits of Additional Spectrum* (Oct. 2010) http://www.fcc.gov/document/mobile-broadband-benefits-additional-spectrum

licenses in similar countries occurring within weeks of each other can yield price differentials of over an order of magnitude. Details include bidding eligibility that impacts the number of potential bidders, the structure and usage rules of the spectrum and other circumstances related to the specific market.[429]

7. Incumbent vs. New Entrant

In general, spectrum rights are more valuable to an incumbent than a new entrant. An incumbent can often leverage existing infrastructure whereas a new entrant cannot. Moreover, incumbents view added spectrum as a savings, i.e., expenditure on additional cell sites avoided. Their incremental revenue per subscriber is also likely to be higher, allowing them to bid more. An established incumbent also has a lower cost of capital. When selling, an incumbent may view the spectrum rights as part of its going-concern value and require a higher price than it would for an asset. Incumbents may also assign "private value" to the spectrum due to the potential foreclosure benefit of using it to block new entrants.

8. License Terms

License terms have a great impact on their value. Issues to consider include the term, renewal expectations, transfer rights and build-out requirements, and ongoing payments, as well potential sharing and/or reuse requirements. As a result of the enormous cumulative impact of different national auction processes, license rules, operation regulations and competitive environments, auction results in one country have limited value in projecting auction valuations in another country. Ongoing payments and transfer rights/secondary market are of particular importance.

a. Ongoing payments

Countries around the world have different policies with respect to ongoing payments in addition to the bidding amount. In the U.S., ongoing payments are generally minimal and restricted to small administrative fees. In the other countries, the situations are different. In the recent Spanish 3.5 GHz auction, for example, the cost of

---

[429] For a detailed discussion of auction structure and policy issues, *see* Martyn Roetter, on behalf of the GSMA, *Spectrum Broadband in the Americas: Policy Issues for Growth and Competition* (Jan. 2011).

PART FIVE: VALUATION

ongoing payment is expected to exceed the auction price.[430] These costs, or lack thereof, must be considered when valuing spectrum and comparing prices across countries

b. Transfer Rights

Spectrum licenses have varying levels of liquidity. In the U.S., the FCC has historically encouraged a secondary market for spectrum. Generally, the FCC permits spectrum licenses transfers unless they would create concerns about FCC policy such as anti-competitive behavior or the proposed acquirer has material character issues. The FCC does not concern itself with transfer prices and does not even record this is its database. In parts of Scandinavia, on the other hand, certain spectrum licenses cannot be sold at a profit. The buyer must earn all of their return through operating a system using the spectrum license.

I. Valuation Trends

Around the time of the introduction of the iPhone in 2008, mobile broadband spectrum license prices soared

Since 1994, the U.S. government has raised over $100 billion in revenue from wireless companies participating in FCC spectrum auctions.[431] Around the time of the introduction of the iPhone in 2008, mobile broadband spectrum license prices soared. The growth of wireless broadband became obvious, but the strategies of operators to deal with it were less transparent. It is now clear that operators have managed the growth via data caps, smaller cell sites, and Wi-Fi offloading, among other strategies. As a result, the upward trajectory in price increases has stalled as shown in Figure 26-4 below:

---

[430] *Operators Spend €438 Million in Spain 5G Spectrum Auction*, Mobile World Live (July 25, 2018) https://www.mobileworldlive.com/featured-content/home-banner/operators-spend-e438m-in-spain-5g-spectrum-auction/.
[431] FCC FY2019 Budget Estimates to Congress (Feb. 2018).

Figure 26-4: Consolidated Spectrum Return Indices

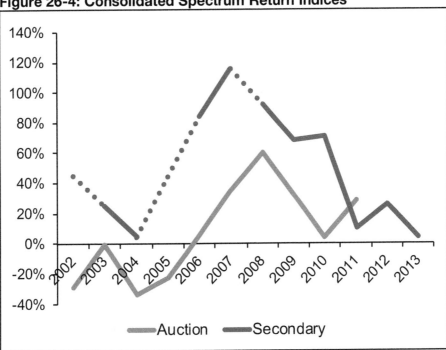

Source: *Scott Wallsten, Technology Policy Institute.*[432]

Dr. Wallsten's analysis in Figure 26-4 is consistent with an international study of 200 mobile wireless auctions showing a decline in relative prices for spectrum global.[433] Nonetheless, great uncertainty remains about future spectrum supply and demand.

1. The Supply Debate

The supply side of the spectrum demand equation is more complicated than the demand side. Much of the uncertainty is due to the difficulty in predicting the outcome and timing of various government efforts to increase spectrum availability. However, the following is known:

The supply side of the spectrum equation is more complicated than the demand side

1. The 2010 National Broadband Plan sought to add 300 MHz of spectrum for mobile broadband before 2015. While it missed this goal, it aims to reach a total of over 500 MHz by 2020. The most significant part of that is the 84 MHz that the FCC pulled back from television broadcasters via the reverse

---

[432] For an explanation of the calculations, *see* Scott Wallsten, Technology Policy Institute, *Is There a Spectrum Crisis? Quantifying Factors Affecting Spectrum License Value (*Feb. 26, 2013) https://techpolicyinstitute.org/wp-content/uploads/2013/01/is-there-really-a-spectrum-cri-2007657.pdf.

[433] Sims, Martin, *Price of Mobile Spectrum Falls in Real Terms*, Policy Tracker (June 20, 2011)

broadcaster incentive auction process enabling 70 MHz (after reduction for guard bands) and auctioned to the wireless industry. The FCC auctioned 65 MHz of additional mobile broadband spectrum in early 2015.

2. The PCAST Report suggests the government share 1,000 MHz of federal spectrum below 3.7 GHz with commercial users. Nearly 500 MHz of government spectrum, although only about half below 3.7 GHz, is already in the NPRM process for shared use.

3. The Spectrum Pipeline Act calls on the NTIA to identify 30 MHz of federally owned wireless communications spectrum below 3 GHz (excluding 1675-1695 MHz) by 2022 and reallocate the spectrum to have the FCC auction it off for commercial or shared use by 2024.

4. The Spectrum Frontiers initiative opened up nearly 11 GHz of high-frequency spectrum for mobile and fixed wireless broadband – licensed use in the 24 GHz, 28 GHz, 37 GHz, 39 GHz, and 47 GHz bands; unlicensed use in the 64 to 71 GHz band; and shared use in the 37 to 37.6 GHz band. Auctions for the the 24 GHz and 28 GHz spectrum licenses are scheduled for late 2018 and 2019.

5. The MOBILE NOW Act instructed the FCC and NTIA to identify at least 255 MHz of federal and non-federal spectrum below 8,000 MHz for mobile and fixed wireless broadband use by December 31, 2022.

6. There is also a movement to force spectrum license users to allow others to use their spectrum when they are not using it.[435]

Cumulatively, these [spectrum allocation] plans, when realized, will massively increase spectrum supply for wireless services

Cumulatively, these plans, when realized, will massively increase spectrum supply for wireless services.

However, as previously discussed, these processes are behind schedule – some observers say hopelessly. Many observers, although a minority, believe that few government agencies will ultimately agree to share spectrum. Others suggest wireless companies will be reluctant to be "second-class citizens" on shared spectrum in large numbers.[436] If

---

[435] For a detailed analysis of this proposal *see*, Michael Calabrese, TPRC 2011, *Use it or Share it: Unlocking the Vast Wasteland of Fallow Spectrum* (Sept. 25, 2011), ssrn: http://ssrn.com/abstract=1992421

[436] For a detailed analysis of this position see: J. Zander, L.K. Rasmussen, K. Sung, P. Mahonen, M. Petrova, R. Jantti & J. Kronander, *On the Scalability of Cognitive Radio:*

so, they will resist investing in the infrastructure needed to deploy on shared network systems widely.

The Broadcast Incentive Auction was a groundbreaking auction to repurpose spectrum

The Broadcast Incentive Auction was a groundbreaking auction to repurpose spectrum for new uses to satisfy the growing demands of consumers. The first of its kind, this auction was authorized by Congress in 2012 and bidding commenced on March 29, 2016. It was comprised of two separate but interdependent options. The first was a "reverse auction," which determined the price at which broadcasters would voluntarily sell their broadcast rights to the spectrum. The second was a "forward auction," which determined the price companies were willing to pay for the spectrum to use for mobile broadband. The auction closed on March 30, 2017, and resulted in repurposing 84 MHz of spectrum - 70 MHz for licensed use and 14 MHz for wireless microphones and unlicensed use. Upon the closing of the auction, the FCC reauthorized and relicensed the facilities of the remaining broadcast television stations that received new channel assignments or that won their auction bid to move to a new frequency band or to channel share. The hundreds of stations nationwide that received new channel assignments are tasked with modifying their existing facilities to transmit on a different frequency. This transition is scheduled for completion by July 2020.[437]

a. Exogenous factors matter: The Aereo, Inc. Wrinkle

The Aereo, Inc. situation created an additional wrinkle for potential spectrum supply

Outside factors can favor a dramatic impact on market value for spectrum. In the U.S. Supreme Court case American Broadcasting Companies v. Aereo Inc. ("Aereo"), Aereo was sued by a collection of major broadcasters who argued that Aereo infringed their copyrighted material because Aereo's streams constituted public performances. Aereo offered a service that allowed subscribers to view live streams of on-the-air television on any Internet-connected device. Broadcasters protested to Aereo's redistribution of this content because Aereo did not pay any broadcasting fees that broadcasters are subject to. The Aereo, Inc. situation created an additional wrinkle for potential spectrum supply. Some broadcasters (including Fox) had

Assessing the Commercial Viability of Secondary Spectrum Access, Wireless Communications, IEEE, vol.20, no.2, 28, 36 (April 2013) http://ieeexplore.ieee.org/stamp/stamp.jsp?tp=&arnumber=6507391&isnumber=6507381

[437] FCC Broadcast Incentive Auction, https://www.fcc.gov/about-fcc/fcc-initiatives/incentive-auctions

publicly indicated that if the Second Circuit decision affirmed Aereo's right to sell its over-the-air broadcasts through the Internet, they may stop broadcasting over the air and only sell to satellite and cable systems. If this had happened, television broadcasters would have had little incentive to keep their spectrum and would have eagerly participated in the auction process. This could have increased spectrum available for reallocation to mobile broadband. Ironically, in this case it would not be the financially weakest broadcasters who would participate, but rather the financially strongest. The financially strongest broadcasters, especially those with network affiliates, have leverage with the cable companies. The smaller ones would be more likely to be dependent on "must carry" rules that are tied to broadcasting over the air.

The case was finally resolved in February 2014, the U.S. Supreme Court heard case. The court ruled in favor of the American broadcasting companies, saying that Aereo violated copyright laws by capturing broadcast signals using tiny antennas and then delivering the captured signals to subscribers for a fee.[438]

2. The Demand Debate

There is little consensus about the rate of future demand growth for spectrum

Like the argument with respect to supply, there is little consensus about the rate of future demand growth. The issue is more fundamental – predicting consumer usage patterns and improvements in spectrum efficiency. Some experts point to high historical demand growth and the increased rollout of smartphones, which use a multiple of the amount of spectrum of other phones. The introduction of 4G devices further increased Internet usage, especially with media downloading. Cisco, for example, reported that 4G traffic accounted for 69% of all mobile data traffic in 2016 and forecast that it will increase to 79% by 2021. Currently, the FCC has allocated approximately 608 MHz to wireless broadband. The "spectrum crunch" side argues that such demand growth will outpace any likely increase in supply. Although, as 5G becomes integrated, demand may grow even further with the increase in IOT and wireless carriers looking to compete as the first broadband providers.

Others say the demand growth is exaggerated.[439] They point to data caps that most operators have put on their new plans. Some evidence

---

[438]Adam Liptak and Emily Steel, *Aereo Loses at Supreme Court, in Victory for TV Broadcasters*, New York Times (June 25, 2014) https://nyti.ms/1mpiMgo

[439] Tim Farrar, *Is Cisco Stacking the Deck with its Mobile Data Numbers?* Gigaom (Feb 9, 2013) http://gigaom.com/2013/02/09/is-cisco-stacking-the-deck-with-its-mobile-data-numbers.

shows that the growth in data traffic has slowed. Newer 3G and 4G protocols are far more spectrally efficient than earlier versions. Additional rapid Wi-Fi off-loading – estimated at close to 60% of wireless traffic in 2016 — is absorbing much of the demand growth. Skeptics of the "spectrum crunch" point to a study cited in the PCAST report indicating that less than 20% of the capacity in prime spectrum bands under 3.7 GHz is utilized even in the most congested areas.[439] The PCAST Report argues that more efficient spectrum use could increase effective capacity by a factor of 1,000.[440]

3. Opportunities

It is rare for an industry as mature as the U.S. wireless industry to have such little consensus about medium-term supply and demand growth. However, a lack of consensus often attracts investors because it creates an opportunity to make money for those who can get it right. Wireless companies are making major spectrum transactions with little industry certainty about future supply that could significantly impact the values of the spectrum that they are trading.

J. Recent Data Points

Prices in the U.S. since June 2005 for licenses at various spectrum frequencies are presented in Figure 26-5.

The lack of consensus attracts investors because it creates an opportunity to make money for those who can get it right

PART FIVE: VALUATION

---

[439] *PCAST Report, supra* note 76, at 99

[440] *PCAST Report, supra* note 76, at iv.

Figure 26-5: Major U.S. Spectrum Transactions

Major Transaction Comps	$/MHz-PoP	Spectrum	Date
Verizon/StraightPath	$0.014	mmWave	Feb-18
Auction 1000	$0.93	600 MHz	Feb-17
Auction 97 (AWS-3 - Paired)	$2.72	AWS-3	Jan-15
Auction 97 (AWS-3 - Unpaired)	$0.52	AWS-3 (unpaired)	Jan-15
Verizon/Cincinnati Bell	$1.19	AWS-1	Apr-14
Auction 96 (H-Bock)	$0.50	AWS-2 (Unpaired)	Feb-14
AT&T/Aloha Partners	$1.30	AWS-1	Jan-14
VZ/T-MUS	$1.72	AWS-1/PCS	Jan-14
T-MUS/VZ	$1.77	700 MHz	Jan-14
ATT/LEAP	$1.24	PCS/AWS	Jul-13
Sprint/Clearwire	$0.30	2.5 GHz	Jul-13
T-MUS/U.S.Cellular	$0.97	AWS-1	Jun-13
DISH/Terrestar	$0.22	AWS-4	Mar-13
DBSD	$0.24	AWS-4	Mar-13
AT&T/Nextwave	$0.34	2.5 GHz	Aug-12
VZ/Spectrum Co	$0.69	AWS	Dec-11
VZ/Leap	$0.53	AWS-1 & PCS	Nov-11

Source: various news sources and Summit Ridge Group, LLC analysis

Figure 26-6 presents estimated spectrum prices as of March 2015.

Figure 26-6: Wall Street Estimated Spectrum Value

Goldman Sachs (March 2015)	Price
Low-Band (under 1 GHz)	$1.69
Mid-band (1GHz - 2.3 GHz)	$2.48
High Band (2.5 GHz)	$0.67

Source: Feldman, Brett; Epstein, Jonathan; Sanchez, Jioren; Laszczyk, Stephan; "Who Has the Best Specrum and What is it Worth?" Goldman Sachs, Inc. (March 5, 2015)

XXVII. Valuation of Orbital Frequency Rights

Orbital frequency rights consist of the right to use specific uplink/downlink radio frequencies (e.g., C-band: 5.950-6.435/3.635-4.210 GHz) at a particular orbital slot (e.g., 95° east longitude). These rights derived from filings with the ITU (described more fully in Chapter VII.B), which is the international organization responsible for, among other matters, the use of the geostationary orbit/radio frequency spectrum among member countries. The specific orbital rights granted to a licensee are vital for a valuation professional to understand since they affect the geography a licensee can serve, the frequencies they can use and the services they can provide.

An orbital slot filing with the ITU provides the license holder with international recognition to operate a communications satellite at a particular position in orbit.

An "Orbital Slot" filing with the ITU provides the license holder with international recognition to operate a communications satellite at a particular longitudinal position in geostationary orbit, transmitting and receiving signals at specific radio frequencies in coordination with nearby satellites using the same radio frequencies to avoid harmful interference.

Factors to consider when valuing orbital frequency rights, also referred to as orbital authorizations can be organized into four categories – regulatory, technical, industry, and other. Following a discussion of these four categories of valuation factors are sections regarding valuation observations and valuation assumptions.

A. Regulatory Factors

Regulatory factors consist primarily of the terms issued by the ITU regarding the use of orbital frequency rights. These terms include the following:

- Geographical Coverage

- Frequency Allotment Conditions

- Bringing-Into-Use ("BIU") dates

- Coordination Agreements

1. Geographical Coverage

When discussing geographical coverage, the core issue is whether the orbital frequency rights provide access to ITU Regions 1, 2, and/or 3. Access to these regions matters due to differences in demographics, climate, level of economic development, the sophistication of telecommunications infrastructure, etc.

Access to these regions also matters since the quality of service providers can offer in a region is affected by the location of an orbital slot. Therefore, when considering geographical coverage, it is also important to consider the location of the orbital slot relative to the desired coverage areas.

2. Frequency Allotment Conditions

ITU frequency allotment conditions allow for the transmission of satellite signals to specific regions using specified bandwidths and frequencies. These allotment conditions affect the value of an orbital frequency right since some frequencies and bandwidths are better suited for the sale of satellite transponder capacity due to climate, level of economic development, demographics, etc.

ITU frequency allotment conditions allow for the transmission of satellite signals to specific regions using specific bandwidths and frequencies

Specific items to consider when looking at allotment conditions include the following:

- The existence of new slots with varying degrees of filing priority
- C- and Ku-bands are increasingly congested by existing users
- Use of steerable beams may have the effect of blocking newcomers
- Use of aging satellites to bring slots into use and block newcomers

a. Frequency Rights

Included in allotment conditions issued by the ITU are provisions that specify the right to use non-band plan and/or plan band frequencies. The ability to use non-Plan frequency bands at specific orbital slots is based on a "first come, first serve" basis but still requires coordination agreements among users. The ability to use Plan band frequencies is based on orbital slot allotments and associated regulations for additional systems.

3. Bringing-Into-Use Dates

Bringing-Into-Use (BIU) dates require the commencement of service by a certain date. BIU dates affect the value of orbital frequency rights if the licensee is at risk of failing to meet the BIU deadline.

4. Coordination Agreements

Coordination Agreements prohibit the use of certain frequencies to minimize signal interference from neighboring satellite. Specific items to consider when looking at coordination agreements include the following:

- Limitations placed on signal transmission regarding countries, bandwidth, and frequency

- Provisional notifications where agreements are reached with some but not all affected networks

- Practical implementation approach (smart, physical positioning) re: operators unwilling to coordinate and "paper" filings

B. Technical Factors

The satellite industry continues to be affected by the unprecedented technological change that will likely be very disruptive to existing players

When valuing an orbital slot authorization, the appraiser must consider certain technical factors. Technical factors include trends in the design and manufacture of satellite and the technical specifications of the specific satellite(s), if any, that occupy the orbital slot to which the orbital frequency rights apply.

1. Technology Trends

The satellite industry continues to be affected by the unprecedented technological change that will likely be very disruptive to existing players. These factors, which are reducing the value of orbital frequency rights, include the following:

a. Shorter Satellite Life

Satellite life is shortening due to satellite capacity entering a world of Moore's Law-type improvement. This front-loads the economic value of satellites and makes a 15-year old data satellite about as useful as a 15-year old laptop. [442]

A specific factor affecting satellite lives is the development of high throughput satellites (HTS). The massive capacity of these satellites has reduced the number of required geostationary satellites and consequently orbital slots. HTS has decreased the value of some orbital slots, particularly when the underlying orbital frequency rights include insufficient spectrum, the orbital slot has a poor look-angle over the desired geography, and the orbital frequency rights are

---

[442] *Should high-throughput satellites last 15 years?,* Space News (Aug. 29, 2016) http://www.spacenewsmag.com/commentary/should-high-throughput-satellites-really-last-15-years/.

PART FIVE: VALUATION

limited due to poor or non-existent coordination agreements. In other cases, HTS technology has increased the value of orbital frequency rights for the most desirable orbital rights. This is because it increases the number of potential customers and revenue an HTS satellite can serve.

b. Cheaper/More Flexible Satellites

Satellites are becoming less expensive and more flexible due to:

- Digital payloads that can change frequencies and power in orbit

- Digital beamforming that can shift antenna coverage in orbit

- All electric propulsion that can lower a satellite's mass by approximately 30-40%.

c. Falling Launch Prices

SpaceX's launch prices are about 50% less than prices charged before SpaceX entering the market. Other launch providers responded by lowering their pricing 20-30%. Additional downward pricing pressure is expected from other reusable launch providers, including Virgin Galactic and Blue Origin.

d. Other

Increasing emphasis is being placed on cheap ground equipment and omnidirectional antennas

Increasing emphasis is being placed on cheap ground equipment and omnidirectional antennas, which lowers the "all in" cost and facilitates mobile applications. Also, the OneWeb NGSO constellation will likely be built with at most one other NGSO constellation to follow. These constellations are mostly focused on consumer data at prices of around $100 Mbps/month. This level of consumer pricing appears probable with some planned GEO systems. If GEO systems can achieve low prices, it diminished the cost advantage of the competing LEO constellations, potentially making them harder to finance.

2. Technology Factors

Examples of items to consider include the following:

- Type of orbital rights including type of orbit and frequencies permitted
- Location of adjacent satellites and analysis of whether the frequencies those satellite use create coordination issues that limit the use of the subject orbital frequency rights
- Technical feasibility of procuring a satellite to fill an orbital slot prior to deadline for bringing into use

C. Industry Factors

The satellite sector is now an approximately $260 billion/year industry globally. Most industry revenue is related to television distribution using Direct to Home (DTS) satellite television. The satellite capacity-leasing sector generates approximately $11 billion per year in revenue.[443]

The satellite sector, like most segments of the telecommunications sector, experienced issues related to over-capacity and investments in technologies that turned out to be uncompetitive.

A major rationalization in the satellite industry has occurred since 2002. Key events in this rationalization process include the following:

- Intelsat bought PanAmSat

- SES bought GE Americom and New Skies

- Eutelsat bought Satmex

- Iridium and Globalstar restructured through the Chapter 11 process

- Several startups folded, most notably, Craig McCaw's Teledesic broadband project.

The primary lesson from this rationalization process is that the lag time for building and launching a satellite (about 3 to 4 years for a single GEO satellite) often allows terrestrial alternatives to develop and leapfrog satellite technology by the time it is ready.

4. Leasing Basics

Traditional wide beam satellites lease capacity on the basis of MHz. Rates are expressed in terms of $/MHz. Rate differentiators include the satellite's geographical coverage area, power levels, the health and age of the satellite if the slot is occupied by a satellite, and the slot's other tenants, which applies especially to video.

D. Valuation Observations

Valuation observations are related to the following:

- Number and timing of transactions

The satellite sector, like most segments of the telecom sector, experienced issues related to over-capacity and investments in technologies that turned out to be uncompetitive

---

[443] Bryce space and technology, prepared for Satellite Industry Association, *2017 State of the Satellite Industry Report* (June 2017) https://www.sia.org/wp-content/uploads/2017/07/SIA-SSIR-2017.pdf.

- Values of satellite service providers

- Motivation for transactions

- Orbital slot impairment charges

1. Number and timing of transactions

Few orbital slot transactions have been completed over the last few years. Lack of orbital slot transactions in the past two years suggests low demand for orbital slots and/or lack of consensus between buyers and sellers regarding the value of orbital slots.

2. Values of satellite service providers

Over the past three years, values of fixed-satellite service FSS operators have declined. Orbital slots values are, in effect, heavily levered because their value derives from the residual value once the costs of building, launching, and operating the satellite are allocated. Therefore, it is likely orbital slot values have declined more than the decline of industry enterprise value.

3. Motive for transactions

There is evidence that some transactions are intended to meet BIU deadlines and preserve orbital slots, which sets the floor for the implied value of an orbital slot intended for development (i.e., if an operator is willing to spend a certain amount to keep an orbital slot, it must be worth at least that amount).

Many potential buyers are emerging state-sponsored satellite operators that are less interested in profit maximization. Instead, the demand for orbital frequency rights may be related to countries such as Azerbaijan Bangladesh, Bolivia, and Turkmenistan seeking to establish "flagship" satellite operators.

The fear of creating unwanted competition is one motivating factor preventing the sale of orbital frequency rights.

4. Orbital slot impairment charges

Publicly traded satellite operators have not recently taken any orbital slot impairment charges. Impairment charges provide a signal regarding the fair value of orbital slots compared to values adjusted during the 2008-2009 financial downturn. Impairment charges are also affected by a lag between (i) market value changes and (ii) accounting adjustments. Finally, there is a lack of clarity regarding the allocation of write-downs between "customer relationships and goodwill" and orbital slots. Write-downs for customer relations (such as Intelsat's from 2015) may mask lower values in orbital slots. Summit Ridge

> *Over the past three years, values of fixed-satellite service operators have declined*

Group is not suggesting anything improper occurred with Intelsat's accounting, but instead is using this example to demonstrate the difficulty of allocating low values between related items.

E. Valuation Assumptions

When valuing orbital frequency rights, certain assumptions are believed to be true. These assumptions include (i) the rights to the orbital frequencies being fully valid; (ii) the licensee will diligently protect the orbital frequency rights by providing appropriate and timely regulatory filings; (iii) the ITU filings that are the basis for the orbital frequency rights provide the most senior level of ITU priority with respect to other operators with nearby satellites that are operational or planned for the subject orbital rights; and (iv) coordination agreements are in place that allows for use of the orbital frequency rights without harmful interference from frequency rights given to neighboring orbital slots.

PART FIVE: VALUATION

XXVIII. Valuation Standards & Accreditation

Formal valuation work requires professionals to follow accepted standards and procedures to ensure their work is credible...

Formal valuation work requires professionals to follow accepted standards and procedures to ensure their work is credible and that others can properly interpret it. Moreover, valuation professionals much have proper training in implementing these procedures to produce credible results.

A. Uniform Standards of Professional Appraisal Practice (USPAP)

USPAP contains the generally accepted standards of the appraisal profession ...

USPAP contains the generally accepted standards of the appraisal profession. In general, formal valuations, particularly for government agencies, such as the IRS, are expected to comply with USPAP standards. The standards involve factors such as requirements for maintaining records of the appraiser's work product, replicability of results, consideration of the liquidity of the asset and others. USPAP applies to all forms of valuation, however compliance is particularly enforced in real estate appraisals related to obtaining mortgages.

1. History

In 1986, nine leading professional appraisal organizations in the U.S. and Canada formed an Ad Hoc Committee on the Uniform Standards of Professional Appraisal Practice (USPAP) in response to the crisis in the savings and loan industry. In 1987, the Committee established the Appraisal Foundation to implement USPAP as the generally accepted set of appraisal standards in the United States.

USPAP was adopted through the enactment by Congress of the Financial Institutions Reform, Recovery, and Enforcement Act ("FIRREA") in 1989.[443] USPAP contains standards for all types of appraisal services, including real estate, personal property, business and mass appraisal. Compliance is required for state-licensed and state-certified appraisers involved in federally related real estate transactions. USPAP is updated every two years so that appraisers have the information they need to deliver unbiased and thoughtful opinions of value.

---

[443] Financial Institutions Reform, Recovery, and Enforcement Act of 1989. https://www.fdic.gov/regulations/laws/rules/8000-3100.html.

2. The Appraisal Foundation

The Appraisal Foundation (Foundation)[444] was authorized as the source of appraisal standards and appraiser qualifications in 1989, when the U.S. Congress FIRREA.

The Foundation is the foremost authority in the U.S. regarding the valuation profession. It is not a membership organization but rather is composed of other organizations. Today with sponsoring organizations and advisory councils, close to one hundred organizations, corporations and government agencies are affiliated with the Foundation.

Under FIRREA, the Foundation sets the Congressionally authorized standards and qualifications for real estate appraisers. It also sets qualifications for personal property appraisers and provides voluntary guidance on recognized valuation methods and techniques for all valuation professionals. This work is intended to advance the valuation profession by ensuring that appraisals are independent, consistent and objective.

The Foundations' independent board, the Appraiser Qualifications Board ("AQB"), promulgates the minimum standards, known as the Uniform Standards of Professional Appraisal Practice known as USPAP.[445]

B. AICPA's SSVS No. 1 Valuation Standard

The valuation standard for members of the American Institute of Certified Public Accountants (AICPA) is the *AICPA Statement on Standards for Valuation Services No. 1 (SSVS No. 1, or the Standard) "Valuation of a Business, Business Ownership Interest, Security, or Intangible Asset."*

The Standard is intended to provide AICPA members with guidelines for developing valuation estimates and reporting on their results. SSVS No. 1 applies to all AICPA members who perform valuation services for various purposes (such as transactions, financings, taxation, financial accounting, bankruptcy, management and financial planning and litigation) as well as for multiple disciplines in the

---

[444] Appraisal Foundation: https://www.appraisalfoundation.org/

[445] Via another independent board, the Appraisers Qualifications Board ("AQB"), the establishes minimum qualifications, known as the Real Property Appraiser Qualification Criteria. Additionally, the AQB has established voluntary Personal Property Appraiser Qualification Criteria. Foundation Sponsors must meet the Personal Property Criteria at a minimum.

profession (including consulting, litigation services, personal financial planning, tax and accounting).[446] SSVS No. 1 are similar to the USPAP guidelines.

C. American Society of Appraisers Accreditation

The American Society of Appraisers ("ASA") is the leading professional association for valuation professionals. Its mission is to foster the public trust of its members and the appraisal profession through compliance with the highest levels of ethical and professional standards. Valuation reports by ASA members are generally required to meet USPAP standards.

The American Society of Appraisers confers four (4) credentials upon qualified candidates: Accredited Member (AM), Accredited Senior Appraiser (ASA), Master Gemologist Appraiser® (MGA®) and Certified in Entity and Intangible Valuation™ (CEIV™). Each credential has its specific education and experience requirements. Obtaining the ASA credential requires relevant work experience, passing the national USPAP) exam, as well as four 27-hour courses, and other qualifications. The ASA is often considered the gold standard credential in the appraisal industry.

D. CFA Institute Accreditation

The CFA Institute, formed in 1947, is a global association of investment professionals. The mission of the CFA Institute is to generate value for core investment management professionals and engaging with the investment management industry to advance ethics, market integrity, and professional standards of practice. It provides continuing education conferences, seminars, webcasts, and publications to allow members and other participants to stay current on developments in the investment industry.

The CFA Institute offers the Chartered Financial Analyst (CFA) designation, the Certificate in Investment Performance Measurement (CIPM) designation, and the Investment Foundations Certificate. Obtaining the CFA designation requires passing three exams (Level I is administered twice a year, while Levels II and III are administered annually), relevant work experience and other qualifications. It is generally considered the most difficult professional accreditation in the financial services industry to acquire.

---

[446] *AICPA Statement on Standards for Valuation Services No. 1 – Fact Sheet.* AICPA https://www.aicpa.org/interestareas/forensicandvaluation/resources/standards.html

APPENDICES

APPENDICES

Appendix A: Spectrum Holdings by Carrier

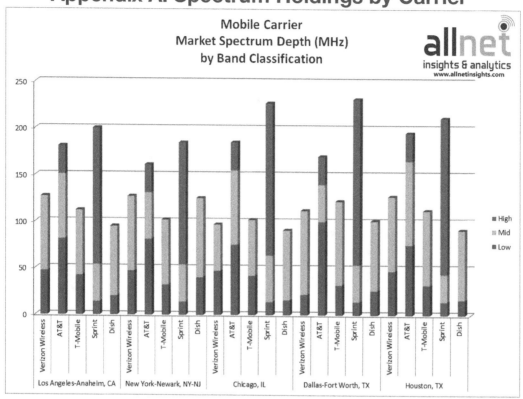

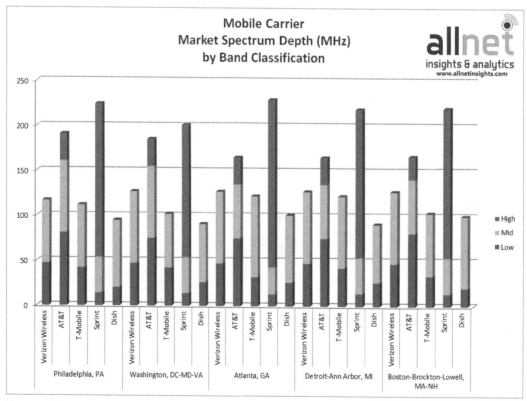

Source: Courtesy of Allnet Insights & Analytics, reprinted with permission

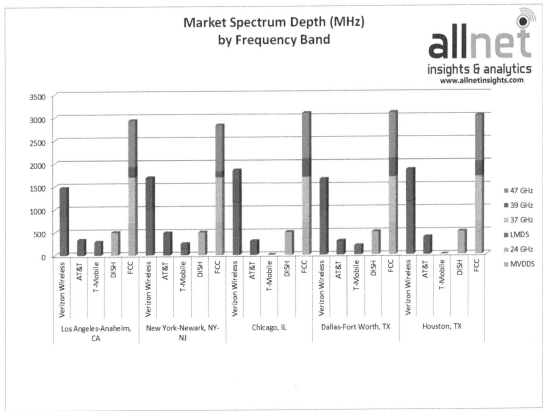

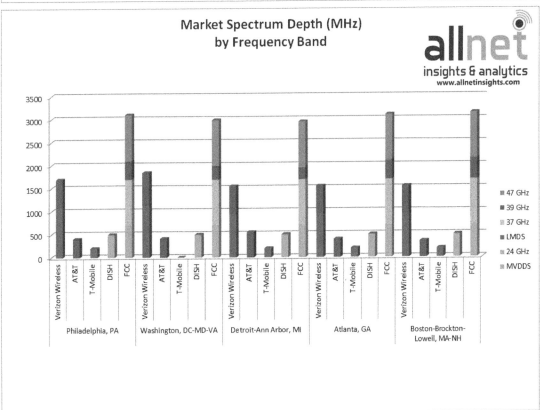

Source: Courtesy of Allnet Insights & Analytics (https://www.allnetinsights.com), reprinted with permission

APPENDICES

insights & analytics
www.allnetinsights.com

CMA Rank	CMA	Market Name	Sq Miles	2014 POPS	Verizon Wireless												
					Total	Low Band	Mid Band	High Band	600MHz	700MHz	Cellular/SMR	AWS-1	AWS-3	PCS	AWS 4 / L Band	WCS	EBS/BRS
1	2	Los Angeles-Anaheim, CA	33,109	17,704,110	127	47	80	0	0	22	25	40	20	20	0	0	0
2	1	New York-Newark, NY-NJ	5,768	17,041,161	127	47	80	0	0	22	25	40	0	40	0	0	0
3	3	Chicago, IL	5,324	8,404,358	97	47	50	0	0	22	25	40	0	10	0	0	0
4	9	Dallas-Fort Worth, TX	8,561	6,857,143	112	22	90	0	0	22	0	40	20	30	0	0	0
5	10	Houston, TX	7,033	6,108,723	107	47	60	0	0	22	25	30	10	20	0	0	0
6	4	Philadelphia, PA	3,587	5,331,294	117	47	70	0	0	22	25	30	20	20	0	0	0
7	8	Washington, DC-MD-VA	3,055	5,168,021	127	47	80	0	0	22	25	30	20	30	0	0	0
8	17	Atlanta, GA	4,383	4,943,920	127	47	80	0	0	22	25	40	20	20	0	0	0
9	5	Detroit-Ann Arbor, MI	4,958	4,653,485	127	47	80	0	0	22	25	40	20	20	0	0	0
10	6	Boston-Brockton-Lowell, MA-NH	4,128	4,606,557	117	47	70	0	0	22	25	40	0	30	0	0	0
11	7	San Francisco-Oakland, CA	3,424	4,594,060	127	47	80	0	0	22	25	40	20	20	0	0	0
12	12	Miami-Fort Lauderdale, FL	3,751	4,532,109	92	22	70	0	0	22	0	40	0	30	0	0	0
13	26	Phoenix, AZ	9,224	4,087,191	132	72	60	0	0	22	50	30	20	10	0	0	0
14	18	San Diego, CA	4,526	3,263,431	127	47	80	0	0	22	25	30	30	20	0	0	0
15	15	Minneapolis-St. Paul, MN-WI	4,870	3,256,107	108	48	60	0	0	22	26	40	0	20	0	0	0
16	19	Denver-Boulder, CO	4,681	3,017,864	107	47	60	0	0	22	25	20	20	20	0	0	0
17	20	Seattle-Everett, WA	4,503	2,839,550	127	47	80	0	0	22	25	40	20	20	0	0	0
18	22	Tampa-St. Petersburg, FL	2,742	2,739,727	127	47	80	0	0	22	25	40	10	30	0	0	0
19	14	Baltimore, MD	2,595	2,737,070	137	47	90	0	0	22	25	40	20	30	0	0	0
20	11	St. Louis, MO-IL	5,092	2,627,456	107	47	60	0	0	22	25	40	10	10	0	0	0
21	30	Portland, OR-WA	3,727	2,185,690	117	47	70	0	0	22	25	30	20	20	0	0	0
22	33	San Antonio, TX	2,545	2,126,810	92	22	70	0	0	22	0	20	20	30	0	0	0
23	93	Las Vegas, NV	8,091	2,069,681	107	47	60	0	0	22	25	20	20	20	0	0	0
24	35	Sacramento, CA	3,521	2,061,310	117	47	70	0	0	22	25	40	20	10	0	0	0
25	91	San Juan-Caguas, PR	1,499	2,038,404	0	0	0	0	0	0	0	0	0	0	0	0	0
26	60	Orlando, FL	2,855	2,005,728	112	22	90	0	0	22	0	40	20	30	0	0	0
27	13	Pittsburgh, PA	3,086	1,968,154	107	47	60	0	0	22	25	40	0	20	0	0	0
28	27	San Jose, CA	1,304	1,894,605	117	47	70	0	0	22	25	30	20	20	0	0	0
29	24	Kansas City, MO-KS	3,365	1,871,407	97	47	50	0	0	22	25	40	0	10	0	0	0
30	75	Austin, TX	2,837	1,825,420	92	22	70	0	0	22	0	20	20	30	0	0	0
31	28	Indianapolis, IN	3,089	1,788,625	127	47	80	0	0	22	25	40	20	20	0	0	0
32	16	Cleveland, OH	3,056	1,759,382	122	72	50	0	0	22	50	40	0	10	0	0	0
33	39	Salt Lake City-Ogden, UT	9,388	1,723,507	117	47	70	0	0	22	25	40	20	10	0	0	0
34	31	Columbus, OH	2,481	1,671,681	127	47	80	0	0	22	25	40	20	20	0	0	0
35	23	Cincinnati, OH-KY-IN	2,165	1,661,531	127	47	80	0	0	22	25	40	0	40	0	0	0
36	46	Nashville-Davidson, TN	4,135	1,618,979	122	47	75	0	0	22	25	40	20	15	0	0	0
37	21	Milwaukee, WI	3,322	1,572,245	102	22	80	0	0	22	0	30	20	30	0	0	0
38	61	Charlotte-Gastonia, NC	1,549	1,442,234	122	72	50	0	0	22	50	30	0	20	0	0	0
39	71	Raleigh-Durham, NC	1,556	1,433,571	132	72	60	0	0	22	50	30	0	30	0	0	0
40	51	Jacksonville, FL	3,698	1,419,127	122	22	100	0	0	22	0	40	20	40	0	0	0
41	72	West Palm Beach-Boca Raton, FL	2,386	1,397,710	92	22	70	0	0	22	0	40	0	30	0	0	0
42	45	Oklahoma City, OK	3,555	1,274,829	88	47	41	0	0	22	25	20	0	21	0	0	0
43	47	Greensboro-Winston-Salem, NC	3,221	1,268,478	122	72	50	0	0	22	50	30	0	20	0	0	0
44	36	Memphis, TN-AR-MS	2,392	1,220,887	101	47	54	0	0	22	25	24	20	10	0	0	0
45	32	Hartford-Bristol, CT	1,607	1,214,295	112	47	65	0	0	22	25	40	0	25	0	0	0
46	43	Norfolk-Virginia Beach, VA-NC	1,946	1,137,565	132	72	60	0	0	22	50	40	0	20	0	0	0
47	25	Buffalo, NY	2,367	1,136,360	107	47	60	0	0	22	25	20	20	20	0	0	0
48	29	New Orleans, LA	3,910	1,110,274	117	47	70	0	0	22	25	40	0	30	0	0	0
49	37	Louisville, KY-IN	1,420	1,091,912	97	47	50	0	0	22	25	40	0	10	0	0	0
50	34	Rochester, NY	4,870	1,058,185	107	47	60	0	0	22	25	30	20	10	0	0	0

Source: Courtesy of Allnet Insights & Analytics (https://www.allnetinsights.com), reprinted with permission

allnet
insights & analytics
www.allnetinsights.com

CMA Rank	CMA	Market Name	Sq Miles	2014 POPS	AT&T												
					Total	Low Band	Mid Band	High Band	600MHz	700MHz	Cellular/SMR	AWS-1	AWS-3	PCS	AWS 4 / L Band	WCS	EBS/BRS
1	2	Los Angeles-Anaheim, CA	33,109	17,704,110	181	81	70	30	0	56	25	10	20	40	0	30	0
2	1	New York-Newark, NY-NJ	5,768	17,041,161	161	81	50	30	0	56	25	0	20	30	0	30	0
3	3	Chicago, IL	5,324	8,404,358	185	75	80	30	0	50	25	20	20	40	0	30	0
4	9	Dallas-Fort Worth, TX	8,561	6,857,143	170	100	40	30	0	50	50	0	20	20	0	30	0
5	10	Houston, TX	7,033	6,108,723	195	75	90	30	0	50	25	20	20	50	0	30	0
6	4	Philadelphia, PA	3,587	5,331,294	191	81	80	30	0	56	25	20	20	40	0	30	0
7	8	Washington, DC-MD-VA	3,055	5,168,021	185	75	80	30	0	50	25	20	20	40	0	30	0
8	17	Atlanta, GA	4,383	4,943,920	165	75	60	30	0	50	25	0	20	40	0	30	0
9	5	Detroit-Ann Arbor, MI	4,958	4,653,485	165	75	60	30	0	50	25	0	20	40	0	30	0
10	6	Boston-Brockton-Lowell, MA-NH	4,128	4,606,557	166	81	60	25	0	56	25	0	20	40	0	25	0
11	7	San Francisco-Oakland, CA	3,424	4,594,060	181	81	70	30	0	56	25	10	20	40	0	30	0
12	12	Miami-Fort Lauderdale, FL	3,751	4,532,109	190	100	60	30	0	50	50	10	30	20	0	30	0
13	26	Phoenix, AZ	9,224	4,087,191	170	50	90	30	0	50	0	20	20	40	0	30	0
14	18	San Diego, CA	4,526	3,263,431	185	75	80	30	0	50	25	20	20	40	0	30	0
15	15	Minneapolis-St. Paul, MN-WI	4,870	3,256,107	174	74	70	30	0	50	24	10	20	40	0	30	0
16	19	Denver-Boulder, CO	4,681	3,017,864	197	75	92	30	0	50	25	30	20	42	0	30	0
17	20	Seattle-Everett, WA	4,503	2,839,550	165	75	60	30	0	50	25	0	20	40	0	30	0
18	22	Tampa-St. Petersburg, FL	2,742	2,739,727	165	75	60	30	0	50	25	0	30	30	0	30	0
19	14	Baltimore, MD	2,595	2,737,070	185	75	80	30	0	50	25	20	20	40	0	30	0
20	11	St. Louis, MO-IL	5,092	2,627,456	184	75	79	30	0	50	25	20	20	39	0	30	0
21	30	Portland, OR-WA	3,727	2,185,690	185	75	80	30	0	50	25	20	20	40	0	30	0
22	33	San Antonio, TX	2,545	2,126,810	210	100	80	30	0	50	50	30	20	30	0	30	0
23	93	Las Vegas, NV	8,091	2,069,681	185	75	80	30	0	50	25	20	20	40	0	30	0
24	35	Sacramento, CA	3,521	2,061,310	185	75	80	30	0	50	25	10	20	50	0	30	0
25	91	San Juan-Caguas, PR	1,499	2,038,404	193	63	100	30	0	38	25	30	20	50	0	30	0
26	60	Orlando, FL	2,855	2,005,728	170	100	40	30	0	50	50	0	20	20	0	30	0
27	13	Pittsburgh, PA	3,086	1,968,154	185	75	80	30	0	50	25	20	20	40	0	30	0
28	27	San Jose, CA	1,304	1,894,605	181	81	70	30	0	56	25	10	20	40	0	30	0
29	24	Kansas City, MO-KS	3,365	1,871,407	185	75	80	30	0	50	25	20	20	40	0	30	0
30	75	Austin, TX	2,837	1,825,420	210	100	80	30	0	50	50	30	20	30	0	30	0
31	28	Indianapolis, IN	3,089	1,788,625	195	75	90	30	0	50	25	30	20	40	0	30	0
32	16	Cleveland, OH	3,056	1,759,382	160	50	80	30	0	50	0	10	20	50	0	30	0
33	39	Salt Lake City-Ogden, UT	9,388	1,723,507	195	75	90	30	0	50	25	10	20	60	0	30	0
34	31	Columbus, OH	2,481	1,671,681	165	75	60	30	0	50	25	10	20	30	0	30	0
35	23	Cincinnati, OH-KY-IN	2,165	1,661,531	185	75	80	30	0	50	25	40	20	20	0	30	0
36	46	Nashville-Davidson, TN	4,135	1,618,979	195	75	90	30	0	50	25	10	20	60	0	30	0
37	21	Milwaukee, WI	3,322	1,572,245	175	75	70	30	0	50	25	20	20	30	0	30	0
38	61	Charlotte-Gastonia, NC	1,549	1,442,234	170	50	90	30	0	50	0	30	20	40	0	30	0
39	71	Raleigh-Durham, NC	1,556	1,433,571	180	50	100	30	0	50	0	30	20	50	0	30	0
40	51	Jacksonville, FL	3,698	1,419,127	160	100	30	30	0	50	50	0	20	10	0	30	0
41	72	West Palm Beach-Boca Raton, FL	2,386	1,397,710	190	100	60	30	0	50	50	10	30	20	0	30	0
42	45	Oklahoma City, OK	3,555	1,274,829	204	75	99	30	0	50	25	40	30	29	0	30	0
43	47	Greensboro-Winston-Salem, NC	3,221	1,268,478	170	50	90	30	0	50	0	30	20	40	0	30	0
44	36	Memphis, TN-AR-MS	2,392	1,220,887	200	75	95	30	0	50	25	30	20	45	0	30	0
45	32	Hartford-Bristol, CT	1,607	1,214,295	173	81	62	30	0	56	25	0	20	42	0	30	0
46	43	Norfolk-Virginia Beach, VA-NC	1,946	1,137,565	160	50	80	30	0	50	0	10	30	40	0	30	0
47	25	Buffalo, NY	2,367	1,136,360	185	75	80	30	0	50	25	30	20	30	0	30	0
48	29	New Orleans, LA	3,910	1,110,274	169	75	80	14	0	50	25	20	30	30	0	14	0
49	37	Louisville, KY-IN	1,420	1,091,912	204	75	99	30	0	50	25	30	20	49	0	30	0
50	34	Rochester, NY	4,870	1,058,185	195	75	90	30	0	50	25	30	20	40	0	30	0

Source: Courtesy of Allnet Insights & Analytics (https://www.allnetinsights.com), printed with permission

APPENDICES

CMA Rank	CMA	Market Name	Sq Miles	2014 POPS	T-Mobile												
					Total	Low Band	Mid Band	High Band	600MHz	700MHz	Cellular/SMR	AWS-1	AWS-3	PCS	AWS 4 / L Band	WCS	EBS/BRS
1	2	Los Angeles-Anaheim, CA	33,109	17,704,110	112	42	70	0	30	12	0	40	0	30	0	0	0
2	1	New York-Newark, NY-NJ	5,768	17,041,161	102	32	70	0	20	12	0	50	0	20	0	0	0
3	3	Chicago, IL	5,324	8,404,358	102	42	60	0	30	12	0	30	0	30	0	0	0
4	9	Dallas-Fort Worth, TX	8,561	6,857,143	122	32	90	0	20	12	0	50	0	40	0	0	0
5	10	Houston, TX	7,033	6,108,723	112	32	80	0	20	12	0	40	10	30	0	0	0
6	4	Philadelphia, PA	3,587	5,331,294	112	42	70	0	30	12	0	40	0	30	0	0	0
7	8	Washington, DC-MD-VA	3,055	5,168,021	102	42	60	0	30	12	0	40	0	20	0	0	0
8	17	Atlanta, GA	4,383	4,943,920	122	42	90	0	20	12	0	50	0	40	0	0	0
9	5	Detroit-Ann Arbor, MI	4,958	4,653,485	122	42	80	0	30	12	0	50	0	30	0	0	0
10	6	Boston-Brockton-Lowell, MA-NH	4,128	4,606,557	103	33	70	0	21	12	0	50	0	20	0	0	0
11	7	San Francisco-Oakland, CA	3,424	4,594,060	112	32	80	0	20	12	0	40	0	40	0	0	0
12	12	Miami-Fort Lauderdale, FL	3,751	4,532,109	142	42	100	0	30	12	0	40	0	50	0	0	0
13	26	Phoenix, AZ	9,224	4,087,191	112	32	80	0	20	12	0	40	10	30	0	0	0
14	18	San Diego, CA	4,526	3,263,431	112	42	70	0	30	12	0	40	0	30	0	0	0
15	15	Minneapolis-St. Paul, MN-WI	4,870	3,256,107	122	42	80	0	30	12	0	40	0	40	0	0	0
16	19	Denver-Boulder, CO	4,681	3,017,864	111	42	69	0	30	12	0	40	0	29	0	0	0
17	20	Seattle-Everett, WA	4,503	2,839,550	122	42	80	0	30	12	0	50	0	30	0	0	0
18	22	Tampa-St. Petersburg, FL	2,742	2,739,727	117	32	85	0	20	12	0	50	0	35	0	0	0
19	14	Baltimore, MD	2,595	2,737,070	102	42	60	0	30	12	0	30	0	30	0	0	0
20	11	St. Louis, MO-IL	5,092	2,627,456	91	31	60	0	31	0	0	30	0	30	0	0	0
21	30	Portland, OR-WA	3,727	2,185,690	102	32	70	0	20	12	0	40	0	30	0	0	0
22	33	San Antonio, TX	2,545	2,126,810	122	42	80	0	30	12	0	40	10	30	0	0	0
23	93	Las Vegas, NV	8,091	2,069,681	122	42	80	0	30	12	0	50	0	30	0	0	0
24	35	Sacramento, CA	3,521	2,061,310	112	32	80	0	20	12	0	40	0	40	0	0	0
25	91	San Juan-Caguas, PR	1,499	2,038,404	115	50	65	0	50	0	0	40	0	25	0	0	0
26	60	Orlando, FL	2,855	2,005,728	122	32	90	0	20	12	0	50	0	40	0	0	0
27	13	Pittsburgh, PA	3,086	1,968,154	92	32	60	0	20	12	0	30	0	30	0	0	0
28	27	San Jose, CA	1,304	1,894,605	122	32	90	0	20	12	0	50	0	40	0	0	0
29	24	Kansas City, MO-KS	3,365	1,871,407	122	42	80	0	30	12	0	30	10	40	0	0	0
30	75	Austin, TX	2,837	1,825,420	122	42	80	0	30	12	0	40	10	30	0	0	0
31	28	Indianapolis, IN	3,089	1,788,625	92	33	58	0	21	12	0	20	10	28	0	0	0
32	16	Cleveland, OH	3,056	1,759,382	122	42	80	0	30	12	0	40	10	30	0	0	0
33	39	Salt Lake City-Ogden, UT	9,388	1,723,507	112	32	80	0	20	12	0	40	10	30	0	0	0
34	31	Columbus, OH	2,481	1,671,681	112	32	80	0	20	12	0	40	10	30	0	0	0
35	23	Cincinnati, OH-KY-IN	2,165	1,661,531	102	42	60	0	30	12	0	10	10	40	0	0	0
36	46	Nashville-Davidson, TN	4,135	1,618,979	82	32	50	0	20	12	0	30	0	20	0	0	0
37	21	Milwaukee, WI	3,322	1,572,245	70	30	40	0	30	0	0	20	0	20	0	0	0
38	61	Charlotte-Gastonia, NC	1,549	1,442,234	90	30	60	0	30	0	0	30	0	30	0	0	0
39	71	Raleigh-Durham, NC	1,556	1,433,571	100	40	60	0	40	0	0	30	10	20	0	0	0
40	51	Jacksonville, FL	3,698	1,419,127	122	32	90	0	20	12	0	50	0	40	0	0	0
41	72	West Palm Beach-Boca Raton, FL	2,386	1,397,710	142	42	100	0	30	12	0	40	10	50	0	0	0
42	45	Oklahoma City, OK	3,555	1,274,829	100	30	70	0	30	0	0	30	10	30	0	0	0
43	47	Greensboro-Winston-Salem, NC	3,221	1,268,478	112	42	70	0	42	0	0	30	10	30	0	0	0
44	36	Memphis, TN-AR-MS	2,392	1,220,887	116	40	76	0	40	0	0	36	10	30	0	0	0
45	32	Hartford-Bristol, CT	1,607	1,214,295	105	32	73	0	20	12	0	50	0	23	0	0	0
46	43	Norfolk-Virginia Beach, VA-NC	1,946	1,137,565	122	42	80	0	30	12	0	40	0	40	0	0	0
47	25	Buffalo, NY	2,367	1,136,360	122	52	70	0	40	12	0	40	0	30	0	0	0
48	29	New Orleans, LA	3,910	1,110,274	102	42	60	0	30	12	0	30	0	30	0	0	0
49	37	Louisville, KY-IN	1,420	1,091,912	112	42	70	0	30	12	0	20	20	30	0	0	0
50	34	Rochester, NY	4,870	1,058,185	122	52	70	0	40	12	0	30	0	40	0	0	0

Source: Courtesy of Allnet Insights & Analytics (https://www.allnetinsights.com), reprinted with permission

| CMA Rank | CMA | Market Name | Sq Miles | 2014 POPS | Sprint | | | | | | | | | | | |
					Total	Low Band	Mid Band	High Band	600MHz	700MHz	Cellular/SMR	AWS-1	AWS-3	PCS	AWS 4 / L Band	WCS	EBS/BRS
1	2	Los Angeles-Anaheim, CA	33,109	17,704,110	200	14	40	146	0	0	14	0	0	40	0	0	146
2	1	New York-Newark, NY-NJ	5,768	17,041,161	185	14	40	131	0	0	14	0	0	40	0	0	131
3	3	Chicago, IL	5,324	8,404,358	227	14	50	163	0	0	14	0	0	50	0	0	163
4	9	Dallas-Fort Worth, TX	8,561	6,857,143	231	14	40	177	0	0	14	0	0	40	0	0	177
5	10	Houston, TX	7,033	6,108,723	211	14	30	167	0	0	14	0	0	30	0	0	167
6	4	Philadelphia, PA	3,587	5,331,294	224	14	40	170	0	0	14	0	0	40	0	0	170
7	8	Washington, DC-MD-VA	3,055	5,168,021	201	14	40	147	0	0	14	0	0	40	0	0	147
8	17	Atlanta, GA	4,383	4,943,920	229	13	30	186	0	0	13	0	0	30	0	0	186
9	5	Detroit-Ann Arbor, MI	4,958	4,653,485	219	14	40	165	0	0	14	0	0	40	0	0	165
10	6	Boston-Brockton-Lowell, MA-NH	4,128	4,606,557	219	14	40	165	0	0	14	0	0	40	0	0	165
11	7	San Francisco-Oakland, CA	3,424	4,594,060	197	14	30	153	0	0	14	0	0	30	0	0	153
12	12	Miami-Fort Lauderdale, FL	3,751	4,532,109	204	14	30	160	0	0	14	0	0	30	0	0	160
13	26	Phoenix, AZ	9,224	4,087,191	220	12	40	168	0	0	12	0	0	40	0	0	168
14	18	San Diego, CA	4,526	3,263,431	228	14	40	174	0	0	14	0	0	40	0	0	174
15	15	Minneapolis-St. Paul, MN-WI	4,870	3,256,107	220	14	30	176	0	0	14	0	0	30	0	0	176
16	19	Denver-Boulder, CO	4,681	3,017,864	220	14	38	168	0	0	14	0	0	38	0	0	168
17	20	Seattle-Everett, WA	4,503	2,839,550	240	14	40	186	0	0	14	0	0	40	0	0	186
18	22	Tampa-St. Petersburg, FL	2,742	2,739,727	235	14	35	186	0	0	14	0	0	35	0	0	186
19	14	Baltimore, MD	2,595	2,737,070	213	14	30	169	0	0	14	0	0	30	0	0	169
20	11	St. Louis, MO-IL	5,092	2,627,456	239	14	50	175	0	0	14	0	0	50	0	0	175
21	30	Portland, OR-WA	3,727	2,185,690	216	14	40	162	0	0	14	0	0	40	0	0	162
22	33	San Antonio, TX	2,545	2,126,810	218	14	40	164	0	0	14	0	0	40	0	0	164
23	93	Las Vegas, NV	8,091	2,069,681	212	14	40	158	0	0	14	0	0	40	0	0	158
24	35	Sacramento, CA	3,521	2,061,310	200	14	30	156	0	0	14	0	0	30	0	0	156
25	91	San Juan-Caguas, PR	1,499	2,038,404	154	0	30	124	0	0	0	0	0	30	0	0	124
26	60	Orlando, FL	2,855	2,005,728	234	14	40	180	0	0	14	0	0	40	0	0	180
27	13	Pittsburgh, PA	3,086	1,968,154	240	14	40	186	0	0	14	0	0	40	0	0	186
28	27	San Jose, CA	1,304	1,894,605	206	14	30	162	0	0	14	0	0	30	0	0	162
29	24	Kansas City, MO-KS	3,365	1,871,407	228	14	40	174	0	0	14	0	0	40	0	0	174
30	75	Austin, TX	2,837	1,825,420	238	14	40	184	0	0	14	0	0	40	0	0	184
31	28	Indianapolis, IN	3,089	1,788,625	236	14	42	180	0	0	14	0	0	42	0	0	180
32	16	Cleveland, OH	3,056	1,759,382	218	14	40	164	0	0	14	0	0	40	0	0	164
33	39	Salt Lake City-Ogden, UT	9,388	1,723,507	224	14	30	180	0	0	14	0	0	30	0	0	180
34	31	Columbus, OH	2,481	1,671,681	250	14	50	186	0	0	14	0	0	50	0	0	186
35	23	Cincinnati, OH-KY-IN	2,165	1,661,531	224	14	30	180	0	0	14	0	0	30	0	0	180
36	46	Nashville-Davidson, TN	4,135	1,618,979	230	13	35	181	0	0	13	0	0	35	0	0	181
37	21	Milwaukee, WI	3,322	1,572,245	218	14	30	174	0	0	14	0	0	30	0	0	174
38	61	Charlotte-Gastonia, NC	1,549	1,442,234	236	14	40	182	0	0	14	0	0	40	0	0	182
39	71	Raleigh-Durham, NC	1,556	1,433,571	230	14	30	186	0	0	14	0	0	30	0	0	186
40	51	Jacksonville, FL	3,698	1,419,127	233	13	40	180	0	0	13	0	0	40	0	0	180
41	72	West Palm Beach-Boca Raton, FL	2,386	1,397,710	224	14	30	180	0	0	14	0	0	30	0	0	180
42	45	Oklahoma City, OK	3,555	1,274,829	230	14	30	186	0	0	14	0	0	30	0	0	186
43	47	Greensboro-Winston-Salem, NC	3,221	1,268,478	221	14	40	167	0	0	14	0	0	40	0	0	167
44	36	Memphis, TN-AR-MS	2,392	1,220,887	230	14	30	186	0	0	14	0	0	30	0	0	186
45	32	Hartford-Bristol, CT	1,607	1,214,295	209	14	40	155	0	0	14	0	0	40	0	0	155
46	43	Norfolk-Virginia Beach, VA-NC	1,946	1,137,565	218	14	30	174	0	0	14	0	0	30	0	0	174
47	25	Buffalo, NY	2,367	1,136,360	240	14	40	186	0	0	14	0	0	40	0	0	186
48	29	New Orleans, LA	3,910	1,110,274	219	14	40	165	0	0	14	0	0	40	0	0	165
49	37	Louisville, KY-IN	1,420	1,091,912	234	14	40	180	0	0	14	0	0	40	0	0	180
50	34	Rochester, NY	4,870	1,058,185	218	14	40	164	0	0	14	0	0	40	0	0	164

Source: Courtesy of Allnet Insights & Analytics (https://www.allnetinsights.com), reprinted with permission

APPENDICES

CMA Rank	CMA	Market Name	Sq Miles	2014 POPS	Dish												
					Total	Low Band	Mid Band	High Band	600MHz	700MHz	Cellular/SMR	AWS-1	AWS-3	PCS	AWS 4 / L Band	WCS	EBS/BRS
1	2	Los Angeles-Anaheim, CA	33,109	17,704,110	95	20	75	0	20	0	0	0	25	10	40	0	0
2	1	New York-Newark, NY-NJ	5,768	17,041,161	125	40	85	0	40	0	0	0	35	10	40	0	0
3	3	Chicago, IL	5,324	8,404,358	91	16	75	0	10	6	0	0	25	10	40	0	0
4	9	Dallas-Fort Worth, TX	8,561	6,857,143	101	26	75	0	20	6	0	0	25	10	40	0	0
5	10	Houston, TX	7,033	6,108,723	91	16	75	0	10	6	0	0	25	10	40	0	0
6	4	Philadelphia, PA	3,587	5,331,294	95	20	75	0	20	0	0	0	25	10	40	0	0
7	8	Washington, DC-MD-VA	3,055	5,168,021	91	26	65	0	20	6	0	0	15	10	40	0	0
8	17	Atlanta, GA	4,383	4,943,920	101	26	75	0	20	6	0	0	25	10	40	0	0
9	5	Detroit-Ann Arbor, MI	4,958	4,653,485	91	26	65	0	20	6	0	0	15	10	40	0	0
10	6	Boston-Brockton-Lowell, MA-NH	4,128	4,606,557	100	20	80	0	20	0	0	0	30	10	40	0	0
11	7	San Francisco-Oakland, CA	3,424	4,594,060	105	30	75	0	30	0	0	0	25	10	40	0	0
12	12	Miami-Fort Lauderdale, FL	3,751	4,532,109	101	36	65	0	30	6	0	0	15	10	40	0	0
13	26	Phoenix, AZ	9,224	4,087,191	91	26	65	0	20	6	0	0	15	10	40	0	0
14	18	San Diego, CA	4,526	3,263,431	91	26	65	0	20	6	0	0	15	10	40	0	0
15	15	Minneapolis-St. Paul, MN-WI	4,870	3,256,107	111	26	85	0	20	6	0	0	35	10	40	0	0
16	19	Denver-Boulder, CO	4,681	3,017,864	101	26	75	0	20	6	0	0	25	10	40	0	0
17	20	Seattle-Everett, WA	4,503	2,839,550	101	26	75	0	20	6	0	0	25	10	40	0	0
18	22	Tampa-St. Petersburg, FL	2,742	2,739,727	91	26	65	0	20	6	0	0	15	10	40	0	0
19	14	Baltimore, MD	2,595	2,737,070	91	26	65	0	20	6	0	0	15	10	40	0	0
20	11	St. Louis, MO-IL	5,092	2,627,456	100	25	75	0	19	6	0	0	25	10	40	0	0
21	30	Portland, OR-WA	3,727	2,185,690	101	26	75	0	20	6	0	0	25	10	40	0	0
22	33	San Antonio, TX	2,545	2,126,810	91	26	65	0	20	6	0	0	15	10	40	0	0
23	93	Las Vegas, NV	8,091	2,069,681	101	26	75	0	20	6	0	0	25	10	40	0	0
24	35	Sacramento, CA	3,521	2,061,310	91	26	65	0	20	6	0	0	15	10	40	0	0
25	91	San Juan-Caguas, PR	1,499	2,038,404	91	26	65	0	20	6	0	0	15	10	40	0	0
26	60	Orlando, FL	2,855	2,005,728	91	26	65	0	20	6	0	0	15	10	40	0	0
27	13	Pittsburgh, PA	3,086	1,968,154	101	26	75	0	20	6	0	0	25	10	40	0	0
28	27	San Jose, CA	1,304	1,894,605	105	30	75	0	30	0	0	0	25	10	40	0	0
29	24	Kansas City, MO-KS	3,365	1,871,407	101	26	75	0	20	6	0	0	25	10	40	0	0
30	75	Austin, TX	2,837	1,825,420	91	26	65	0	20	6	0	0	15	10	40	0	0
31	28	Indianapolis, IN	3,089	1,788,625	90	25	65	0	19	6	0	0	15	10	40	0	0
32	16	Cleveland, OH	3,056	1,759,382	101	26	75	0	20	6	0	0	25	10	40	0	0
33	39	Salt Lake City-Ogden, UT	9,388	1,723,507	91	26	65	0	20	6	0	0	15	10	40	0	0
34	31	Columbus, OH	2,481	1,671,681	91	26	65	0	20	6	0	0	15	10	40	0	0
35	23	Cincinnati, OH-KY-IN	2,165	1,661,531	101	26	75	0	20	6	0	0	25	10	40	0	0
36	46	Nashville-Davidson, TN	4,135	1,618,979	101	26	75	0	20	6	0	0	25	10	40	0	0
37	21	Milwaukee, WI	3,322	1,572,245	86	16	70	0	10	6	0	0	20	10	40	0	0
38	61	Charlotte-Gastonia, NC	1,549	1,442,234	81	16	65	0	10	6	0	0	15	10	40	0	0
39	71	Raleigh-Durham, NC	1,556	1,433,571	91	16	75	0	10	6	0	0	25	10	40	0	0
40	51	Jacksonville, FL	3,698	1,419,127	91	16	75	0	10	6	0	0	25	10	40	0	0
41	72	West Palm Beach-Boca Raton, FL	2,386	1,397,710	101	36	65	0	30	6	0	0	15	10	40	0	0
42	45	Oklahoma City, OK	3,555	1,274,829	91	26	65	0	20	6	0	0	15	10	40	0	0
43	47	Greensboro-Winston-Salem, NC	3,221	1,268,478	86	16	70	0	10	6	0	0	20	10	40	0	0
44	36	Memphis, TN-AR-MS	2,392	1,220,887	81	16	65	0	10	6	0	0	15	10	40	0	0
45	32	Hartford-Bristol, CT	1,607	1,214,295	115	40	75	0	40	0	0	0	25	10	40	0	0
46	43	Norfolk-Virginia Beach, VA-NC	1,946	1,137,565	101	26	75	0	20	6	0	0	25	10	40	0	0
47	25	Buffalo, NY	2,367	1,136,360	91	16	75	0	10	6	0	0	25	10	40	0	0
48	29	New Orleans, LA	3,910	1,110,274	96	16	80	0	10	6	0	0	30	10	40	0	0
49	37	Louisville, KY-IN	1,420	1,091,912	101	26	75	0	20	6	0	0	25	10	40	0	0
50	34	Rochester, NY	4,870	1,058,185	91	26	65	0	20	6	0	0	15	10	40	0	0

Source: Courtesy of Allnet Insights & Analytics (https://www.allnetinsights.com), reprinted with permission

Appendix B: ITU Regions

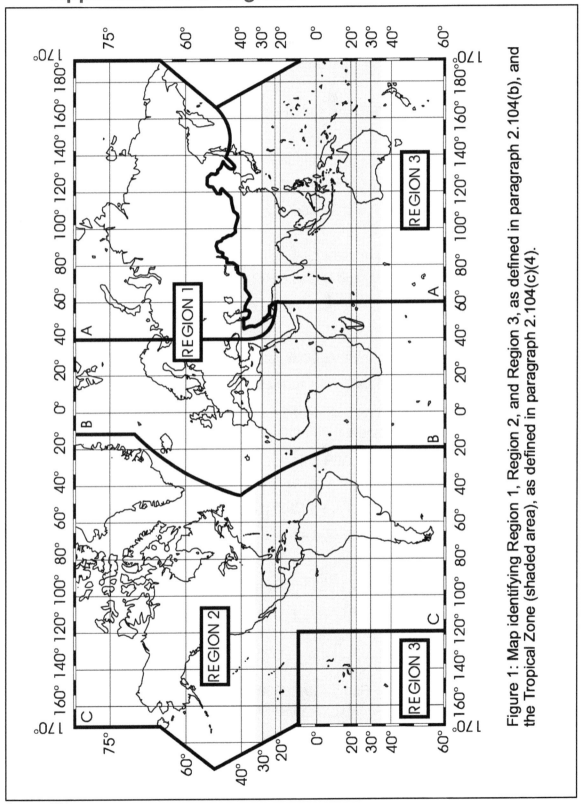

Figure 1: Map identifying Region 1, Region 2, and Region 3, as defined in paragraph 2.104(b), and the Tropical Zone (shaded area), as defined in paragraph 2.104(c)(4).

Source: ITU

Appendix C: FCC Geographical Licensing Area

The FCC has a long history of using a variety of territory sizes ranging from the 734 Cellular Market Areas ("CMAs") to a single national license. Maps of the different geographical licensing areas are included after the area descriptions below. A summary of these licensing areas are as follows:

Cellular Market Areas ("CMAs") [Used for Original Cellular Services and Still Used in Some Recent Auctions]

- 734 total areas. Composed of 306 Metropolitan Statistical Areas ("MSAs") and 428 Rural Service Areas (RSAs). Used for:

  - Cellular Radiotelephone Service - 47 CFR § 22.909 (824 to 894 MHz: Blocks A-B);

  - Interactive Video and Data Service (IVDS) - 47 CFR § 95.803 (Segments: A (218.0 to 218.5 MHz) and B (218.5 to 219.0 MHz)); and

  - Parts of other mobile wireless spectrum auctions including 700 MHz, and AWS.

"Trading Area" Divisions [Used in Many Early Auctions]

- **Basic Trading Areas ("BTAs")** - 491 total areas. Used for:

  - Multipoint Distribution Service (MDS) - 47 CFR § 21.924 (2150 to 2162, 2596 to 2680 MHz: Channels 1, 2(2A), E1-E4, F1-F4, H1-H3)

  - Narrowband PCS - 47 CFR § 24.102 (901 to 902, 930 to 931 MHz: Channels 25 to 26);

  - Broadband PCS - 47 CFR § 24.202 (1850 to 1990 MHz: Blocks C-F); and

  - Local Multipoint Distribution Service (LMDS) - 47 CFR § 101.1007 (27.5 to 31.3 GHz: Blocks A-B).

- **Major Trading Areas ("MTAs")** - 52 total areas. Used for:

  - Narrowband PCS - 47 CFR § 24.102 (901 to 902, 930 to 931 MHz, 940 to 941 MHz: Channels 18 to 24);

  - Broadband PCS - 47 CFR § 24.202 (1850 to 1990 MHz: Blocks A-B); and

  - Specialized Mobile Radio (SMR) 900 MHz - 47 CFR § 90.661 (896 to 901 MHz and 935 to 940 MHz: Channel Blocks A-T).

- **Regional PCS Areas ("RPCs")**. Aggregation of MTAs into 5 regions. Used for:

  - Narrowband PCS - 47 CFR § 24.102 (901 to 902, 930 to 931 MHz, 940 to 941 MHz: Channels 18 to 24);

  - Broadband PCS - 47 CFR § 24.202 (1850 to 1990 MHz: Blocks A-B); and

- o Specialized Mobile Radio (SMR) 900 MHz - 47 CFR § 90.661 (896 to 901 MHz and 935 to 940 MHz: Channel Blocks A-T).

"Economic Area" Divisions [Newer System Often Used Alongside CMAs]

- **[Basic] Economic Areas ("BEAs" or more commonly "EAs")** – 176 total areas. Used for:

  - o General Wireless Communications Service (GWCS) - 47 CFR § 26.102 (4660-4685 MHz: Channel Blocks A-E);

  - o Specialized Mobile Radio (SMR) 800 MHz - 47 CFR § 90.681 & 90.903 (806-821/851-866 MHz: Spectrum Blocks A-C);

  - o 220 MHz - 47 CFR § 90.761 (220-222 MHz: Channel Assignments A-E);

  - o Location and Monitoring Service (LMS) - 47 CFR § 90.7 (3 Spectrum Blocks (1) 904.000-909.750 MHz and 927.750-928.000 MHz; (2) 919.750-921.750 MHz and 927.500-927.750 MHz; and (3) 921.750-927.250 MHz and 927.250-927.500 MHz);

  - o 38.6-40.0 GHz Band (39 GHz) - 47 CFR § 101.64 (38.6-40.0 GHz: Channels 1-14 with paired blocks A-B);

  - o AWS-1; and

  - o 700 MHz (portions) and AWS (portions).

- **Major Economic Areas ("MEAs")**. Aggregation of BEAs (EAs) into 52 regions. Used for:

  - o Wireless Communications Service (WCS) - 47 CFR § 27.6 (Paired Channel Blocks A (2305 to 2310 MHz and 2350 to 2355 MHz) and B (2310 to 2315/2355 to 2360 MHz));

  - o 929 MHz Paging - 47 CFR § 90.493 (Channels A-L: 929.0125 to 929.9625 MHz); and

  - o 931 MHz Paging - 47 CFR § 22.531 (Channels AA-BK: 931.0125 to 931.9875 MHz).

- **Regional Economic Areas ("REAs")**. Aggregation of MEAs into 12 regions. Used for:

  - o Wireless Communications Service (WCS) - 47 CFR § 27.6 (Unpaired Channel Blocks C (2315-2320 MHz) and D (2345-2350 MHz)).

- **[Regional] Economic Area Groupings ("[R]EAGs")**. Aggregation of BEAs(EAs) into six regions. Used for:

  - o 220 MHz - 47 CFR § 90.761 (220 to 222 MHz: Channel Assignments F-J); and

- 700 MHz - 47 CFR § 27.6 (746 to 764 and 776 to 794 MHz: Blocks A-D).

- **VHF Public Coast Station Areas ("VCPs")**. Aggregations of BEAs (EAs) into 42 areas. Used for:

  - VHF Public Coast Stations 47 CFR § 80.371(c)(1)(B).

Other Geographic Groupings

- **Television Market Areas ("TMAs")**. 210 television markets. These are almost always referred to as "DMAs" (Designated Market Areas), but DMAs are technically a Neilsen term. Used for:

  - Determining areas for the cable must-carry/retransmission consent election. (47 CFR § 76.55)

    - Cable Television Service 47 CFR 76 Subpart D

  - Children's Television Programming Report (Form 398)

- **Emergency Alert Local Areas ("EASs")**. Used for:

  - Emergency Alert System 47 CFR § 11.21

- **Nationwide Area ("NWAs")**. Used for:

  - Narrowband PCS - 47 CFR § 24.102 (901 to 902 MHz, 930 to 931 MHz and 940 to 941 MHz: Channels 1 to 11).

The Relationship of the FCC license territories is summarized in Figure AIV-1 below.

Figure AIV-1: FCC License Territory Relationships

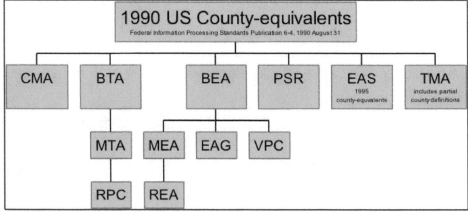

Source: FCC

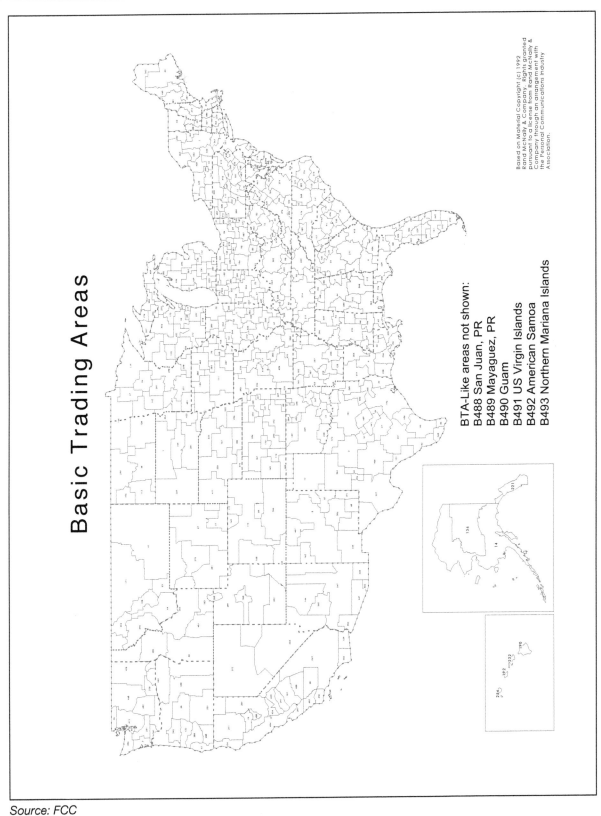

Basic Trading Areas

BTA-Like areas not shown:
B488 San Juan, PR
B489 Mayaguez, PR
B490 Guam
B491 US Virgin Islands
B492 American Samoa
B493 Northern Mariana Islands

Source: FCC

There are 491 Basic Trading Areas.

Cellular Market Areas (CMAs)

Metropolitan Statistical Areas (MSAs) and Rural Service Areas (RSAs)

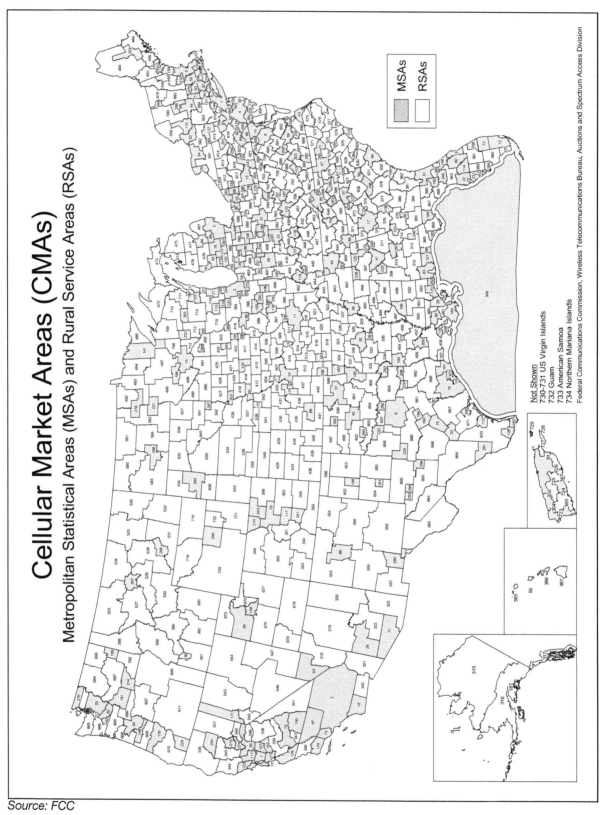

MSAs
RSAs

Not Shown
730-731 US Virgin Islands
732 Guam
733 American Samoa
734 Northern Mariana Islands
Federal Communications Commission, Wireless Telecommunications Bureau, Auctions and Spectrum Access Division

Source: FCC

There are 734 CMAs (Cellular Market Area): 306 MSAs (Metropolitan Statistical Area) plus 428 RSAs (Rural Service Area).

Economic Areas (EAs)

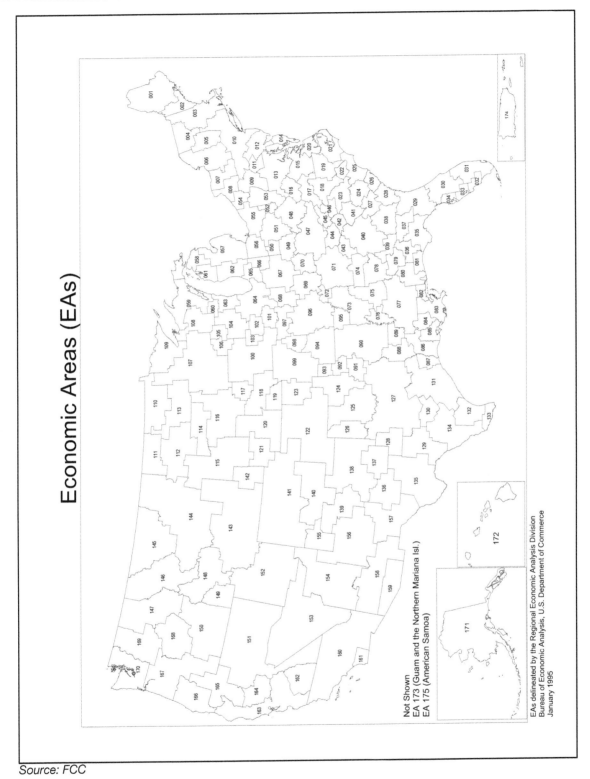

Not Shown
EA 173 (Guam and the Northern Mariana Isl.)
EA 175 (American Samoa)

EAs delineated by the Regional Economic Analysis Division
Bureau of Economic Analysis, U.S. Department of Commerce
January 1995

Source: FCC

There are 176 Economic Areas.

Major Economic Area (MEA)

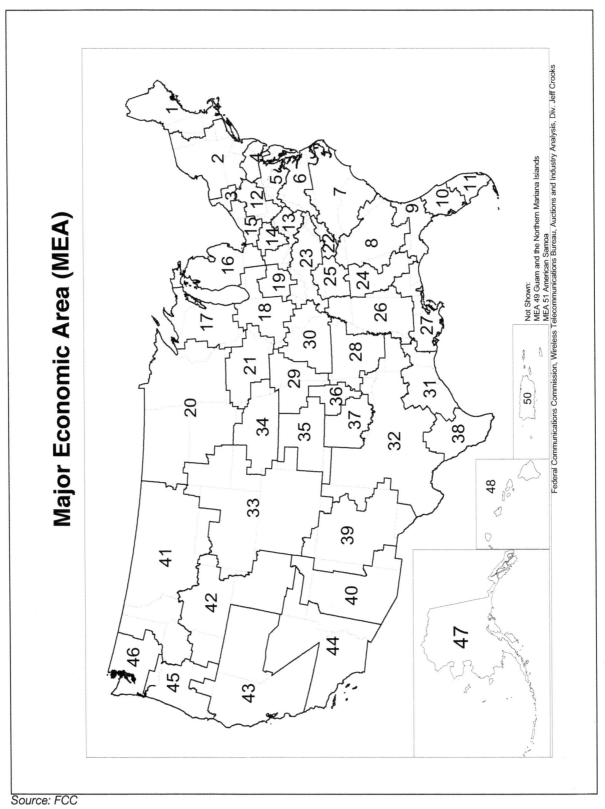

Not Shown:
MEA 49 Guam and the Northern Mariana Islands
MEA 51 American Samoa

Federal Communications Commission, Wireless Telecommunications Bureau, Auctions and Industry Analysis, Div. Jeff Crooks

Source: FCC

There are 52 Major Economic Areas.

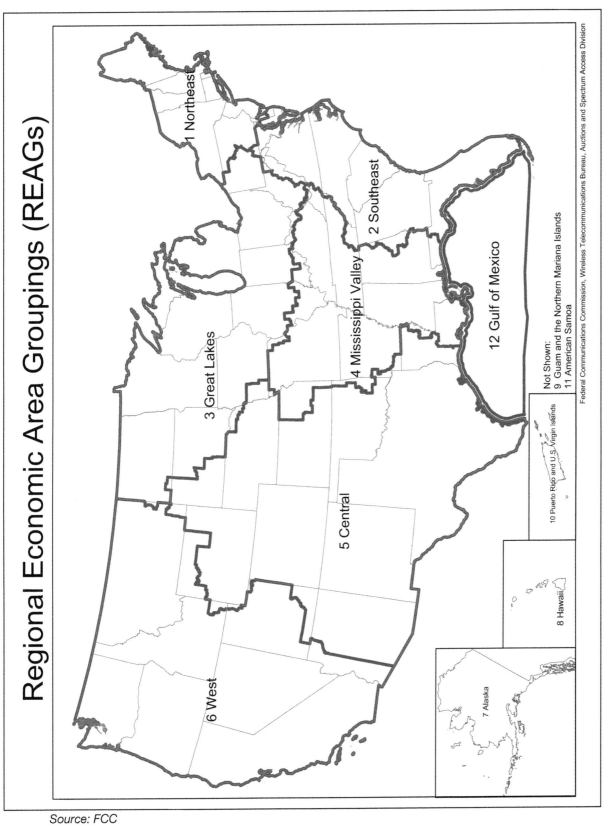

Regional Economic Area Groupings (REAGs)

1 Northeast

2 Southeast

3 Great Lakes

4 Mississippi Valley

12 Gulf of Mexico

5 Central

6 West

10 Puerto Rico and U.S. Virgin Islands

8 Hawaii

7 Alaska

Not Shown:
9 Guam and the Northern Mariana Islands
11 American Samoa

Federal Communications Commission, Wireless Telecommunications Bureau, Auctions and Spectrum Access Division

Source: FCC

There are 12 Regional Economic Areas.

Appendix D: Radio Spectrum Frequencies

Band name	Abbreviation	ITU Band	Frequency and Wavelength in Air	Examples of Uses
Tremendously low frequency	TLF		< 3 Hz > 100,000 km	Natural and man-made electromagnetic noise
Extremely low frequency	ELF		3–30 Hz 100,000 km – 10,000 km	Communication with submarines
Super low frequency	SLF		30–300 Hz 10,000 km – 1000 km	Communication with submarines
Ultra low frequency	ULF		300–3000 Hz 1000 km – 100 km	Submarine communication, communication within mines
Very low frequency	VLF	4	3–30 kHz 100 km – 10 km	Navigation, time signals, submarine communication, wireless heart rate monitors, geophysics
Low frequency	LF	5	30–300 kHz 10 km – 1 km	Navigation, time signals, AM longwave broadcasting (Europe and parts of Asia), RFID, amateur radio
Medium frequency	MF	6	300–3000 kHz 1 km – 100 m	AM (medium-wave) broadcasts, amateur radio, avalanche beacons
High frequency	HF	7	3–30 MHz 100 m – 10 m	Shortwave broadcasts, citizens' band radio, amateur radio and over-the-horizon aviation communications, RFID, over-the-horizon radar, Automatic Link Establishment (ALE) / Near Vertical Incidence Skywave (NVIS) radio communications, marine and mobile radio telephony
Very high frequency	VHF	8	30–300 MHz 10 m – 1 m	FM, television broadcasts and line-of-sight ground-to-aircraft and aircraft-to-aircraft communications. Land Mobile and Maritime Mobile communications, amateur radio, weather radio
Ultra high frequency	UHF	9	300–3000 MHz 1 m – 100 mm	Television broadcasts, microwave ovens, microwave devices/communications, radio astronomy, mobile phones, wireless LAN, Bluetooth, ZigBee, GPS and two-way radios such as Land Mobile, FRS and GMRS radios, amateur radio
Super high frequency	SHF	10	3–30 GHz 100 mm – 10 mm	Radio astronomy, microwave devices/communications, wireless LAN, most modern radars, communications satellites, satellite television broadcasting, DBS, amateur radio
Extremely high frequency	EHF	11	30–300 GHz 10 mm – 1 mm	Radio astronomy, high-frequency microwave radio relay, microwave remote sensing, amateur radio, directed-energy weapon, millimeter wave scanner
Terahertz or Tremendously high frequency	THz or THF	12	300–3,000 GHz 1 mm – 100 μm	Terahertz imaging – a potential replacement for X-rays in some medical applications, ultrafast molecular dynamics, condensed-matter physics, terahertz time-domain spectroscopy, terahertz computing/communications, sub-mm remote sensing, amateur radio

Source: Wikipedia and Summit Ridge Group, LLC analysis

Appendix E: Glossary

- **3G:** Third Generation of mobile technologies. 3G decreased spectrum costs, enabled customers to achieve higher data transmission rates (mobile systems: more than 384 Kbps; stationary systems: more than 2 Mbps) and improved efficiency in the use of spectrum. Comes in different transmission formats such as W-CDMA, UMTS, CDMA 2000, TD-CDMA, DECT and Mobile WiMAX.

- **3GPP:** (Third Generation Partnership Project). An international umbrella group for telecom regulation coordination.

- **4G:** Fourth Generation of mobile technologies. 4G decreased spectrum costs even beyond 3G. It enables customers to achieve higher data transmission rates – as high as 1GB/Sec.

- **Adaptive Beam Steering:** Technique that steers beams to follow user mobility and overcome the effects of blockage using intelligent prediction algorithms and rapid beam switching methods.

- **Advanced Antenna Techniques:** Four-way receive diversity that supports up to 8x8 MIMO

- **AMPS:** Advanced Mobile Phone Service.

- **Artificial Intelligence:** Machine intelligence that drives change in network design and network management

- **ATC:** Ancillary Terrestrial Component. Using satellite telephony spectrum to let MSS provide service terrestrially at the same time as using it to provide service via satellite. The use of ATCs in Mobile Satellite Services was introduced in 2003.

- **Autonomous Networks:** A self-optimizing network that can identify and mitigate problems as they occur.

- **AWS:** Advanced Wireless Spectrum: 1710 to 1755 MHZ for uplink and 2110 to 2155 for downlink. In the U.S. this was broken up into six blocks (A-F) that have been subject to auctions since 2006.

- **Bandplan:** A regulatory plan for using frequencies in a specific frequency band. It includes numerous technical details about the band including the channel division, licensing, modulation and other information.

- **Beamforming:** A MIMO technique that uses multiple antennas to control the direction of a wave by weighing the magnitude and phase of individual antenna signals in an array of multiple antennas.

- **Big Data:** A massive amount of data, both structured and unstructured that is analyzed to reveal patterns and trends.

APPENDICES

- **BRS:** Broadband Radio Service: Used for general-purpose networking. Uses microwave frequencies between 2.5 and 2.7 GHz. Increasingly in demand for mobile wireless applications.

- **Cable Technology DOCSIS 3.1:** Technology that will enable cable networks to reach substantially higher speeds. DOCSIS 3.1 is the fourth generation on DOCSIS standard developed by Cable Labs.

- **Carrier Aggregation:** Enables bands of spectrum that are not adjacent to one another to be combined.

- **C-band:** 3.4 to 4.3 GHz (receive) and 4.25 to 6.425 GHz (transmit). Used primarily for satellite transmission and desirable in tropical areas due to its resistance to rain fade. Many countries are considering reallocating the lower portion of the receive band for terrestrial broadband.

- **CEPT:** European Conference of Postal and Telecommunications Administrations. A European regional coordinating body for European telecom and postal issues.

- **CDMA:** (Code Division Multiple Access). A spread-spectrum technology that allows multiple users to transmit over the same physical frequency channel but prevents interference by coding each transmission.

- **Central Office Re-architected as a Data Center (CORD):** The shift in equipment from proprietary gear to commoditized servers that run on open software in a central office.

- **CEPT:** (European Conference of Postal and Telecommunications Administration). European regional telecommunication regulating body.

- **CITL:** (Inter-American Telecommunication Commission). A regional telecom coordinating body for the Americas.

- **Communications Act of 1934:** Authorized the creation of the FCC.

- **Container Technology:** Technology that enables software to be spread across a data center of the network in small packages.

- **C-RAN:** Centralized radio access networks that separate the radio and antenna from a digital baseband path and pools multiple baseband units in a central office, which leverages distributed base station architecture.

- **Device to Device Communications (D2D):** Direct communication between two mobile devices that enhances spectral efficiency.

- **Distributed Massive MIMO:** Addresses the issue of antenna form factor constraints by utilizing the formation of a large number of antenna elements opportunistically in both transmission and reception.

- **Duplex Gap:** The space between the uplink and downlink frequencies in paired spectrum blocks.

- **EBS:** Educational Broadcasting System.

- **EDGE:** (Enhanced Data Rates for GSM Evolution). An advanced version of GPRS.

- **Downlink:** Transmission from the base station to the user.

- **FCC:** The Federal Communications Commission. An independent agency of the U.S. government that works in the areas of broadband, competition, the spectrum, the media, public safety and homeland security.

- **FDD:** Frequency Division Duplexing. A technology that uses different frequencies for the send and receive signals to minimize interference. FDD is the most common duplexing technology in the U.S.. This is in contract with TDD (Time Division Duplexing).

- **Fiber Technologies:** Transmits data in the form of pulses of light through extremely thin strands of glass.

- **Frequency Division Duplex (FDD):** A technique where the transmitter and receiver operate at different carrier frequencies.

- **FSS:** Fixed Satellite Services.

- **Full Dimension MIMO:** A scalable implementation of massive MIMO that leverages the 3D channel mode to achieve better performance by considering the individual multiplexing in the elevation plane.

- **G.Fast:** The newest form of DSL technology that is projected to offer speeds of 1 Gbps.

- **GPS:** Global Positioning Satellite. A satellite systems run by the U.S. defense department. It emits a timing signal that can be triangulated to determine geographic position.

- **GPRS:** General Packet Radio Service. GSM (see above) expanded for data.

- **GSM:** Global System for Mobile Communication. A standard developed by the European Telecommunications Standards Institute for protocols for second generation (2G) mobile phones.

- **GWCS:** General Wireless Communication Service. A communications band at 4.660 to 4.685 GHz.

- **Hertz:** one hertz is one frequency wave. Frequency is frequently referred to by the number of waves (hertz) produced in a second.

APPENDICES

- **Hyper Convergence in Hardware:** A software-centric infrastructure system with an architecture that integrates compute, storage, networking, and virtualization resources into a commodity hardware box supported by one single vendor.

- **IEEE:** Institute of Electrical and Electronic Engineers.

- **Internet of Things (IoT):** The Internetworking of vehicles, applications devices, and infrastructure in everyday life.

- **ITU:** (International Telecommunications Union). Global coordinating body for radio spectrum. The ITU is based in Geneva, Switzerland.

- **ITU-R:** The division of the ITU that handles most spectrum issues.

- **Ka-band:** 26.5 to 40 GHz. This satellite band has historically suffered from significant weather-related interference. However, new higher-powered satellites over the past 10 to 15 years have largely overcome this problem. This band is heavily used in state of the art satellite broadband systems.

- **Ku-band:** 12 to 18 GHz. Used primarily in satellite communications. Most commercial satellite television signals in the U.S. and Europe are transmitted in Ku-band. Although not as resistant to rain fade as C-band, its higher frequency allows consumers to use much smaller reception antennas.

- **L-band:** 1 to 2 GHz (1452.96 to 1492.624 MHz harmonized by CEPT. Used for satellite radio and MSS applications as well terrestrial mobile broadband .

- **LMDS:** Local Multipoint Distribution Service. Used for broadband wireless. Intended initially for wireless digital television. Uses the 31.0 to 31.3 GHz frequency. Now being considered for broadband back-haul and last mile broadband access in certain areas.

- **LTE:** Long Term Evolution. A fourth-generation version of GSM with data rates as high as 1 GB/Sec.

- **LTE License Assisted Access (LAA):** Delivers coverage and capacity to mobile users by using the 5 GHz unlicensed band and licensed spectrum.

- **LTE-U Technology:** Augments a carrier's 4G LTE service by utilizing the unlicensed spectrum in the 5 GHz range.

- **LORAN:** (LOng RAnge Navigation). A low-frequency timing and positioning system that has largely been replaced by global positioning satellites (GPS).

- **Massive MIMO:** Technology that uses hundreds of antennas at base stations to further increase capacity and system throughput with special multiplexing and time-division duplexing (TDD). It is seen as one of the critical enablers of 5G networks.

- **Millimeter Waves (mmWaves):** Spectrum frequency bands at 30-300 GHz that are considered to have the ability to support high rates, low latency, and flexible connectivity for 5G. Has also been used to refer to the 24-28 GHz frequency bands.

- **MMDS:** Multichannel Multipoint Distribution Service (see BRS).

- **Mobile Edge Computing (MEC):** An emerging technology that provides the advantages of low latency and high bandwidth at the edge of RAN that is going to be used in 5G deployment.

- **MSS:** (Mobile Satellite Services). For the provision of mobile services using satellites. Only since the introduction of ATCs in Mobile Wireless Services in 2003 has there been an integration of both satellite and terrestrial uses in one frequency band. Bands that provide MSS are the S-band and L-band.

- **Narrowbanding:** A regulatory reduction in the amount of spectrum allocated to a frequency band.

- **Network Function Virtualization (NFV):** A network architecture that separately packages functions from dedicated hardware into individual network functions, which are then run on a virtual server. It is designed to consolidate and deliver the network components needed to support a fully virtualized infrastructure.

- **NFV Infrastructure:** Infrastructure platform over which NFVs are deployed.

- **NFV Management and Orchestration (NFV MANO):** Provides the framework for managing and orchestrating all NFV infrastructure resources.

- **Network Slicing:** A form of virtualization that allows network operators to divide RAN into multiple end-to-end networks, encompassing from radio access to the core network.

- **Non-Orthogonal Multiple Access (NOMA):** A technique used boost spectral efficiency through an intra-cell multiplexing scheme further.

- **NTIA:** (National Telecommunications and Information Administration). An agency within the department of commerce that regulates and administers spectrum allocated for government use.

- **Ofcom:** The British telecom regulatory body.

- **OpenStack:** A cloud computing system that manages large pools of storage, compute, and network resources through the Internet.

- **Orbital Slot:** The location in space allocated for a satellite in a specific frequency band.

- **Paired Spectrum:** Spectrum that is allocated in two blocks, one authorized for uplink transmission and one authorized for downlink transmission.

- **PCAST:** President's Council of Advisors on Science and Technology. In 2012, this group issued an influential report recommending spectrum sharing as a means to increase spectral efficiency.

- **PCS:** (Personal Communication Services). In North America, wireless voice and data services on the 1850 - 1990 MHz band.

- **Quadrature Amplitude Modulation (QAM):** Bandwidth enhancement technique that conveys data by modulating the amplitude of separate carrier waves out of phase by 90 degrees and the resultant output consists of both amplitude and phase variations. QAM enables more data to be transmitted on the same carrier signal.

- **RF:** (Radio Frequency). Typically refers to spectrum between 3 kHz and 300 GHz.

- **S-band:** 2 to 4 GHz. Used for satellite MSS applications.

- **Self-Organizing Network (SON):** The automation of critical tasks in the configuration and optimization of networks that aims to reduce installation and network management costs.

- **Smart Radio:** A radio that can use multiple frequencies and determine the appropriate frequency to use based on the design criteria.

- **Software Defined Network (SDN):** A network architecture approach that facilitates network management by enabling a network to be centrally programmed and updated using software applications. SND replaces traditional, proprietary network hardware.

- **Software Defined Wide Area Network (SD-WAN):** A specific application of SDN applied to wide area network connections, which are used to connect enterprise networks over large geographic areas.

- **Spatial Multiplexing:** Transmits multiple independently and separately encoded data streams through multiple antenna elements.

- **Spectrum Sharing:** The simultaneous usage of a specific radio frequency band in a specific geographic area by many independent entities.

- **Spectrum Sharing with Cellular Systems:** A proposed system of spectrum sharing and resource allocation over D2D communication to mitigate against the risk to the existing cellular network.

- **TDD:** (Time Division Duplexing). A technology that separates the send and receive signals by time. This technology is advantageous when usage is asymmetrical. TDD is common in China.

- **TDMA:** (Time Division Multiple Access). A channel access method that allows users to share the same frequency by dividing transmissions into different time slots.

- **Ultra Densification:** Creates more layers of cells and manages shared spectrum resources intelligently to increase capacity to keep up with the growing demand for bandwidth.

- **UMTS:** (Universal Mobile Telecommunications System). A 3G version of GMS (see above).

- **Uplink:** transmission to the base station.

- **Virtual Network Functions (VNF):** The functional component of network infrastructures that provides a well-defined functional behavior.

- **VSAT:** (Very Small Aperture Terminal). A small satellite dish used for a variety of satellite communications needs including corporate networks.

- **Wi-Fi:** A format for transmitting broadband data across short distances to unlicensed consumer devices.

- **WCS:** Wireless Communication Services.

- **White Spaces:** Unused frequency in the broadcasting band plan.

- **WiMAX:** Worldwide Interoperability for Microwave Access. A format/standard for information transmission, mainly to provide fixed wireless broadband services. WiMAX can be used in a variety of spectrum bands, such as 700 MHz, 2.4 GHz, 3.5 GHz and 5.8 GHz, although the main ones for which there is support are the WCS and BRS bands.

- **WRC:** (World Radio Conference). An event run by the ITU that revises and reviews Radio Regulations, the international treaty governing the use of radio spectrum and satellite orbits.

APPENDICES

Appendix F: Index

APPENDICES

APPENDICES

Appendix G: Bonus Track: Ode to the Spectrum Handbook

We hope you found the Spectrum Handbook 2018 helpful. If you'd like to celebrate, we've included this poem below:

You won't believe what I've seen
It was the Spectrum Handbook 2018

Studying wireless, wireline and satellite
It will keep you up all night

No baloney
Learn about Marconi
He was one of the faves
With the radio waves

Everything you never knew
About the ITU

There was 3G, 4G and now 5G
All coming at me
To give capacity for IoT

Kilohertz, Megahertz and Gigahertz
But that's not the worst
Bandwidth demand is about to burst

Beamforming
Is performing

Shannon's Limit is not dead
But MIMO turns it on its head

Carriers try to be efficient
But it is not sufficient

We need more spectrum
And we expect to get some

Chairman Pai
Says he is going to try

He knows he can't hide
From what's happening worldwide

Net neutrality
Was a fatality

But the flames are flaring
For spectrum sharing

And a rebrand
Of the C-band

They say millimeter wave is the save
But carriers must be brave
Because it compels
more small cells

Don't doubt it,
Read all about it

You won't believe what can be seen
In the Spectrum Handbook 2018

CPSIA information can be obtained
at www.ICGtesting.com
Printed in the USA
LVHW060814211218
600389LV00001B/1/P

9 780989 296243